A Handbook Series on
Electromagnetic Interference and
Compatibility

Volume 2

Grounding
and
Bonding

Michel Mardiguian

Interference Control Technologies, Inc.
Gainesville, Virginia

Interference Control Technologies, Inc.
Route 625, Gainesville, VA 22065
TEL: (703) 347-0030   FAX: (703) 347-5813

Library of Congress Catalog Card Number: 88-80528
ISBN: 0-944916-02-3

Dedication

To Benjamin Franklin:

A great philosopher and statesman,
and a mediocre lightning conductor.

Other Books in the 12-Volume Series

VOLUME 1
Fundamentals of Electromagnetic Compatibility

VOLUME 2
Grounding and Bonding

VOLUME 3
Electromagnetic Shielding

VOLUME 4
Filters and Power Conditioning

VOLUME 5
EMC in Components and Devices

VOLUME 6
EMI Test Methodology and Procedures

VOLUME 7
EMC in Telecommunications

VOLUME 8
EMI Control Methodology and Procedures

VOLUME 9
United States Commercial Standards

VOLUME 10
European and International Commercial Standards

VOLUME 11
Military EMC Standards

VOLUME 12
Supporting Military EMC Standards

Contents

Table of Contents

Common Terms and Abbreviations in EMC Literature

Prefixes for Decimal Multiples

10^{12}	tera	T
10^{9}	giga	G
10^{6}	mega	M
10^{3}	kilo	k
10^{2}	hecto	h
10	deka	da
10^{-1}	deci	d
10^{-2}	centi	c
10^{-3}	milli	m
10^{-6}	micro	μ
10^{-9}	nano	n
10^{-12}	pico	p

Technical Terms

absolute .... abs
alternating current............ ac
American wire gage .... AWG
ampere............................. A
ampere per meter............. A/m
ampere-hour..................... Ah
amplitude modulation....... AM
amplitude probability
  distribution.................... APD
analog to digital .... A/D
analog-to-digital converter. ADC or
  A/D
  converter
anti-jamming.................... AJ
arithmetic logic unit .... ALU
audio frequency................ AF
automatic data processing. ADP
automatic frequency control AFC
automatic gain control ...... AGC

average .... avg
bandwidth........................ BW
binary coded decimal........ BCD
bit.................................... b
bit-error rate .... BER
bits per second................. bps
British thermal unit.......... Btu
broadband........................ BB
byte .... B
bytes per second.............. Bps
centimeter-gram-second .... cgs
central processing unit...... CPU
characters per second .... cps
common-mode coupling .... CMC
common-mode rejection
  ratio............................. CMRR
complementary metal-oxide
  semiconductor .... CMOS
continuous wave............... CW
coulomb C
cubic centimeter.............. cm^3
decibel .... dB
decibel above 1 milliwatt .. dBm
decibel above 1 volt.......... dBV
decibel above 1 watt......... dBW
degree Celsius.................. °C
degree Fahrenheit .... °F
degree Kelvin................... °K
diameter........................... dia
differential-mode coupling. DMC
digital multimeter............. DMM
digital to analog .... D/A
digital voltmeter.............. DVM
digital-to-analog converter. DAC or
  D/A conv.

Common Terms and Abbreviations in EMC Literature

diode-transistor logic .... DTL
direct current .... dc
double pole double throw . DPDT
double sideband .... DSB
double sideband suppressed
  carrier.......................... DSB-SC
dual in-line package.......... DIP
electric field..................... E-field
electromagnetic
  compatibility .... EMC
electromagnetic
  interference................... EMI
electromagnetic pulse .... EMP
electromotive force .... EMF
electron volt .... eV
electronic countermeasures ECM
electrostatic discharge ...... ESD
emitter-coupled logic .... ECL
extremely high frequency . EHF
extremely low frequency... ELF
farad............................... F
fast Fourier transform ...... FFT
field intensity .... FI
field intensity meter .... FIM
field-effect transistor......... FET
foot................................. ft or '
frequency......................... freq
frequency division multiplex FDM
frequency modulation .... FM
frequency shift keying ...... FSK
gauss .... G
gram............................... g
ground .... gnd
ground loop coupling........ GLC
ground support equipment GSE
hazards of electromagnetic
  radiation to ordnance..... HERO
henry .... H
hertz (cycles per second)... Hz
high frequency .... HF
high-power transistor-
  to-transistor logic .... HTTL
high-speed complementary
  metal-oxide
  semiconductor .... HCMOS
high-threshold logic .... HTL
hour................................ hr
inch................................. in or "
inch per second .... ips
industrial, scientific and
  medical .... ISM
infrared............................ IR
input/output .... I/O
inside dimension.............. ID

instantaneous automatic
  gain control................... IAGC
insulated-gate field-effect
  transistor...................... IGFET
integrated circuit IC
interference-to-noise ratio . I/N
intermediate frequency ..... IF
joule .... J
junction field-effect
  transistor...................... JFET
kilogram .... kg
kilohertz........................... kH
kilovolt............................. kV
kilowatt............................ kW
kilowatt-hour .... kWh
lambert L
large-scale integration....... LSI
least significant bit........... LSB
length l
length (of cable) .... l_c
line impedance stabilization
  network........................ LISN
line of sight..................... LOS
liter................................. l
local oscillator .... LO
low frequency................... LF
lower sideband .... LSB
lumen............................... lm
lux lx
magnetic field .... H-field
master oscillator power
  amplifier....................... MOPA
maximum.......................... max
maxwell .... Mx
mean time between failure MTBF
mean time to failure......... MTTF
mean time to repair.......... MTTR
medium frequency
  (300 kHz to 3 MHz)...... MF
metal-oxide semiconductor MOS
metal-oxide semiconductor
  field-effect transistor...... MOSFET
metal-oxide varistor.......... MOV
meter .... m
microfarad........................ μF
microhenry....................... μH
micron (10^{-6} meter)......... μ
micro-ohm........................ $\mu \Omega$
microwave .... MW
mile .... mi
military specification .... MIL-SPEC
military standard.............. MIL-STD
milliamp........................... mA

million instructions per second	MIPS	pulse position modulation	PPM
millisecond	ms	pulse repetition frequency	PRF
millivolt	mV	pulse-amplitude modulation	PAM
milliwatt	mW	pulse-code modulation	PCM
minimum	min	pulse-duration modulation	PDM
minimum discernable signal	MDS	pulse-width modulation	PWM
minute	min	quasipeak	QP
modulator-demodulator	modem	radiation hazard	RADHAZ
most significant bit	MSB	radio frequency	RF
multilayer board	MLB	radio interference and field intensity	RI-FI
multiplex, multiplexer	mux	radio-frequency interference	RFI
nanofarad	nF	random access memory	RAM
nanohenry	nH	receiver	RX
nanosecond	ns	reference	ref
narrowband	NB	relative humidity	RH
negative	neg	resistance-inductance-capacitance	RLC
negative-positive-negative (transistor)	npn	return to zero	RTZ
negative-to-positive (junction)	n-p	revolutions per minute	rpm
newton	N	roentgen	R
noise equivalent power	NEP or P_n	root-mean-square	rms
		second	s
non-return to zero	NRZ	sensitivity time control	STC
N-type metal-oxide semiconductor	NMOS	shielding effectiveness	SE
		sideband	SB
nuclear electromagnetic pulse	NEMP	siemens	S
		signal-to-interference (ratio)	S/I
oersted	Oe	signal-to-noise (ratio)	S/N
ohm	Ω	silicon controlled rectifier	SCR
ohm-centimeter	Ωcm	single sideband	SSB
ohms per square	Ω/sq	square meter	m^2
ounce	oz	standing-wave ratio	SWR
outside dimension	OD	super high frequency	SHF
peak	pk	super low frequency	SLF
peak-to-peak	p-p	surface acoustic wave	SAW
phase lock loop	PLL	surface-mount technology	SMT
phase modulation	PM	surface-mounted component	SMC
positive	pos	surface-mounted device	SMD
positive-negative-positive (transistor)	pnp	television	TV
		temperature coefficient	TC
positive-to-negative (junction)	p-n	tesla	T
pound (sterling)	£	time division multiplex	TDM
pound per square centimeter	p/cm²	transistor-to-transistor logic	TTL
		ultra high frequency (360 MHz to 3 GHz)	UHF
pound per square inch	psi	ultraviolet	UV
power factor	PF	very high frequency (30 MHz to 300 MHz)	VHF
printed circuit board	PCB	very high-speed integrated circuit	VHSIC
private branch exchange	PBX		
P-type metal-oxide semiconductor	PMOS	very large-scale integration	VLSI
pulse per second	pps	very low frequency (3 kHz to 30 kHz)	VLF

Common Terms and Abbreviations in EMC Literature

volt	V		length (coil turn, ground loop, etc.)	l
volt meter	VM		length in millimeters	l_{mm}
voltage standing wave ratio	VSWR		magnetic susceptibility	χ
voltage-to-frequency converter	VFC		magnetizing force	H
voltampere	VA		parasitic capacitance	C_p
volt-ohm meter	VOM		permeability of free space	μ_0
watt	W		permeability of medium relative to μ_0	μ_r
waveguide beyond cuttoff	WGBCO		phase constant	β
weber	Wb		radius	r
words per minute	wpm		relative permittivity	ϵ_r
yard	yd		resistance (in ohms)	R
			rise time	τ_r

Mathematical Functions and Operators

		shield thickness	d
absolute value	abs	time	t
approximately equal	$\approx$	time constant, transmission factor	τ
argument	arg	velocity, volume	V
cosine	cos	wavelength	λ
cosine (hyperbolic)	cosh		
cotangent	cot		
cotangent (hyperbolic)	coth		
determinant	det		
dimension	dim		
exponential	exp		
imaginary	im		
inferior	inf		
limit	lim		
logarithm, common (base$_{10}$)	log		
logarithm, Napierian (base$_e$)	ln		
sine	sin		
tangent	tan		
tangent (hyperbolic)	tanh		

Common Variables in EMC Equations

attenuation constant, absorption factor	α
Boltzmann's constant	K
capacitance (in farads)	C
charge	Q
coefficient of self-inductance	L
conductance in mho	G
conductivity, propagation constant, leakage coefficient, deviation	σ
current	I
dielectric constant, permittivity	ϵ
frequency (in Hz)	f
impedance	Z
induced voltage	E
inductance (in henrys)	L
infinity	∞

Acknowledgements

My thanks go out to Jeff Eckert for his cordial and efficient editing. I am certainly indebted to Hugh Denny whose works have been very inspirational in the making of this book and are utilized in many places. I am also grateful to Ralph Morrison whose expertise in low-frequency instrumentation grounding (an often overlooked area) has helped me substantially.

Foreword

In the 1900s and 1920s, the proliferation of electrical machinery and appliances caused many fires and casualties because practices for protection against electrical hazards were not yet understood (or enforced). As a result, a strong emphasis was put on the grounding and earthing of electrical equipment. Because most lightning and power-fault control relies on a low-impedance path to earth, the rage was "ground, ground, ground." Never mind the rationale, just strive for a good, low-resistance ground. Our predecessors passed along this enduring legacy.

Regrettably, over the ensuing years most electronic engineers and technicians have been indoctrinated with the idea that a "good ground" is synonymous with good EMI control. Among other misconceptions, the word ground is sometimes used when in fact bond (connect via a low-impedance, direct means) is meant. Generally, the word ground is substituted for the word return, which adds to the confusion. In this respect, a ground is any kind of low-impedance path for current to return to its source. This impedance is low but finite, so there will be a difference in potential along its length.

Today, lightning and power faults fall into the broad category of electromagnetic interference (EMI). Its cure, electromagnetic compatibility (EMC), has emerged as a separate science. Most of the time, the EMC engineer inherits an earthing and grounding situation which is optimized for power fault and hazard protection but not for noise reduction.

The most important observation about grounding is that an effective grounding system must be designed, like any other portion of the circuit. It is wishful thinking to expect that a grounding arrangement will perform well just by chance. A good ground does not just happen; it has to be well conceived and accurately calculated, and all configurations must be weighed with regard to dimensions and frequencies, just like any functional circuit.

We hope that this book will help designers, technicians and field engineers to optimize the functionality and reliability of their equipment by providing an orderly and methodic approach to grounding. Such an approach is highly preferable to the set of empirical and even contradictory recipes that are too often employed.

Michel Mardiguian

Chapter 1

Introduction to Grounding

The subject of grounding often intertwines with EMI control; for example, where and when should a signal reference or a cable shield be grounded? Other issues relate to buildings, shielded enclosures, equipments and filters, and each has its own grounding requirements. As it happens, grounding is one of the least understood but most significant culprits in the entire intrasystem EMI problem.

There are primarily two purposes for grounding devices, cables, equipments and systems: to prevent a shock hazard in the event that an equipment frame or housing may develop a high voltage due to lightning or an accidental breakdown of wiring or components, and to reduce EMI due to electrical-field, common impedance, or other forms of interference coupling. There may exist a third purpose, specific to some vehicles, airships, etc., where the system body constitutes one conductor of the power distribution network.

1.1 The Environment

Traditionally, systems were grounded for safety. This is still a prime consideration where tradition, habits and safety laws generally overrule any noise-control aspect because either:

1. Historically, safety standards existed first, so the corresponding techniques and practices have dictated the way

buildings, plants, etc. were built.

2. Even for new installations, the safety of people and the prevention of fire or explosion prevail over the functionality of electronic devices, which is deemed to be more manageable.

But the grounding of an equipment has a much broader connotation than the correct operation of this lone equipment or the protection of people using it.

An electronic system usually comprises many diverse circuits. For present purposes, a circuit is considered to be any collection of passive and active elements combined to perform a specific function, i.e., attenuate, amplify, rectify, detect, filter or otherwise alter a waveform. A grounding path is also considered to be a circuit or part of a circuit.

Whether distances between individual circuits are large or small, the entire system must function as an integral unit. Each circuit must perform its intended function and supply an output to a designated load, in an interference free manner, in the presence of extraneous signals. Grounding of circuits is an essential ingredient of this process.

Typically, a system must operate in an environment containing many potentially incompatible (error-producing or damage-threatening) voltages and currents as illustrated in Fig. 1.1. For example, within a facility are power sources (operating at frequencies specified as dc, 50 Hz, 60 Hz, and 400 Hz); very low frequency (VLF) signals from monitors, indicators and other specialized devices; and audio frequency voltages and currents associated with voice communications and control systems. In the higher frequency region of the spectrum there are radio frequency (RF) signals, ranging from VLF to microwaves used for broadcast communications, surveillance, tracking and other functions. Extending from audio frequencies into the RF region are the broadband data and communications systems, both analog and digital. Lightning discharges and stray earth currents further contribute to the noise environment. These various signals, falling in overlapping frequency ranges and representing a wide range of amplitudes, pose a definite threat of interference (and possible damage) to devices unless care is taken to minimize their coupling into susceptible circuits. Equipment, system and facility grounding is important in minimizing interference from sources internal or external to a system.

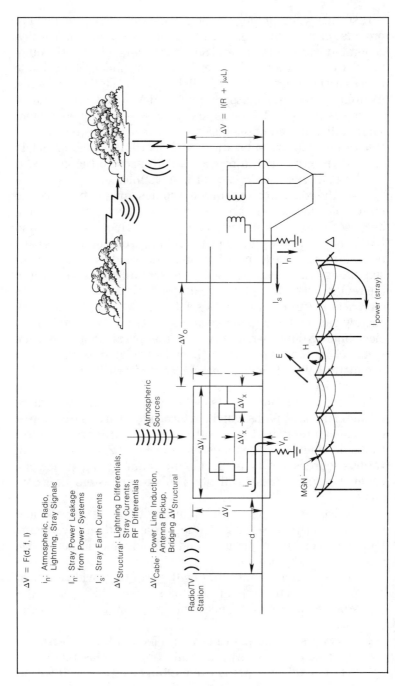

Figure 1.1—Grounding Scenario

1.3

Historically, grounding requirements arose from the need to provide protection from lightning strokes and industrially-generated static electricity. Structures and electrical equipment were connected to earth, i.e., grounded, to provide necessary conduction paths for lightning and static discharges. As utility power transmission systems developed, grounding to earth was found to be necessary for personnel and equipment safety. All major components of a transmission system such as generating stations, substations and distribution elements had to be earth grounded to provide a path back to the generator for the fault currents in case of line trouble.

With the development of electronics, metal became the preferable choice for structural and enclosure construction because it provides fire protection, mechanical strength and EMI control. As a result, many grounding problems are perhaps related to the presence of metal. The ready availability of something which can be used as a **ground** tends to obscure the real reason why a ground is needed. Metal associated with electrical circuitry poses a possible shock hazard which frequently can lead to arguments about **earthing** the metal for an electronic ground when perhaps the parts should not be metallic in the first place. (Double-insulated tools, which eliminate exposed, energizable metal surfaces, do not need to be grounded.)

Multiple electronic circuits and equipment often must share common metallic paths which, in turn, may also serve as power returns, lightning discharge paths, integral portions of electromagnetic shields, etc., as illustrated in Fig. 1.2. Currents from various sources may be present in the common impedance of a conductive path. This frequently leads to undesired EMI coupling.

Effective grounding is the realization of an appropriate reference network serving multiple roles without producing EMI between user circuits and equipment. Functionally, grounds typically provide:

1. Low-resistance connection with earth to provide a return path between the fault and the source. This lessens the voltage hazard until fuses blow or breakers trip (Fig. 1.3a).

2. A low-resistance path between electrical and electronic equipment and nearby metallic objects. This minimizes personnel danger in the event of an electrical fault within the equipment (Fig. 1.3a).

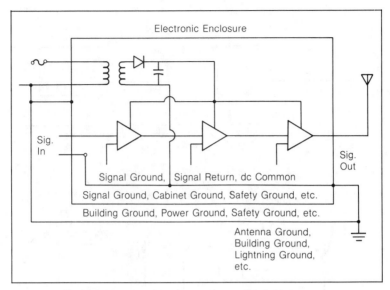

Figure 1.2—The Multiple Functions of Grounds

3. A preferential path between the point of impingement of a lightning stroke on an exposed object and the earth (Fig. 1.3b).
4. A path for bleeding off static charge before the potential becomes high enough to produce a spark or an arc (Fig. 1.3c).
5. A common reference plane of low relative impedance between electronic devices, circuits, and systems.
6. A reference plane for long-wave antenna systems.

Many electronic grounding systems simultaneously involve two or more of these functions. For example, one interconnected metallic system or network may serve both safety and EMI control functions and also perform as part of an antenna system.

Frequently, such multiple roles are in conflict either in terms of operational requirements or in terms of implementation techniques. This book is to foster an understanding of the electromagnetic properties of grounding networks. In this way, designers can appropriately configure networks needed in particular facilities, systems, equipment and circuits and have a high degree of confidence in their performance.

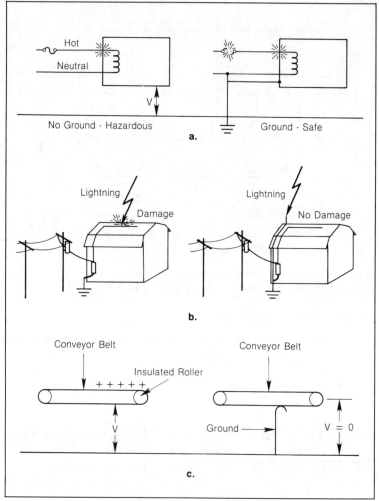

Figure 1.3—The Varied Functions of Grounding

1.2 Terms and Definitions: Grounding or Earthing?

Certainly the most abused word in the electronic engineer's lexicon is "ground" (Fig. 1.4). For instance, when one says that if you **ground** the cable shield at the receiving end, interference will be reduced, does this really mean **ground**? **Earth**? **Safety green**? Or does it mean **connect to**? And if it means **connect** or **bond**, how is this done and how is the **ground** configured? Etc., etc. Sometimes any one of the following words is meant as a substitute for ground, depending upon the context (the list is not exhaustive):

earth	return	connection	safety
reference	bond	chassis	frame
ground plane	green wire	grid	housing
stake	cold-water pipe	ground rod	enclosure

The time is long overdue to propose some definitions, so here goes. First, we shall speak of the noun rather than the verb.

Ground: A concept only to support other concepts such as **ground loop,** but otherwise to be avoided in favor of one of the following terms:

Earth: The soil in which a safety conductor (rod, grid, plate) is driven or buried to provide a low-impedance sink for fault and lightning currents.

Reference: Some object whose potential (often 0 V with respect to earth) is the one to which analog and logic circuits, equipments and systems can be related or benchmarked.

Return: The low (reference) side of a wire pair (e.g., neutral), outer jacket of a coax or conductor providing a path for intentional current to get back to the source.

Bond: The mechanism used to joint two metal surfaces via a low-impedance path.

Connection: A mechanical joint between two electrical conductors, often including an intermediary conductor such as a jumper, pigtail or shield braid.

Here are some examples:

1. **Right:** Connect the chassis reference to green safety wire.

   Wrong: Ground the chassis to safety wire.

2. **Right:** Bond the cover plate to the metallic housing via screws and electrical gaskets.

   Wrong: Ground the cover plate to the housing ground via screws and gaskets.

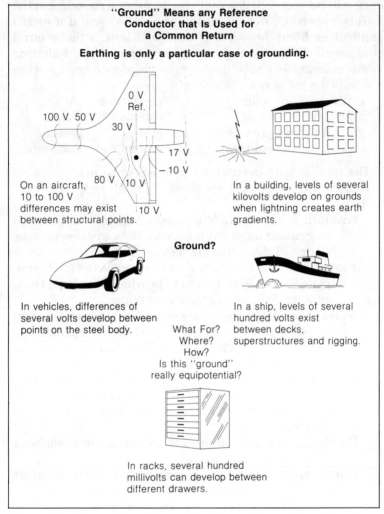

"Ground" Means any Reference Conductor that Is Used for a Common Return

Earthing is only a particular case of grounding.

On an aircraft, 10 to 100 V differences may exist between structural points.

In a building, levels of several kilovolts develop on grounds when lightning creates earth gradients.

Ground?

In vehicles, differences of several volts develop between points on the steel body.

What For?
Where?
How?
Is this "ground" really equipotential?

In a ship, levels of several hundred volts exist between decks, superstructures and rigging.

In racks, several hundred millivolts can develop between different drawers.

Figure 1.4—"Ground" can be a misleading, ambiguous term if one does not consider its electrical parameters.

1.3 Rationale for Grounding

This section presents an overview of why grounding is important. Most of the shock hazard and fault-clearance grounding applications which will be seen in this section stem from the fact that ac distribution generally is done with an earthed neutral. Therefore it may be necessary to briefly remind the reader why electrical power is supplied with an earthed neutral in the first place.

Figure 1.5a shows that a perfectly floated source would be harmless to people touching bare conductors: there is no possible return path. However, in 1.5b we see that in reality there is no such a thing as a perfectly floated network. Especially with power utilities, as soon as some length of wire rests above ground, stray capacitances are created which can range from 3 to 10 pF/m for overhead wires to 30 to 100 pF/m for buried armored cables. Therefore at 60 Hz, 300 m of line would offer a leakage impedance to ground of 1 to 3 MΩ for overhead lines and 100 to 300 kΩ for buried lines. For the human body touching it, this represents a 0.1 to 1 mA current source (for a 115 Vac supply) or 0.2 to 2 mA (for a 230 Vac supply). Consequently, to obviate the hazards of floated distribution, companies usually connect their neutral to earth, which also creates a path for lightning and power fault clearance.

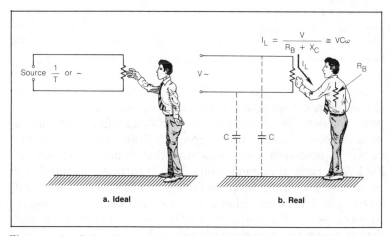

Figure 1.5—Safety Issue with a Supposedly Floated Power Network

1.3.1 Electrical Shock Hazards

Ac power distribution in private homes, buildings, hospitals and industrial sites is governed by local and national codes. In the U.S.A., the National Fire Protection Association (NFPA)

has issued NFPA-STD-70 **National Electrical Code,** dealing with standards on wiring and electrical devices. One requirement is that with each outgoing phase and neutral wire there must be a safety ground (green) wire.[1] The same applies for three-wire, 115/115/230 Vac systems in which a second hot wire (red) is added as shown in Fig. 1.6.

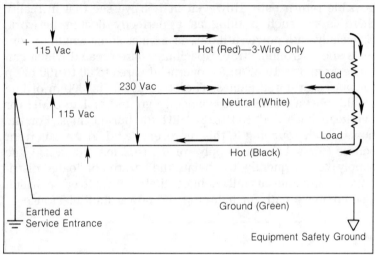

Figure 1.6—Standard 2- and 3-Wire Electrical Wire Coding in U.S.A.

Look at the equipment in Fig. 1.7 and assume first that its chassis is not connected to the safety ground. If the hot side were accidentally shorted to the equipment frame, the latter would become 115 Vac hot to ground. (Notice that no fuse will blow.) If someone were touching that frame as shown in Fig.1.7a, a path of current would return through his hand and continue through the body and out either (1) the other hand if it were touching some other reference such as another grounded piece or (2) the soles of the feet to a concrete floor and thence to the building ground.

If the person's body resistance is as low as 1,000 Ω, 115 mA will be flowing through it. Unfortunately, 75 mA of current through the body could be fatal. These **shock** hazards can be avoided by tying the frame to the neutral earthing point via the green wire as is done in a modern ac power cord.

Now, Fig. 1.7b shows that if the same fault as in 1.7a exists (e.g., damaged insulation or a live part accidentally touching the case), two things will result:

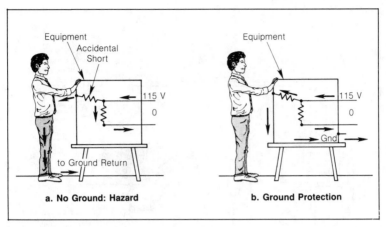

Figure 1.7—Safety and Shock Hazards with and without Equipment Grounds

1. A fuse or circuit breaker will probably trigger, alerting the user that something is not right.
2. Even if the user ignores this warning, when he touches the frame it will be at the ground potential and no danger will exist. However, to be able to say that the frame is at the ground potential, the grounding conductor must have a sufficiently low impedance such that the Z × I product of the fault current does not create a hazardous voltage shift. All the same, all the metal parts between the touched zone and the safety wire must be capable of carrying the fault current without excessive voltage build-up.

This is the basis of the shock protection aspect of grounding.

Figure 1.8 shows another facet of this safety issue, in a medical application. In Fig. 1.8a, a vacuum cleaner with a three-wire power cord is plugged into a wall outlet on the same circuit as an electrocardiogram (ECG or EKG) monitor. The third wire is grounded to the outer case, but the motor windings are exposed to damp dust. This provides a path for a "winding-to-outer-case" short circuit. This short would cause the case to rise to line voltage, but the case is grounded to protect the operator. In this example, the unit has not failed completely but has developed a fault that permits 1 A to flow down the ground wire and back to the power distribution panel.

1.11

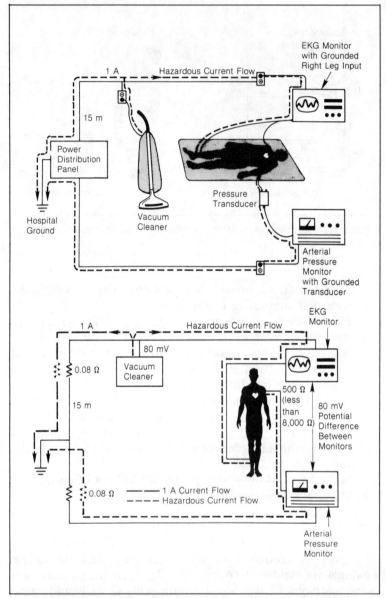

Figure 1.8—Microshock Hazard in Hospitals (Courtesy of IEEE Spectrum)

Figure 1.8b shows an analysis of the incident. If the panel is 15 m distant and the wiring is AWG 12, the ground wire has 0.08 Ω resistance. The hazard here is that the vacuum cleaner caused a difference in ground potential between the two devices. This allows a potentially lethal current to flow through the patient via the catheter.

More details on standards and mandatory grounding techniques will be covered in Chapter 4 of this book.

1.3.2 Power Fault Clearout

While a direct short between phase and neutral (or more generally a hot wire and its return) is normally taken care of by the fuse, circuit breakers or other current limiters, there are several abnormal conditions which could not be detected by these devices. Examples include but are not limited to:

1. Rodents and moisture causing insulation damage between wires (or windings) and chassis
2. Aging and thermal cycling of insulation materials
3. Mechanical damage during installation or manipulations
4. Environmental contaminants
5. Hot wire connected to chassis by mistake
6. Sustained arc to ground subsequent to a temporary overvoltage

These conditions are hazardous for several reasons:

1. Fault currents flowing in the grounds may raise the equipment frames to hazardous potential above earth (see Section 1.3.1).
2. Energy in a fault arc can be sufficient to vaporize copper or aluminium.
3. Large fault currents develop heat by Joule effect, creating burn and fire hazards.
4. Burning insulation generates toxic smoke.

Provided that the neutral is earthed at the source (e.g., the secondary of the power utility transformer), any first fault to ground, at building wiring level or equipment level, will appear as a phase-to-neutral short (see Fig. 1.6) and will trip a fuse or a circuit breaker. This will interrupt the hazardous current and alert the user.

1.3.3 Lightning Hazard

Grounding and earthing relate to lightning protection in several ways:

1. Lightning rods and aerials and their associated down conductors need a low-impedance path to sink the lightning currents to earth.
2. Currents indirectly induced by lightning electromagnetic fields could develop hazardous voltages between equipments or between equipment and ground.
3. Lightning overvoltage arrestors of any kind need a low-impedance path to ground to work efficiently.

In the case of buildings, lightning aerials and their earthing must be capable of draining the most severe lightning currents (e.g., 30 kA or 100 kA) without producing excessive voltage drops. In aircraft, all structures which can be hit by or carry lightning currents must be capable of carrying a worst-case 100 kA/10 µs current between two extremities without damaging internal equipment or causing a transient in excess of 500 V.

1.3.4 Electrostatic Drainage

The accumulation of static electricity on equipment, on materials being handled, and on operating personnel creates a serious hazard when flammable liquids, gases, dusts or explosives are present. For both the sake of human lives and prevention of property damage, the buildup of static electricity has to be avoided. Besides the catastrophic issues mentioned above, there are many reasons for controlling static electricity:

1. To facilitate handling and processing of textile fibers, granulates and paper in corresponding industries
2. To reduce the damage to integrated circuits during manufacturing and handling

Not widely known or remembered is also the fact that any ungrounded object above the earth's surface will develop some voltage gradient due to its exposure to ambient electrical fields, even at dc or low frequencies. For instance, the value of a normal, "fine weather" static field is about 100 V/m. This value increases drastically under certain conditions such as the proximity of high-voltage overhead lines or stormy weather.

Many static problems can be solved by bonding the various parts of an equipment together and grounding the entire system to earth reference.

Figure 1.9 shows the situation of a person underneath a high-voltage overhead power line. The value of line-to-body capacitance, which in fact is the value of line-to-ground capacitance in a fictitious "tube" composed of the human body, results in about 0.8 to 1 pF of coupling capacitance. For a 400 kV line at 50/60 Hz, this corresponds to a body current of about 120 μA (or if we relate to the electrical field directly below the wires, 17 μA/kV/m). This current is not even perceptible, the threshold of perception being in the 1 mA range.

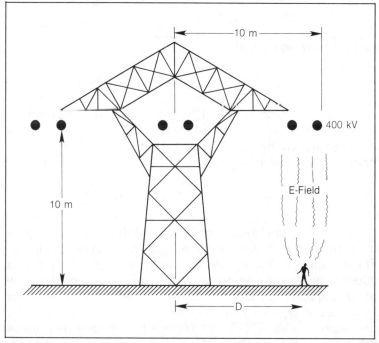

Figure 1.9—E-Field Exposure underneath a High-Voltage Line (continued next page)

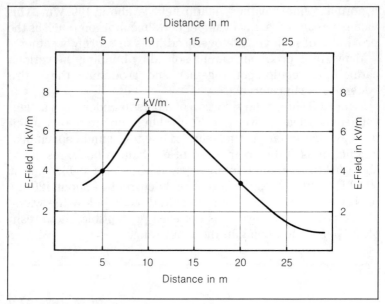

Figure 1.9—(continued)

If now we look at Fig. 1.10, where we see ungrounded structures, the voltages at the ungrounded fence (point A) or the ungrounded metal roof (point B) are set by the capacitive bridge C_1, C_2, that is:

$$V_A \text{ or } V_B = V_o \times \frac{X_{c2}}{X_{c1} + X_{c2}} = V_o \frac{C_1}{C_1 + C_2}$$

Since the length of wire or the area of the roof can be quite large, the charging effect of these capacitors can be significant. For instance, a few square meters of corrugated roof or a hundred meters of ungrounded fence can represent 30 to 100 pF of coupling capacitance C_1. From the same 400 kV, 50/60 Hz line, this corresponds to a current source of 3 to 10 mA seen by the person's body. This is not yet overly hazardous but felt as unpleasant. If, now, the rate of change of the E-field is no longer 50 or 60 Hz but a faster one (such as occurs during a lightning storm) the current may reach many times the above values. The danger disappears if points A or B are grounded.

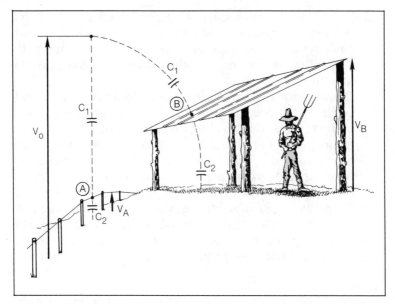

Figure 1.10—Aggravated Exposure by Ungrounded Metal Structures

1.3.5 Electromagnetic Interference (EMI) Control

This fifth reason for grounding encompasses all the noise reduction, RFI, EMP and other aspects. The borderline is somewhat ambiguous because lightning could have been classified as an EMI manifestation as well. But what is meant here is more the control of erroneous behavior of electronic circuits caused by electromagnetic influence. Although it is a regrettable myth to believe that "grounding" something will immediately eliminate electrical noise (in fact, in many cases, this will not solve the problem and could even aggravate it), there are several cases where grounding and earthing are necessary to reduce electromagnetic interference:

1. Anything acting as a Faraday shield (Faraday cage, transformer shields, cable shields, filter cases) needs to be connected to the same conductor as the EMI return path, and this return path is often the structure or earth reference.

2. If one wants to reduce common-impedance coupling between equipments, the common return that these two equipments are sharing must be a low-impedance path. This often is chosen, for the better or worse, as the structure.

3. Electrostatic discharge: if the static drainage recommended in 1.3.4 does not occur, the charge buildup will ultimately result in an abrupt discharge. In addition to the explosion and fire hazards mentioned before, this causes a transient electrical noise. Some ESD fixes consist of bonding and grounding equipment frames to improve their Faraday cage performance.

4. Hardening against electromagnetic pulse (and more specifically nuclear EMP) requires similar grounding and earthing precautions as for lightning. Additional difficulties stem from the rise time, which is 100 times faster.

1.4 Conflicts between Safety and EMI Control Considerations

The most common areas of disagreement between safety and EMI relate to filters and ground loop problems.

1.4.1 Conflicts Due to EMI Filters

To help reduce EMI in equipment of all types, it is common practice today to use filters at the power line entry in equipment. Here, either capacitors or filters are placed from both hot and neutral lines to the ground wire to bypass EMI. (The neutral line is also a source of EMI.) If the choice of these capacitors were left entirely up to the EMI specialist, he would prefer to put all possible RF bypassing to chassis via large-value capacitors. Unfortunately, this would create a safety issue. If we look at the same scenario as we had in Fig. 1.7, we see now in Fig. 1.11 an equipment which is connected to earth via its safety wire and equipped with a capacitive filter. If the operator is touching the frame, he is actually touching the phase (hot) wire through the impedance X_c (at 60 or 50 Hz) of the capacitor. This is of no consequence since the person's body resistance is shunted by the chassis-to-earth safety wire.

Note that the equipment has no electrical fault yet.

Now, as a first fault let's assume that the connection to earth via the green safety wire is missing: broken ground pin, loose wire terminal, illicit use of a two-wire extender for a three-wire power cord, etc. The equipment is still working perfectly, and nothing warns the user that this equipment could be dangerous to touch. However, if the user touches the equipment metallic case, the only path to ground is now his body resistance. For this reason, the U.S. National Electrical Code previously limited the use of such capacitors to 0.1 μF at 60 Hz, corresponding to a leakage reactive current of 5 mA. Thus, if an individual touched an equipment frame and the frame was not grounded, the maximum current through the body would be limited to the 5 mA.

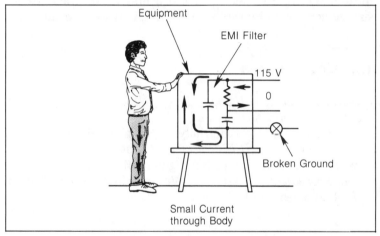

Figure 1.11—Equipment Connected to Earth and Equipped with a Capacitive Filter

Another kind of shock hazard exists due to either several devices with EMI filters operating off the same circuit or one device developing a short to frame. Both situations involve **microshock** hazards in hospitals, clinics and medical centers in which catheters via electrodes from EKG, arterial pressure monitors and similar biophysical instruments are in direct contact with the heart. When a high-impedance leakage or direct short develops in an equipment, such as when an ordinary appliance shares a common ground (green wire) with the medical instruments, a substantial current may flow in the ground wire. Most current will return directly to the power distribution panel, but some will follow another path directly through the heart as shown in Fig. 1.8.[2]

1.4.2 Conflicts Due to Ground Loop Isolation

As shown in Chapter 5 of this book and demonstrated analytically in Ref. 3 and many others, the EMI engineer in many instances would be perfectly happy if he could "float" either the electrical reference or the chassis of his equipment versus structure or earth. This would open "ground loops" and avoid circulation of common-mode current. Unfortunately (or fortunately, for the health of the users) these practices are strictly controlled by safety rules which always prevail.

1.5 References

1. *National Electrical Code (NEC)*, NFPA-STD-70 (National Fire Protection Association).
2. Friedlander, G.D., "Electricity in Hospitals: Elimination of Lethal Hazards," (*IEEE Spectrum*, Sept. 1971; pp. 40-51).
3. White, Donald R.J. and Mardiguian, M., *EMI Methodology and Procedures*, (Gainesville, Virginia: Interference Control Technologies, Inc.).

1.6 Bibliography

1. Ianovici, M., *Compatibilite Electro Magnetique*, (Ecole Polytechnique de Lausanne).
2. Herman, J.R., *Electromagnetic Ambients and Man-Made Noise*, (Gainesville, Virginia: Interference Control Technologies, Inc.).

Chapter 2

Ground Path Impedance

The behavior of any conductor used for grounding must be known from dc up to the highest frequency of concern. Every element (conductor) of a grounding system, whether it be for power grounding, signal grounding or lightning protection, has properties of resistance, capacitance and inductance. Shields and drain wires of signal cables, the green wire power ground and lightning down conductors have these properties. The resistance property is exhibited by all metals. The resistance of a ground path conductor is a function of the material, its length and its cross-sectional area. The capacitance associated with a ground conductor is determined by its geometric shape, its proximity to other conductors and the nature of the intervening dielectric. The inductance is a function of its size, geometry, length and, to a limited extent, the relative permeability of the metal.

2.1 DC Resistance and AC Impedances of Ground Paths

Intuitively, people relate the efficiency of a grounding conductor to its cross section: "the heavier, the better." Although this is true for dc and very low frequencies, it is not so when frequencies become higher and higher or current rise times become shorter and shorter. For instance, Fig. 2.1 shows that a round conductor with a 6 mm diameter is 100 times less resistive at dc than a 0.6 mm diameter wire. But its high-frequency impedance is only twice less. On the other hand, Fig. 2.1 reveals that a metal plane is always less impedant than virtually any wire or strap. This will be explained in detail in the following sections.

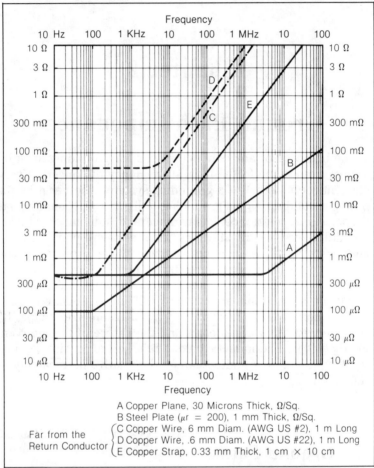

Figure 2.1—Impedances of Metal Planes and Conductors

A situation commonly encountered is that of a ground cable (power or signal) running along in the proximity of a ground plane. A representative circuit of this **simple** ground path is illustrated by Fig. 2.2.[1] The effects of the resistive elements of the **circuit** will predominate at very low frequencies. The relative influence of the reactive elements will increase at increasing frequencies. At some frequency, the magnitude of the inductive reactance ($j\omega L$) equals the magnitude of the capacitive reactance ($1/j\omega C$) and the circuit becomes resonant.

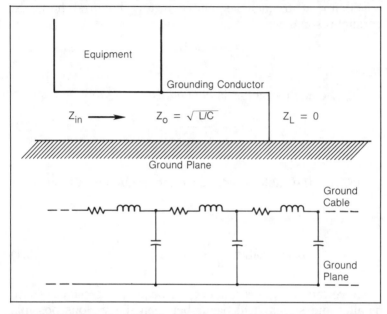

Figure 2.2—Equivalent Circuit of Ground Cable Parallel to a Ground Plane

The frequency of the primary (or first) resonance can be determined from:

$$f = \frac{1}{2\pi\sqrt{LC}} \qquad (2.1)$$

where,

    L = total cable inductance
    C = net capacitance between the cable and the ground plane

At resonance, the impedance presented by the grounding path will either be high or low, depending on whether it is parallel or series resonant, respectively. (In this context, the terms **parallel** and **series resonance** are used by similarity with a parallel LC or a series LC circuit.) At parallel resonance, the impedance seen looking into one end of the cable will be much higher than expected from $R + j\omega L$. For good conductors, e.g., copper and aluminum, $R < \omega L$; thus $j\omega L$ generally provides an accurate estimate of the impedance of a ground conductor at frequencies above a few hundred hertz. At parallel resonance:

$$Z_p = Q\omega L \qquad (2.2)$$

where,

Q, the quality factor, is defined as:

$$Q = \frac{\omega L}{R_{(ac)}} \qquad (2.3)$$

where,

$R_{(ac)}$ = the cable resistance at the frequency of resonance

Then:

$$Z_p = Q\omega L = \frac{\omega L}{R_{(ac)}} \times \omega L = \frac{\omega^2 L^2}{R_{(ac)}} \qquad (2.4)$$

Above the primary resonance, subsequent resonances (both parallel and series) will occur between the various possible combinations of inductances and capacitances (including parasitics) in the path. Series resonances in the grounding **circuit** will also occur between the inductances of line (wire) segments and one or more of the shunt capacitances. The impedance of a series resonant path is:

$$Z_s = \frac{\omega L}{Q} \qquad (2.5)$$

Therefore,

$$Z_s = \omega L \left(\frac{\omega L}{R_{(ac)}}\right)^{-1} = R_{(ac)} \qquad (2.6)$$

The series resonant impedance is equal to the series ac resistance of the particular inductance and capacitance in resonance. (At the higher-ordered resonances, where the resonant frequency is established by line [wire] segments and not the total path, the series impedance of the path to ground may be less than predicted from a consideration of the entire ground conductor length.) An understanding of the high-frequency behavior of a grounding conductor is simplified by viewing it as a transmission line.

If the ground is considered uniform along its run, well-known techniques can be used to describe the voltages and currents along the line as a function of time and distance. If the resistance elements in Fig. 2.2 are small relative to the inductances and capacitances, the grounding path has a characteristic impedance, Z_0, equal to $\sqrt{L/C}$ where L and C are the per-unit-length values of inductance and capacitance. The situation illustrated in Fig. 2.2 is of particular interest in equipment grounding. The input impedance of the grounding path, i.e., the impedance to ground seen by the equipment case, is:

$$Z_{in} = jZ_0 \times \tan \beta x \qquad (2.7)$$

where,

$\beta = \omega\sqrt{L/C}$ = the phase constant for the transmission line

x = the length of the path from the box to the short

Where βx is less than $\pi/2$ radians, i.e., when the electrical path length is less than $\lambda/4$, the input impedance of the short circuited line is inductive with a value ranging from $0(\beta x = 0)$ to ∞ ($\beta x = \pi/2$ radians). As βx increases beyond $\pi/2$ radians in value, the impedance of the grounding path cycles alternately between its open and short circuit values.

Thus, from the vantage point of the device or component which is grounded, the impedance is analogous to that offered by a short circuited transmission line. Where $\beta x = \pi/2$, the impedance offered by the ground conductor behaves like a lossless parallel LC resonant circuit. Just below resonance, the impedance is inductive; just above resonance, it is capacitive; while at resonance, the impedance is real and quite high (infinite in the perfectly lossless case). Resonance occurs at values of x equal to integer multiples of one-quarter wavelength, such as a one-half wavelength, three-quarter wavelength, etc.

Typical ground networks are complex circuits of resistances, inductances and capacitances with frequency-dependent properties including both parallel and series resonances.

Resonance effects in a grouding path are illustrated in Fig. 2.3, and Fig. 2.4 shows the swept frequency behavior of a grounding strap.[1] The relative effectiveness of a grounding conductor as a function of frequency is directly related to its impedance behavior. It is evident from Fig. 2.3 that, for maximum effectiveness, **ground conductor lengths should be a small portion of the wavelength at the frequency of the signal of concern.** Most effective performance is obtained at frequencies well below the first resonance.

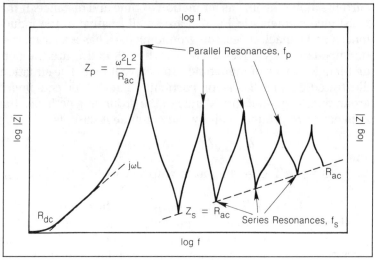

Figure 2.3—Typical Impedance vs. Frequency Behavior of a Grounding Conductor

Antenna effects are related to circuit resonance behavior. Ground conductors will act as antennas to radiate or pick up potential interference energy, depending upon their lengths relative to a wavelength, i.e., their efficiency. This fact permits a wavelength-to-physical-length ratio to be derived for ground conductors. The efficiency of a conductor as an antenna is related to its radiation resistance. Radiation resistance is a direct measure of the energy radiated from the antenna.

A good measure of performance for a wire is a quarter-wave monopole, which has a radiation resistance of 36.5 Ω. An antenna which transmits or receives 10 percent or less in comparison with a monopole logically can be defined as inefficient. To be effective, a ground wire should be an inefficient antenna, which means that it should exhibit a radiation resistance of 3.65 Ω or less. A monopole antenna with a length of less than λ/12 will have a radiation resistance of less than 3.65 Ω. The radiation resistance, i.e., the fictitious resistance which would dissipate the same power as the one the antenna radiates for the same current, varies as l^2/λ^2. A convenient criterion for a **poor** antenna, i.e., a good ground wire, is that its length is λ/12 or less. Thus, a rule of thumb in the design of an effective grounding system is to maintain ground wires exposed to potentially interfering signals at lengths less than 1/20 of the interfering signal wavelength.

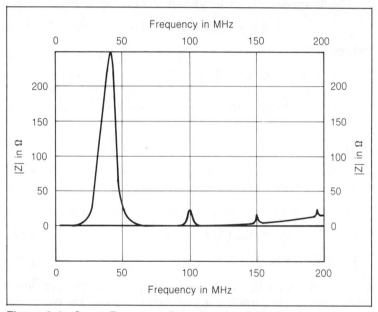

Figure 2.4—Swept Frequency Behavior of a Grounding Strap

2.2 Wire and Circular Conductors

The total impedance of a conductor, for $l \ll \lambda$ is given by:

$$Z = R_{(ac\ or\ dc)} + j\omega\ (L_{ext} + L_{int})\qquad(2.8)$$

R is the real part of the impedance and is equal to

$$R = \rho\frac{l}{S}\qquad(2.9)$$

where,

ρ = resistivity in ohms × meters at the temperature
   of concern

l = length in meters

S = cross section in square meters

The equation is also applicable to ρ, l and S in centimeters.

When frequency increases, the skin effect causes the current to leave progressively the center core of the conductor. Consequently, the effective cross section available for the current to flow decreases.

The ac resistance for a cylindrical conductor is:

$$R_{ac} = R_{dc} \, (d/4\delta + 1/4) \qquad (2.10)$$

where,

d = wire diameter in mm

$$\delta^* = \text{skin depth in mm} \simeq \frac{0.066}{\sqrt{\sigma_r \mu_r \, F_{MHz}}}$$

with,

σ_r = relative conductivity = 1 for copper

μ_r = relative permeability = 1 for copper

Therefore, for a copper wire at room temperature and for $d/2 > \delta$,

$$R_{ac} = R_{dc} \, (3.78 \times d \, \sqrt{F} + 1/4) \qquad (2.11)$$

for F in MHz and d in mm.

The external self-inductance L_{ext} is by far the most critical of the parasitic (i.e., undesired) effect in a grounding conductor. The internal inductance caused by the magnetic field **inside** the metal of the wire is of second order and is generally neglected in the calculation of a grounding conductor impedance.

For one wire above a ground plane, or a wire pair far from a ground plane:

For $h < l$(or $D < 2l$) in Fig. 2.5,

---

* Skin depth is defined as the surface thickness in which 63 percent of the current (or $1 - 1/e$) is concentrated at a given frequency.

2.8

$$L_{ext} = 0.2 \ (\ln \frac{4h}{d}) \ \mu H/m \qquad (2.12A)$$

For $h > l$ (or $D > 2l$)

$$L_{ext} = 0.2 \ (\ln \frac{4l}{d}) \ \mu H \qquad (2.12B)$$

where,

h = height above ground plane in meters
D = distance between the two wires (if a pair)
   = 2h (by image method)
d = wire diameter in meters
l = wire length in meters
ln = natural logarithm

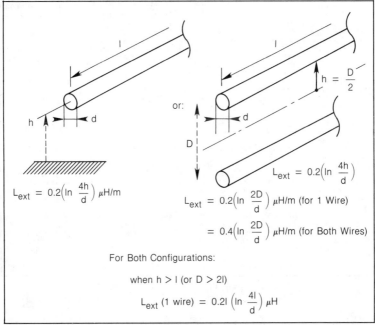

For Both Configurations:

when $h > l$ (or $D > 2l$)

$$L_{ext} \ (1 \ wire) = 0.2l \left(\ln \frac{4l}{d}\right) \mu H$$

Figure 2.5—External Self-Inductance

The first equation shows that increasing h for a given diameter d will increase L_{ext}. It seems that this increase would go on forever, but beyond a certain height (exactly when h exceeds l), the flux produced by the current in the loop formed by the wire and its return is no longer uniform. So L no longer increases with h, and Eq. (2.12b) applies, which is the free-space inductance of the wire. For a rough approximation and for ordinary types of layout, L_{ext} can be approximated by 1 μH/m or 10 nH/cm. Table 2.1 lists the resistance and inductance of round wires, and Table 2.2 lists the impedance at any frequency (up to l = λ/4) of three typical wire sizes. Table 2.3 displays the equivalence between American AWG, diameter, cross section and resistance for solid annealed copper wire.

Table 2.1—Resistance and Inductance of Straight Wires from AWG #0 to 34

Diam	AWG	R/L	10 cm	20 cm	30 cm	50 cm	70 cm	1 m	2 m	3 m	5 m	7 m	10 m	20 m	30 m
8.2	0	Res/μ	32	64	96	160	225	322	645	967	1,613	2,259	3,227	6,455	9,683
		Ind/n	62	153	254	474	710	1,086	2,450	3,918	7,042	10,329	15,470	33,712	53,001
6.5	2	Res/μ	51	102	153	56	358	512	1,026	1,539	2,565	3,592	5,132	10,265	15,398
		Ind/n	67	162	267	497	743	1,132	2,543	4,057	7,273	10,654	15,933	34,639	54,392
5.2	4	Res/μ	81	162	244	408	570	816	1,631	2,447	4,080	5,712	8,161	16,322	24,484
		Ind/n	71	171	281	520	775	1,179	2,635	4,196	7,505	10,978	16,397	35,567	55,783
4.1	6	Res/μ	129	259	389	648	907	1,297	2,594	3,892	6,488	9,083	12,976	25,954	38,931
		Ind/n	76	180	295	543	807	1,225	2,728	4,335	7,737	11,303	16,860	36,494	57,174
3.2	8	Res/μ	206	412	618	1,031	1,443	2,062	4,126	6,189	10,316	14,443	20,634	41,269	61,904
		Ind/n	80	189	309	566	840	1,271	2,821	4,474	7,969	11,627	17,324	37,422	58,566
2.6	10	Res/μ	328	655	983	1,640	2,296	3,280	6,561	9,842	16,404	22,967	32,810	65,621	98,432
		Ind/n	85	199	323	589	872	1,318	2,913	4,613	8,200	11,952	17,788	38,349	59,957
2	12	Res/m	0.5	0.1	1.5	2.5	3.5	5	10	15	25	36	51	103	156
		Ind/n	90	208	336	612	905	1,364	3,006	4,753	8,432	12,277	18,252	39,277	61,348
1.6	14	Res/m	.08	1.6	2.4	4	5.6	8	16	24	40	57	82	165	248
		Ind/n	94	217	350	635	937	1,410	3,099	4,892	8,664	12,601	18,715	40,204	62,739
1.3	16	Res/m	1	2	3	6	8	12	25	39	65	91	131	263	395
		Ind/n	99	226	364	659	969	1,457	3,191	5,031	8,896	12,926	19,179	41,132	64,131
1	18	Res/m	2	4	6	10	14	20	41	62	104	146	209	418	628
		Ind/n	103	235	378	682	1,002	1,503	3,284	5,170	9,128	13,250	19,643	42,059	65,522
0.8	20	Res/m	3	6	9	16	22	32	66	99	166	232	332	666	999
		Ind/n	108	245	392	705	1,034	1,549	3,377	5,309	9,360	13,575	20,107	42,987	66,913
0.6	22	Res/m	5	10	15	26	36	52	105	158	264	370	529	1,060	1,590
		Ind/n	113	254	406	728	1,067	1,596	3,470	5,448	9,592	13,900	20,570	43,914	68,305
0.5	24	Res/m	8	16	24	42	58	83	168	252	421	589	842	1,685	2,529
		Ind/n	117	263	420	751	1,099	1,642	3,562	5,587	9,823	14,224	21,034	44,842	69,696
0.4	26	Res/m	13	26	39	66	93	133	267	401	669	937	1,340	2,680	4,021
		Ind/n	122	273	434	774	1,132	1,688	3,655	5,726	10,055	14,549	21,498	45,769	71,087
0.3	28	Res/m	21	42	63	106	148	213	425	639	1,065	1,491	2,131	4,263	6,394
		Ind/n	127	282	448	798	1,164	1,735	3,748	5,865	10,287	14,873	21,962	46,697	72,478
0.25	30	Res/m	34	67	101	168	236	338	677	1,016	1,694	2,372	3,389	6,776	10,168
		Ind/n	131	291	461	821	1,197	1,781	3,841	6,005	10,519	15,198	22,425	47,624	73,870
0.2	32	Res/m	54	107	161	268	376	538	1,077	1,616	2,694	3,772	5,389	10,779	16,168
		Ind/n	136	300	475	844	1,229	1,828	3,933	6,144	10,751	15,523	22,889	48,552	75,261
0.16	34	Res/m	85	170	256	428	599	856	1,713	2,570	4,284	5,998	8,569	17,139	25,709
		Ind/n	140	310	489	867	1,261	1,874	4,026	6,283	10,983	15,847	23,353	49,479	76,652

μ = microhm,   m = milliohm   n = nanohenry

A phenomenon which is too often forgotten or overlooked is the proximity effect of two neighboring wires. Like for skin effect in a single conductor, proximity effect results from magnetic field influence reacting on the very currents which caused that field to exist. Just like with electrostatic charges, currents in the same direction "repel" each other while currents in opposite directions "attract" each other (Fig. 2.6). The result is a nonuniform current density in the conductors. With large currents and large dI/dt, these repulsion/attraction forces can actually move conductors, as when power and ground buses are thrown out of their clamps during lightning surges.

Table 2.2—Impedance of Straight Circular Copper Wires*

FREQ.	AWG#2, D = 6.54 mm				AWG#10, D = 2.59 mm				AWG#22, D = 0.64 mm			
	l=1 cm	l=10 cm	l=1 m	l=10 m	l=1 cm	l=10 cm	l=1 m	l=10 m	l=1 cm	l=10 cm	l=1 m	l=10 m
10 Hz	5.13 μ	51.4 μ	517 μ	5.22 m	32.7 μ	327 μ	3.28 m	32.8 m	529 μ	5.29 m	52.9 m	529 m
20 Hz	5.14 μ	52.0 μ	532 μ	5.50 m	32.7 μ	328 μ	3.28 m	32.8 m	529 μ	5.29 m	53.0 m	530 m
30 Hz	5.15 μ	52.8 μ	555 μ	5.94 m	32.8 μ	328 μ	3.28 m	32.9 m	529 μ	5.30 m	53.0 m	530 m
50 Hz	5.20 μ	55.5 μ	624 μ	7.16 m	32.8 μ	329 μ	3.30 m	33.2 m	530 μ	5.30 m	53.0 m	530 m
70 Hz	5.27 μ	59.3 μ	715 μ	8.68 m	32.8 μ	330 μ	3.33 m	33.7 m	530 μ	5.30 m	53.0 m	530 m
100 Hz	5.41 μ	66.7 μ	877 μ	11.2 m	32.9 μ	332 μ	3.38 m	34.6 m	530 μ	5.30 m	53.0 m	530 m
200 Hz	6.20 μ	99.5 μ	1.51 m	20.6 m	33.2 μ	345 μ	3.67 m	39.6 m	530 μ	5.30 m	53.0 m	530 m
300 Hz	7.32 μ	137 μ	2.19 m	30.4 m	33.7 μ	365 μ	4.11 m	46.9 m	530 μ	5.30 m	53.0 m	531 m
500 Hz	10.1 μ	219 μ	3.59 m	50.3 m	35.3 μ	425 μ	5.28 m	64.8 m	530 μ	5.31 m	53.2 m	533 m
700 Hz	13.2 μ	303 μ	5.01 m	70.2 m	37.7 μ	500 μ	6.66 m	84.8 m	530 μ	5.32 m	53.4 m	537 m
1 kHz	18.1 μ	429 μ	7.14 m	100 m	42.2 μ	632 μ	8.91 m	116 m	531 μ	5.34 m	53.9 m	545 m
2 kHz	35.2 μ	855 μ	14.2 m	200 m	62.5 μ	1.13 m	16.8 m	225 m	536 μ	5.48 m	56.6 m	589 m
3 kHz	52.5 μ	1.28 m	21.3 m	300 m	86.3 μ	1.65 m	25.0 m	336 m	545 μ	5.71 m	60.9 m	656 m
5 kHz	87.3 μ	2.13 m	35.6 m	500 m	137 μ	2.72 m	41.5 m	559 m	571 μ	6.39 m	72.9 m	835 m
7 kHz	122 μ	2.98 m	49.8 m	700 m	189 μ	3.79 m	58.1 m	783 m	609 μ	7.28 m	87.9 m	1.04 Ω
10 kHz	174 μ	4.26 m	71.2 m	1.00 Ω	268 μ	5.41 m	82.9 m	1.11 Ω	681 μ	8.89 m	113 m	1.39 Ω
20 kHz	348 μ	8.53 m	142 m	2.00 Ω	533 μ	10.8 m	165 m	2.23 Ω	1.00 m	15.2 m	207 m	2.63 Ω
30 kHz	523 μ	12.8 m	213 m	3.00 Ω	799 μ	16.2 m	248 m	3.35 Ω	1.39 m	22.0 m	305 m	3.91 Ω
50 kHz	871 μ	21.3 m	356 m	5.00 Ω	1.33 m	27.0 m	414 m	5.58 Ω	2.20 m	36.1 m	504 m	6.48 Ω
70 kHz	1.22 m	29.8 m	498 m	7.00 Ω	1.86 m	37.8 m	580 m	7.82 Ω	3.04 m	50.2 m	704 m	9.06 Ω
100 kHz	1.74 m	42.6 m	712 m	10.0 Ω	2.66 m	54.0 m	828 m	11.1 Ω	4.31 m	71.6 m	1.00 Ω	12.9 Ω
200 kHz	3.48 m	85.3 m	1.42 Ω	20.0 Ω	5.32 m	108 m	1.65 Ω	22.3 Ω	8.59 m	142 m	2.00 Ω	25.8 Ω
300 kHz	5.23 m	128 m	2.13 Ω	30.0 Ω	7.98 m	162 m	2.48 Ω	33.5 Ω	12.8 m	214 m	3.01 Ω	38.7 Ω
500 kHz	8.71 m	213 m	3.56 Ω	50.0 Ω	13.3 m	270 m	4.14 Ω	55.8 Ω	21.4 m	357 m	5.01 Ω	64.6 Ω
700 kHz	12.2 m	298 m	4.98 Ω	70.0 Ω	18.6 m	378 m	5.80 Ω	78.2 Ω	30.0 m	500 m	7.02 Ω	90.4 Ω
1 MHz	17.4 m	426 m	7.12 Ω	100 Ω	26.6 m	540 m	8.28 Ω	111 Ω	42.8 m	714 m	10.0 Ω	129 Ω
2 MHz	34.8 m	853 m	14.2 Ω	200 Ω	53.2 m	1.08 Ω	16.5 Ω	223 Ω	85.7 m	1.42 Ω	20.0 Ω	258 Ω
3 MHz	52.3 m	1.28 Ω	21.3 Ω	300 Ω	79.8 m	1.62 Ω	24.8 Ω	335 Ω	128 m	2.14 Ω	30.1 Ω	387 Ω
5 MHz	87.1 m	2.13 Ω	35.6 Ω	500 Ω	133 m	2.70 Ω	41.4 Ω	558 Ω	214 m	3.57 Ω	50.1 Ω	646 Ω
7 MHz	122 m	2.98 Ω	49.8 Ω	700 Ω	186 m	3.78 Ω	58.0 Ω	782 Ω	300 m	5.00 Ω	70.2 Ω	904 Ω
10 MHz	174 m	4.26 Ω	71.2 Ω	1.00 kΩ	266 m	5.40 Ω	82.8 Ω	1.11 kΩ	428 m	7.14 Ω	100 Ω	1.29 kΩ
20 MHz	348 m	8.53 Ω	142 Ω	2.00 kΩ	532 m	10.8 Ω	165 Ω	2.23 kΩ	857 m	14.2 Ω	200 Ω	2.58 kΩ
30 MHz	523 m	12.8 Ω	213 Ω	3.00 kΩ	798 m	16.2 Ω	248 Ω	3.35 kΩ	1.28 Ω	21.4 Ω	301 Ω	3.87 kΩ
50 MHz	871 m	21.3 Ω	356 Ω	5.00 kΩ	1.33 Ω	27.0 Ω	414 Ω	5.58 kΩ	2.14 Ω	35.7 Ω	501 Ω	6.46 kΩ
70 MHz	1.22 Ω	29.8 Ω	498 Ω	7.00 kΩ	1.86 Ω	37.8 Ω	580 Ω	7.82 kΩ	3.00 Ω	50.0 Ω	702 Ω	9.04 kΩ
100 MHz	1.74 Ω	42.6 Ω	712 Ω	10.0 kΩ	2.66 Ω	54.0 Ω	828 Ω	11.1 kΩ	4.28 Ω	71.4 Ω	1.00 kΩ	12.9 kΩ
200 MHz	3.48 Ω	85.3 Ω	1.42 kΩ	20.0 kΩ	5.32 Ω	108 Ω	1.65 kΩ	22.3 kΩ	8.57 Ω	142 Ω	2.00 kΩ	25.8 kΩ
300 MHz	5.23 Ω	128 Ω	2.13 kΩ	30.0 kΩ	7.98 Ω	162 Ω	2.48 kΩ	33.5 kΩ	12.8 Ω	214 Ω	3.01 kΩ	38.7 kΩ
500 MHz	8.71 Ω	213 Ω	3.56 kΩ	50.0 kΩ	13.3 Ω	270 Ω	4.14 kΩ	55.8 kΩ	21.4 Ω	357 Ω	5.01 kΩ	64.6 kΩ
700 MHz	12.2 Ω	298 Ω	4.98 kΩ	70.0 kΩ	18.6 Ω	376 Ω	5.80 kΩ	78.2 kΩ	30.0 Ω	500 Ω	7.02 kΩ	90.4 kΩ
1 GHz	17.4 Ω	426 Ω	7.12 kΩ		26.6 Ω	540 Ω	8.28 kΩ		42.8 Ω	714 Ω	10.0 kΩ	

AWG = American Wire Gage
D = wire diameter in mm
l = wire length in cm or m
μ = microhms
m = milliohms
Ω = ohms

Non-Valid Region for which l ≥ λ/4

*(Values Derived from Free-Space Inductance, when the Conductor Is Far from Its Return Circuit or Plane)

Table 2.3—Properties of Annealed Copper Wire

AWG No.	Diameter		Cross-Sectional Area		Resistance in Ohms	
	mils	mm	cmil	mm²	per 1,000 ft	per km
4/0	460.0	11.7	211,600	107.2	0.049	0.161
3/0	409.6	10.4	167,800	85.0	0.062	0.203
2/0	364.8	9.3	133,100	67.4	0.078	0.256
1/0	324.9	8.3	105,500	53.4	0.098	0.322
1	289.3	7.3	83,690	42.4	0.124	0.407
2	257.6	6.5	66,370	33.6	0.156	0.512
4	204.3	5.2	41,740	21.1	0.248	0.814
6	162.0	4.1	26,250	13.3	0.395	1.296
8	128.5	3.3	16,510	8.4	0.628	2.060
10	101.9	2.6	10,380	5.3	0.999	3.278
12	80.8	2.1	6,530	3.3	1.588	5.210
14	64.1	1.6	4,107	2.1	2.525	8.284
16	50.8	1.3	2,583	1.3	4.016	13.176
18	40.3	1.0	1.624	0.8	6.385	20.948
20	31.9	0.8	1.022	0.5	10.150	33.300

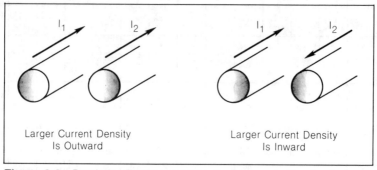

Larger Current Density Is Outward

Larger Current Density Is Inward

Figure 2.6—Proximity Effects between Two Discrete Conductors

2.3 Straps and Flat Buses

Table 2.4[1] lists the per unit length resistance, R/l, of representative grounding/bonding straps as calculated from:

$$R/l = \frac{\rho}{A} \qquad (2.13)$$

where,

ρ = resistivity of the material
A = cross sectional area of the strap, in consistent units

Table 2.4—Resistance Properties of Grounding Straps

Strap Size in cm	Unit Length Resistance in $\mu\Omega$/cm		
	Copper	Aluminum	Steel
0.05 × 0.5	69.2	107.6	388.9
0.05 × 1.0	34.6	53.8	194.5
0.05 × 2.0	17.3	26.9	97.2
0.05 × 5.0	6.9	10.8	38.8
0.05 × 10.0	3.5	5.4	19.7
0.1 × 0.5	34.6	53.8	194.5
0.1 × 1.0	17.3	26.9	97.2
0.1 × 2.0	8.7	13.5	48.9
0.1 × 5.0	3.5	5.4	19.7
0.1 × 10.0	1.7	2.7	9.6

Assessment of the capacitance associated with a ground conductor requires knowledge of its surroundings. The inductance, however, may be calculated for rectangular conductors from:

$$L = 0.0021 \left[\ln \frac{2l}{b + c} + 0.5 + 0.2235 \frac{b + c}{l} \right] \mu H \quad (2.14)$$

where,

b = width of the strap
c = thickness of the strap
l = length of the strap in centimeters

Tables 2.5 and 2.6 give the inductance and impedance values of typical rectangular straps of selected dimensions. Figures 2.7 through 2.9 illustrate the relative behavior of the inductance of rectangular straps as a function of length, width and thickness, respectively.[1] Observe that the inductance does decrease with increasing width and increases with increasing length. Thus, a recommendation frequently encountered is that of restricting the length-to-width ratio to 5:1 for grounding and bonding straps.

Table 2.5—Inductance of Various Straps

Width b in cm	Thickness c in mm	L, in μH for:		
		l = 15 cm	l = 30 cm	l = 100 cm
1	0.2	0.115	0.30	1.15
	1	0.1	0.27	1.11
	2	0.08	0.22	0.8
2.5	0.2	0.09	0.22	1
	1	0.08	0.2	0.90
	2	0.07	0.17	0.80
5	0.2	0.07	0.19	0.85
	1	0.066	0.18	0.83
	2	0.06	0.16	0.75

Table 2.6—Impedance of Copper Straps*

FREQ.	0.3 mm × 10 mm Strap				1 mm × 10 mm Strap				2 mm × 50 mm Strap			
	l=3 cm	l=10 cm	l=1 m	l=10 m	l=3 cm	l=10 cm	l=1 m	l=10 m	l=15 cm	l=50 cm	l=1 m	l=10 m
10 Hz	173 μ	574 μ	5.74 m	57.4 m	52.4 μ	172 μ	1.72 m	17.2 m	30.1 μ	108 μ	180 μ	1.90 m
20 Hz	174 μ	574 μ	5.74 m	57.5 m	53.3 μ	172 μ	1.73 m	17.3 m	34.4 μ	130 μ	201 μ	2.36 m
30 Hz	175 μ	574 μ	5.75 m	57.5 m	54.1 μ	172 μ	1.73 m	17.5 m	38.8 μ	151 μ	232 μ	2.98 m
50 Hz	176 μ	575 μ	5.75 m	57.6 m	55.8 μ	173 μ	1.76 m	17.9 m	47.4 μ	195 μ	312 μ	4.40 m
70 Hz	178 μ	575 μ	5.76 m	57.9 m	57.5 μ	175 μ	1.79 m	18.6 m	56.0 μ	238 μ	404 μ	5.93 m
100 Hz	181 μ	576 μ	5.79 m	58.3 m	60.0 μ	177 μ	1.86 m	19.9 m	69.0 μ	304 μ	549 μ	8.29 m
200 Hz	189 μ	581 μ	5.92 m	60.9 m	68.5 μ	192 μ	2.24 m	26.4 m	112 μ	522 μ	1.05 m	16.3 m
300 Hz	198 μ	589 μ	6.14 m	65.0 m	76.9 μ	215 μ	2.75 m	34.7 m	155 μ	739 μ	1.57 m	24.3 m
500 Hz	215 μ	614 μ	6.79 m	76.6 m	93.8 μ	275 μ	3.97 m	53.1 m	242 μ	1.17 μ	2.61 m	40.5 m
700 Hz	233 μ	615 μ	7.66 m	91.3 m	111 μ	346 μ	5.30 m	72.5 m	328 μ	1.61 μ	3.65 m	56.7 m
1 kHz	259 μ	721 μ	9.25 m	116 m	136 μ	462 μ	7.37 m	102 m	457 μ	2.26 μ	5.22 m	81.1 m
2 kHz	345 μ	1.04 m	15.5 m	210 m	220 μ	874 μ	14.4 m	201 m	889 μ	4.44 μ	10.4 m	162 m
3 kHz	432 μ	1.43 m	22.4 m	309 m	304 μ	1.29 m	21.5 m	302 m	1.32 m	6.62 μ	15.6 m	243 m
5 kHz	605 μ	2.25 m	36.7 m	510 m	473 μ	2.15 m	35.8 m	503 m	2.84 m	11.0 m	26.1 m	405 m
7 kHz	779 μ	3.11 m	51.0 m	712 m	642 μ	3.00 m	50.2 m	704 m	3.05 m	15.3 m	36.5 m	567 m
10 kHz	1.04 m	4.40 m	72.7 m	1.01 Ω	895 μ	4.29 m	71.7 m	1.00 Ω	4.34 m	21.9 μ	52.2 m	810 m
20 kHz	1.91 m	8.75 m	145 m	2.02 Ω	1.74 m	8.57 m	143 m	2.01 Ω	8.66 m	43.6 μ	104 m	1.62 Ω
30 kHz	2.77 m	13.1 m	217 m	3.04 Ω	2.58 m	12.8 m	215 m	3.01 Ω	13.0 m	65.4 μ	156 m	2.43 Ω
50 kHz	4.51 m	21.8 m	362 m	5.07 Ω	4.27 m	21.4 m	358 m	5.03 Ω	21.6 m	109 μ	261 m	4.05 Ω
70 kHz	6.24 m	30.5 m	507 m	7.10 Ω	5.95 m	30.0 m	501 m	7.04 Ω	30.2 m	152 μ	365 m	5.67 Ω
100 kHz	8.84 m	43.7 m	725 m	10.1 Ω	8.42 m	42.8 m	716 m	10.0 Ω	43.2 m	218 μ	522 m	8.10 Ω
200 kHz	17.5 m	87.4 m	1.45 Ω	20.2 Ω	16.9 m	85.7 m	1.43 Ω	20.1 Ω	86.4 m	436 μ	1.04 Ω	16.2 Ω
300 kHz	26.2 m	131 m	2.17 Ω	30.4 Ω	25.3 m	128 m	2.15 Ω	30.1 Ω	129 m	653 μ	1.56 Ω	24.3 Ω
500 kHz	43.5 m	218 m	3.62 Ω	50.7 Ω	42.2 m	214 m	3.58 Ω	50.3 Ω	216 m	1.09 Ω	2.61 Ω	40.5 Ω
700 kHz	60.8 m	305 m	5.07 Ω	71.0 Ω	59.1 m	300 m	5.01 Ω	70.4 Ω	302 m	1.52 Ω	3.65 Ω	56.7 Ω
1 MHz	86.9 m	437 m	7.25 Ω	101 Ω	84.4 m	428 m	7.16 Ω	100 Ω	432 m	2.18 Ω	5.22 Ω	81.0 Ω
2 MHz	173 m	874 m	14.5 Ω	202 Ω	169 m	857 m	14.3 Ω	201 Ω	863 m	4.36 Ω	10.4 Ω	162 Ω
3 MHz	260 m	1.31 Ω	21.7 Ω	304 Ω	253 m	1.28 Ω	21.5 Ω	301 Ω	1.29 Ω	6.53 Ω	15.6 Ω	243 Ω
5 MHz	434 m	2.18 Ω	36.2 Ω	507 Ω	422 m	2.14 Ω	35.8 Ω	503 Ω	2.16 Ω	10.9 Ω	26.1 Ω	405 Ω
7 MHz	607 m	3.05 Ω	50.7 Ω	710 Ω	590 m	3.00 Ω	50.1 Ω	704 Ω	3.02 Ω	15.2 Ω	36.5 Ω	567 Ω
10 MHz	867 m	4.37 Ω	72.5 Ω	1.01 kΩ	843 m	4.28 Ω	71.6 Ω	1.00 kΩ	4.32 Ω	21.8 Ω	52.2 Ω	810 Ω
20 MHz	1.73 Ω	8.74 Ω	145 Ω	2.02 kΩ	1.69 Ω	8.57 Ω	143 Ω	2.01 kΩ	8.63 Ω	43.6 Ω	104 Ω	1.62 kΩ
30 MHz	2.60 Ω	13.1 Ω	217 Ω	3.04 kΩ	2.53 Ω	12.8 Ω	215 Ω	3.01 kΩ	13.0 Ω	65.3 Ω	156 Ω	2.43 kΩ
50 MHz	4.33 Ω	21.8 Ω	362 Ω	5.07 kΩ	4.21 Ω	21.4 Ω	358 Ω	5.03 kΩ	21.6 Ω	109 Ω	261 Ω	4.05 kΩ
70 MHz	6.07 Ω	30.5 Ω	507 Ω	7.10 kΩ	5.90 Ω	30.0 Ω	501 Ω	7.04 kΩ	30.2 Ω	152 Ω	365 Ω	5.67 kΩ
100 MHz	8.67 Ω	43.7 Ω	725 Ω	10.1 kΩ	8.43 Ω	42.8 Ω	716 Ω	10.0 kΩ	43.2 Ω	218 Ω	522 Ω	8.10 kΩ
200 MHz	17.3 Ω	87.4 Ω	1.45 kΩ	20.2 kΩ	16.9 Ω	85.7 Ω	1.43 kΩ	20.1 kΩ	86.3 Ω	436 Ω	1.04 kΩ	16.2 kΩ
300 MHz	26.0 Ω	131 Ω	2.17 kΩ	30.4 kΩ	25.3 Ω	128 Ω	2.15 kΩ	30.1 kΩ	130 Ω	653 Ω	1.56 kΩ	24.3 kΩ
500 MHz	43.3 Ω	218 Ω	3.62 kΩ	50.7 kΩ	42.1 Ω	214 Ω	3.58 kΩ	50.3 kΩ	216 Ω	1.09 kΩ	2.61 kΩ	40.5 kΩ
700 MHz	60.7 Ω	305 Ω	5.07 kΩ	71.0 kΩ	59.0 Ω	300 Ω	5.01 kΩ	70.4 kΩ	302 Ω	1.52 kΩ	3.65 kΩ	56.7 kΩ
1 GHz	86.7 Ω	437 Ω	7.25 kΩ		84.3 Ω	428 Ω	7.16 kΩ		432 Ω	2.18 kΩ	5.22 kΩ	81.0 kΩ

Strap dimensions are thickness × width in mm

l = strap length in cm or m
μ = microhms
m = milliohms
Ω = ohms

▨ Value Subject To Error Where l $\geq$ λ/20

*(Worst-case values derived from free-space inductance, when the conductor is far from its return circuit or plane.)

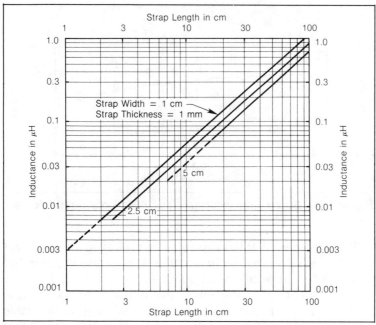

Figure 2.7—Ground Strap Inductance as a Function of Length and for Different Strap Widths. Note that for length/width < 2, the model becomes inapplicable since the strap behaves more like a ground plane.

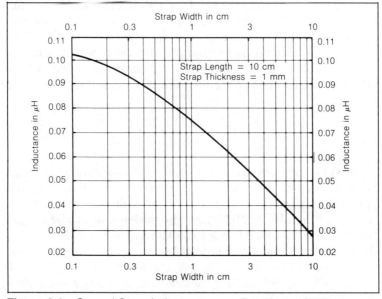

Figure 2.8—Ground Strap Inductance as a Function of Width

2.15

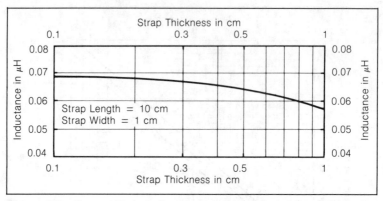

Figure 2.9—Ground Strap Inductance as a Function of Strap Thickness

The behavior of the strap reactance relative to a straight round wire, as a function of length-to-width ratio is illustrated by Fig. 2.10.[1] Note that a 5:1 length-to-width ratio indicates a reactance of about 45 percent of that of a straight round wire. It also must be noted that a 5:1 length-to-width is the value below which Eq. (2.14) starts to give pessimistic (too high) inductance values since a very wide strap will approach the condition of a ground plane, which is described in next section.

The previous values are valid for a straight strap. If the strap is bent into a "U" shape as in Fig 2.11, the self-inductance will be higher, and the self-resonant frequency of the strap will be lower. As explained in Section 2.1, for the general case of a ground path a ground strap has its parasitic inductance L which will resonate with its parasitic capacitance C, at a frequency:

$$f_o = \frac{1}{2\pi\sqrt{LC}}$$

As will be seen in Section 3.3, the self-capacitance of a strap is of little meaning since it is generally paralleled by the parasitic capacitance of the two structures being bonded, which is generally much higher. The designer has to be careful not to use straps which will have an *in situ* resonance within the operating frequency range of his equipment. Using shorter and wider straps or using several straps in parallel will decrease L, thereby shifting the resonant frequency to a higher number.

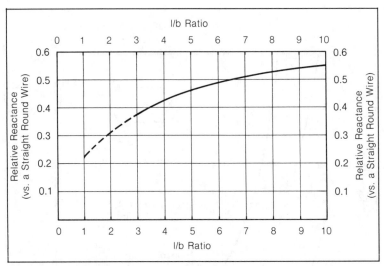

Figure 2.10—Relative Inductive Reactance vs. Length-to-Width Ratio of Flat Straps, Compared to that of a Round Wire

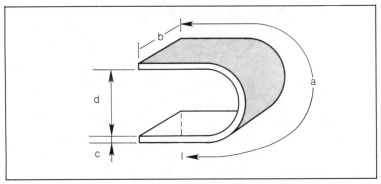

Figure 2.11—"U"-Shaped Ground Strap, Showing More Inductance

Figure 2.12 shows the resonant frequencies associated with a 50 cm by 30 cm cabinet, chassis or circuit board separated from a ground plane with various thicknesses of air space and Teflon®. It is grounded to the ground plane with 1 cm × 1 mm ground strap of varying lengths.

Note that practical and reasonable lengths of less than 30 cm can easily produce resonant behavior in the HF region. These resonances can be particularly important in EMI control in strong radiated environments by actually enhancing pickup rather than suppressing it.

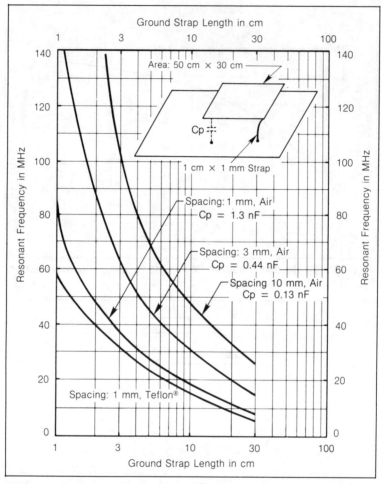

Figure 2.12—Ground Strap Resonance Effects

2.4 Ground Planes

Even large sheet ground planes do not offer zero imped-ances, although they will offer three to four orders of magni-tude less impedance than a single small wire. Typical ground plane impedances in ohms per square (Ω/sq) are given in Table 2.7. For direct comparison with straight copper wires, see

2.18

Table 2.2. The dc resistance, R_{dc}, of a metal ground plane is:

$$R_{dc} = \frac{\rho l}{A} \qquad (2.15)$$

$$= \frac{1,000 \, l}{\sigma l t}$$

$$R_{dc} = \frac{1,000}{\sigma t} \; \Omega/sq \qquad (2.16)$$

where,

ρ = resistivity of the metal in $\Omega \times$ m, such that

$R = \rho \dfrac{l}{A}$ will be in Ω

σ = $\sigma_c \, \sigma_r$ conductivity of the metal = $1/\rho$
σ_c = 5.80×10^7 mhos/m for copper
σ_r = conductivity relative to copper
   = 0.17 for cold-rolled steel
t = metal thickness in mm

Thus Eq. (2.16) becomes:

$$R_{dc} = \frac{17.2}{\sigma_r t} \; \mu\Omega/sq \qquad (2.17)$$

The reactance of a metal ground plane is:*

$$Z_{RF} = \frac{369 \, \sqrt{\mu_r \, f/\sigma_r}}{1 - e^{-t/\delta}} \; \mu\Omega/sq \qquad (2.18)$$

where,

μ_r = permeability relative to copper
   = 200 for cold-rolled steel
f = frequency in MHz
δ = skin depth in cm

$$= \frac{0.066}{\mu_r \sigma_r \, f_{MHz}} \text{ for any metal}$$

---

*See page 1.12 of *Electromagnetic Shielding Materials and Performance*, published by Don White Consultants, Inc., 1975.

For instance, as soon as skin depth δ becomes less than thickness t (i.e., beyond 10 kHz for 1 mm of copper or beyond 1 MHz for 0.1 mm of copper):

$$Z_{RF} \text{ for copper planes} \quad = 369 \sqrt{F_{MHz}} \quad \mu\Omega/sq$$
$$Z_{RF} \text{ for aluminum planes} \quad = 476 \sqrt{F_{MHz}} \quad \mu\Omega/sq$$
$$Z_{RF} \text{ for ordinary steel planes} \quad = 12.6 \sqrt{F_{MHz}} \quad m\Omega/sq$$

The concept of ohms per square is explained in Fig. 2.13. Here it is apparent that no matter how large the square sample, its resistance will keep the same value.

Table 2.7—Metal Ground Plane Impedances in Ohms/Square

Freq.	COPPER, COND-1, PERM-1						STEEL, COND-0.17, PERM-200					
	t = 0.03	t = 0.1	t = 0.3	t = 1	t = 3	t = 10	t = 0.03	t = 0.1	t = 0.3	t = 1	t = 3	t = 10
10 Hz	574 μ	172 μ	57.4 μ	17.2 μ	5.74 μ	1.75 μ	3.38 m	1.01 m	338 μ	101 μ	38.5 μ	40.3 μ
20 Hz	574 μ	172 μ	57.4 μ	17.2 μ	5.75 μ	1.83 μ	3.38 m	1.01 m	338 μ	102 μ	49.5 μ	56.6 μ
30 Hz	574 μ	172 μ	57.4 μ	17.2 μ	5.75 μ	1.95 μ	3.38 m	1.01 m	338 μ	103 μ	62.3 μ	69.3 μ
50 Hz	574 μ	172 μ	57.4 μ	17.2 μ	5.76 μ	2.30 μ	3.38 m	1.01 m	338 μ	106 μ	86.2 μ	89.6 μ
70 Hz	574 μ	172 μ	57.4 μ	17.2 μ	5.78 μ	2.71 μ	3.38 m	1.01 m	338 μ	110 μ	105 μ	106 μ
100 Hz	574 μ	172 μ	57.4 μ	17.2 μ	5.82 μ	3.35 μ	3.38 m	1.01 m	338 μ	118 μ	127 μ	126 μ
200 Hz	574 μ	172 μ	57.4 μ	17.2 μ	6.04 μ	5.16 μ	3.38 m	1.01 m	340 μ	157 μ	179 μ	179 μ
300 Hz	574 μ	172 μ	57.4 μ	17.2 μ	6.38 μ	6.43 μ	3.38 m	1.01 m	342 μ	199 μ	219 μ	219 μ
500 Hz	574 μ	172 μ	57.4 μ	17.3 μ	7.36 μ	8.27 μ	3.38 m	1.01 m	350 μ	275 μ	283 μ	283 μ
700 Hz	574 μ	172 μ	57.4 μ	17.3 μ	8.55 μ	9.77 μ	3.38 m	1.01 m	362 μ	335 μ	335 μ	335 μ
1 kHz	574 μ	172 μ	57.4 μ	17.5 μ	10.4 μ	11.6 μ	3.38 m	1.01 m	385 μ	403 μ	400 μ	400 μ
2 kHz	574 μ	172 μ	57.5 μ	18.3 μ	16.1 μ	16.5 μ	3.38 m	1.02 m	495 μ	566 μ	566 μ	566 μ
3 kHz	574 μ	172 μ	57.5 μ	19.5 μ	20.3 μ	20.2 μ	3.38 m	1.03 m	623 μ	693 μ	694 μ	694 μ
5 kHz	574 μ	172 μ	57.6 μ	23.0 μ	26.2 μ	26.1 μ	3.38 m	1.06 m	862 μ	896 μ	896 μ	896 μ
7 kHz	574 μ	172 μ	57.8 μ	27.1 μ	30.9 μ	30.9 μ	3.38 m	1.10 m	1.05 m	1.06 m	1.06 m	1.06 m
10 kHz	574 μ	172 μ	58.2 μ	33.5 μ	36.9 μ	36.9 μ	3.38 m	1.18 m	1.27 m	1.26 m	1.26 m	1.26 m
20 kHz	574 μ	172 μ	60.4 μ	51.6 μ	52.2 μ	52.2 μ	3.40 m	1.57 m	1.79 m	1.79 m	1.79 m	1.79 m
30 kHz	574 μ	172 μ	63.8 μ	64.3 μ	63.9 μ	63.9 μ	3.42 m	1.99 m	2.19 m	2.19 m	2.19 m	2.19 m
50 kHz	574 μ	173 μ	73.6 μ	82.7 μ	82.6 μ	82.6 μ	3.50 m	2.75 m	2.83 m	2.83 m	2.83 m	2.83 m
70 kHz	574 μ	173 μ	85.5 μ	97.7 μ	97.7 μ	97.7 μ	3.62 m	3.35 m	3.35 m	3.35 m	3.35 m	3.35 m
100 kHz	574 μ	175 μ	104 μ	116 μ	116 μ	116 μ	3.85 m	4.03 m	4.00 m	4.00 m	4.00 m	4.00 m
200 kHz	575 μ	183 μ	161 μ	165 μ	165 μ	165 μ	4.95 m	5.66 m	5.66 m	5.66 m	5.66 m	5.66 m
300 kHz	575 μ	195 μ	203 μ	202 μ	202 μ	202 μ	6.23 m	6.93 m	6.94 m	6.94 m	6.94 m	6.94 m
500 kHz	576 μ	230 μ	262 μ	261 μ	261 μ	261 μ	8.62 m	8.96 m	8.96 m	8.96 m	8.96 m	8.96 m
700 kHz	578 μ	271 μ	309 μ	309 μ	309 μ	309 μ	10.5 m	10.6 m	10.6 m	10.6 m	10.6 m	10.6 m
1 MHz	582 μ	335 μ	369 μ	369 μ	369 μ	369 μ	12.7 m	12.6 m	12.6 m	12.6 m	12.6 m	12.6 m
2 MHz	604 μ	516 μ	522 μ	522 μ	522 μ	522 μ	17.9 m	17.9 m	17.9 m	17.9 m	17.9 m	17.9 m
3 MHz	638 μ	643 μ	639 μ	639 μ	639 μ	639 μ	21.9 m	21.9 m	21.9 m	21.9 m	21.9 m	21.9 m
5 MHz	736 μ	827 μ	826 μ	826 μ	826 μ	826 μ	28.3 m	28.3 m	28.3 m	28.3 m	28.3 m	28.3 m
7 MHz	855 μ	977 μ	977 μ	977 μ	977 μ	977 μ	33.5 m	33.5 m	33.5 m	33.5 m	33.5 m	33.5 m
10 MHz	1.04 m	1.16 m	1.16 m	1.16 m	1.16 m	1.16 m	40.0 m	40.0 m	40.0 m	40.0 m	40.0 m	40.0 m
20 MHz	1.61 m	1.65 m	1.65 m	1.65 m	1.65 m	1.65 m	56.6 m	56.6 m	56.6 m	56.6 m	56.6 m	56.6 m
30 MHz	2.03 m	2.02 m	2.02 m	2.02 m	2.02 m	2.02 m	69.4 m	69.4 m	69.4 m	69.4 m	69.4 m	69.4 m
50 MHz	2.62 m	2.61 m	2.61 m	2.61 m	2.61 m	2.61 m	89.6 m	89.6 m	89.6 m	89.6 m	89.6 m	89.6 m
70 MHz	3.09 m	3.09 m	3.09 m	3.09 m	3.09 m	3.09 m	106 m	106 m	106 m	106 m	106 m	106 m
100 MHz	3.69 m	3.69 m	3.69 m	3.69 m	3.69 m	3.69 m	126 m	126 m	126 m	126 m	126 m	126 m
200 MHz	5.22 m	5.22 m	5.22 m	5.22 m	5.22 m	5.22 m	179 m	179 m	179 m	179 m	179 m	179 m
300 MHz	6.39 m	6.39 m	6.39 m	6.39 m	6.39 m	6.39 m	219 m	219 m	219 m	219 m	219 m	219 m
500 MHz	8.26 m	8.26 m	8.26 m	8.26 m	8.26 m	8.26 m	283 m	283 m	283 m	283 m	283 m	283 m
700 MHz	9.77 m	9.77 m	9.77 m	9.77 m	9.77 m	9.77 m	335 m	335 m	335 m	335 m	335 m	335 m
1 GHz	11.6 m	11.6 m	11.6 m	11.6 m	11.6 m	11.6 m	400 m	400 m	400 m	400 m	400 m	400 m
2 GHz	16.5 m	16.5 m	16.5 m	16.5 m	16.5 m	16.5 m	566 m	566 m	566 m	566 m	566 m	566 m
3 GHz	20.2 m	20.2 m	20.2 m	20.2 m	20.2 m	20.2 m	694 m	694 m	694 m	694 m	694 m	694 m
5 GHz	26.1 m	26.1 m	26.1 m	26.1 m	26.1 m	26.1 m	896 m	896 m	896 m	896 m	896 m	896 m
7 GHz	30.9 m	30.9 m	30.9 m	30.9 m	30.9 m	30.9 m	1.06 Ω	1.06 Ω	1.06 Ω	1.06 Ω	1.06 Ω	1.06 Ω
10 GHz	36.9 m	36.9 m	36.9 m	36.9 m	36.9 m	36.9 m	1.26 Ω	1.26 Ω	1.26 Ω	1.26 Ω	1.26 Ω	1.26 Ω

t is in units of mm
μ = microhms
m = milliohms
Ω = ohms

NOTE: Do not use table at frequencies in MHz above $5/l_m$ since the separation distance in meters, l_m, of two grounded equipments will exceed 0.05 λ where error becomes significant.

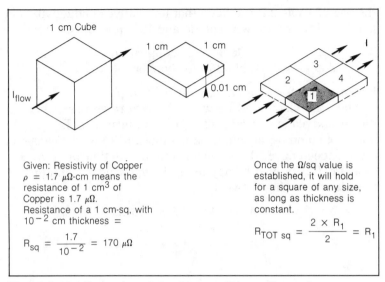

Given: Resistivity of Copper
$\rho = 1.7$ $\mu\Omega$-cm means the
resistance of 1 cm^3 of
Copper is 1.7 $\mu\Omega$.
Resistance of a 1 cm-sq, with
10^{-2} cm thickness =

$$R_{sq} = \frac{1.7}{10^{-2}} = 170 \ \mu\Omega$$

Once the Ω/sq value is
established, it will hold
for a square of any size,
as long as thickness is
constant.

$$R_{TOT \ sq} = \frac{2 \times R_1}{2} = R_1$$

Figure 2.13—Illustration of the Ohm-per-Square Concept

Finally, the impedance of a metal ground plane at any frequency including dc is:

$$Z = (R_{dc} + j \ Z_{RF}) \ [1 + |\tan 1 \ (2\pi d/\lambda)|] \qquad (2.19)$$
$$\simeq R_{dc} + jZ_{RF} \text{ for } d \leq 0.005 \ \lambda \qquad (2.19A)$$

Therefore, the impedance between two points in a ground plane will approximate the ohms per square of Eq. (2.19A) provided the ground plane is at least as wide as the distance between the two ground points, and this distance d is short compared with a wavelength λ.

Equation (2.19A) is tabulated in Table 2.7 for both copper and cold-rolled steel, from 10 Hz to 10 GHz, for six different thicknesses: 0.03 (about 1 mil), 0.1, 0.3, 1, 3 and 10 mm.

Examine Table 2.7 and note that the dc resistance governs at 10 Hz for the thin metals (t = 0.03 mm). However, the RF impedance already applies at 10 Hz for the thick metals because they are several skin depths thick. For the same frequency above about 100 MHz for copper, the RF impedances are the same for different thicknesses. This also applies for steel above about 10 MHz because the skin depth is much less than metal thickness.

The impedance of any other metal may be determined with

the use of Table 2.7, provided that its relative conductivity and permeability are known. The dc and RF impedances are:

$$R_{dc} = \text{from Table 2.7 (for copper)} / \sigma_r$$
$$Z_{RF} = \text{from Table 2.7 (for copper)} \times \sqrt{\mu_r / \sigma_r}$$

For instance, for aluminum, $\sigma_r = 0.6$ and $\mu_r = 1$.

When the distance d between the two reference points on the ground plane exceeds $\lambda/20$, the simplification in Eq. (2.19A) does not stand because neglecting $\tan(2\pi d/\lambda)$ would cause an error exceeding +30 percent in the calculation of Z. In this case, Eq. (2.19) must be applied strictly, giving a ground plane impedance varying between:

$$Z = 2 \times Z_x \text{ for d } = \lambda/8, 3\,\lambda/8 \ldots.(2k+1)\,\lambda/8$$
$$Z = Z_x \qquad \text{for d } = \lambda/2, 3\,\lambda/2 \ldots. k\,\lambda/2$$
$$Z = \infty \qquad \text{for d } = \lambda/4, 3\,\lambda/4 \ldots.(2k+1)\,\lambda/4$$

where,

Z_x = the impedance given by Eq. (2.19A) or found in Table 2.7. This is shown conceptually in Fig. 2.14.

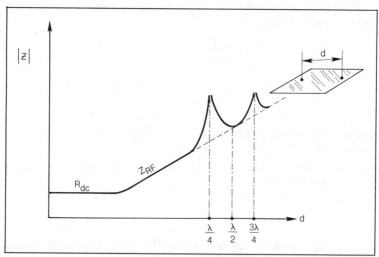

Figure 2.14—Domain of Applicability and Limits of the Ground Plane Impedance Values Found in Table 2.7

Figure 2.15 shows an example of ground voltage distributions on a metal plane used with RF circuitry. All voltages are referenced to the point where the ground strap is bonded to the chassis. The "hot spots" can be visualized by the circuit on the right where the currents returning from different loads to the source common can build up more voltage drop at some places due to higher concentration.

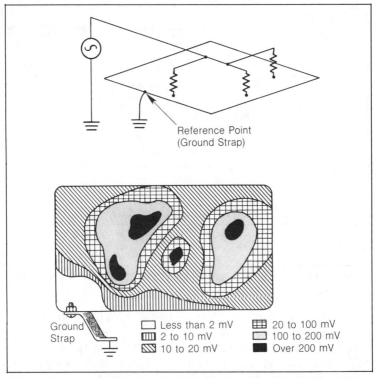

Figure 2.15—Typical Chassis-Potential Pattern at a Specific Frequency

Another interesting feature of ground plane configurations is the almost universal situation where the ground plane is the return path for a wire meandering above it. By the same phenomena as proximity effect (Section 2.2), when F increases, the current tends to flow so as to form the minimum loop surface. In other words, the current "seeks" the lower-impedance path. A classical experiment to demonstrate this consists of feeding the wire-above-plane circuit of Fig. 2.16 with a powerful signal generator. With a steel plate and enough current, above few megahertz one will see the area just under the wire becoming progressively dark red as frequency is increased. That might induce an interesting question: Why are ground planes so efficient when only a thin, filament-like zone is actually used?

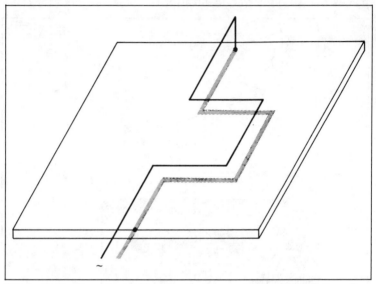

Figure 2.16—Experiment Showing the Concentration of HF Return Current underneath the Incoming Wire

The reason is that even though the current does not "utilize" much of the metal outside the shade of the upper wire (or trace), there is no H-field which can surround the plane (see Fig. 2.17). As a result, the self-inductance of the wire-above-ground is diminished while the distributed capacitance is increased.

The values found in Table 2.7 can be used to approximate the impedance of metal plane samples which are not square. For instance, the impedance of a rectangular plate with length L and width W can be found by:

$$Z_{ohms} = Z_{table} \times L/W$$

provided that L/W does not exceed 10, above which gross errors would occur (except for dc). At this point the element would start behaving like a wire due to external self-inductance. The surface impedance of a short beam or cylinder can be calculated similarly by using the developed area and comparing it to a rectangular plane.

2.24

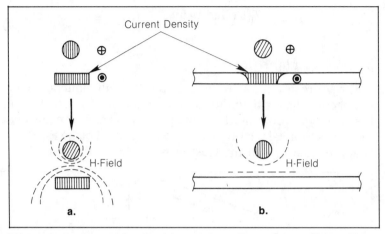

Figure 2.17—Current Density (a) in a Wire or Trace Pair and (b) in a Wire-Above-Plane Situation

Illustrative Example 2.1

Determine the impedance between two ends in a steel cable tray measuring 2 m × 0.50 m, 1 mm thick, for an interfering signal caused by a 27 MHz CB transmitter.

The wavelength for 27 MHz is 11 m, so $d/\lambda = 2/11$. Since distance d exceeds $\lambda/20$, Eq. (2.19) must be applied and corrected by the aspect ratio d/w:

$$Z = Z_{RF} [1 + \tan (2\pi d/\lambda)] \times d/w$$

From Table 2.7 for 1 mm steel at 27 MHz, Z_{RF} is about 65 mΩ/sq. So,

$$Z = 65 [1 + \tan (2\pi \times 2/11)] \times 2/0.50 = 828 \text{ m}\Omega$$

2.5 Beams, Girders and Other Irregular Shapes

With some modifications Eq. (2.19), given for ground planes, can be used to approximate the impedance of other configurations. For example, Fig. 2.18 shows a metal member having a perimeter p and a length *l*. The RF impedance of a given section of that bar will be:

$$Z \approx \frac{Z_{RF} \text{ (Gnd plane)} \times l_{mm}}{p_{mm}} \qquad (2.20)$$

provided that $l/p \leq 10$

The l/p restriction is to assure that the self-inductance will not become larger than the surface inductance, at which point the member would start behaving as a wire. The equivalent thickness t for calculating Z_{RF} from the ground plane Eq. (2.19) is approximately half the least cross sectional dimension.

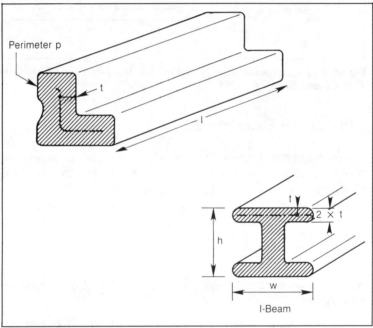

Figue 2.18—Impedance of Beams with Irregular Cross Sections

The dc resistance of a bar, derived from the basic $R = \rho l/s$ formula, is given by:

$R = 17.2\, l/A$	$\mu\Omega$ for copper	(2.21A)
$R = 29\, l/A$	$\mu\Omega$ for alunimium	(2.21B)
$R = 101\, l/A$	$\mu\Omega$ for steel	(2.21C)

where,

l = length of the bar in mm
A = cross section in mm^2

The actual impedance of the beam or girder is the complex addition of R_{dc} and Z_{RF}, but usually it is an acceptable approximation to use R_{dc} for low frequencies and Z_{RF} alone at high frequencies.

Illustrative Example 2.2

Two pieces of equipment are grounded to a steel girder, with a 3 m separation between grounding points. The girder is an I-beam having the following characteristics:
 1. a cross section A of 25 cm^2
 2. a perimeter p of 90 cm
 3. a metal thickness t of 6 mm
Find:
 A. its dc resistance
 B. its impedance at 400 Hz
 C. its impedance against a lightning stroke current with 0.5 μs rise time

A. The dc resistance, from Eq. (2.21C), and taking $l = 3.10^3$ mm, is:

$$R = 101 \times 3,000/2,500 = 121 \ \mu\Omega$$

B. From Table 2.7, the value of Z_{RF} for a steel plate with thickness t = 6 mm/2 at 400 Hz is 250 μΩ by interpolation. Since $l/p < 10$, Eq. (2.20) can be used. So:

$$Z_{400 \ Hz} = 250 \ \mu\Omega \times \frac{3,000 \ mm}{900 \ mm} = 833 \ \mu\Omega$$

As can be seen, the RF reactance already overrides the dc resistance.
C. The second corner frequency of the Fourier spectrum (or bandwidth) corresponding to a transition of 0.5 μs is:

$$1/\pi\tau_r = 637 \ kHz$$

From Table 2.7, the value of Z_{RF} at 637 kHz is 9.9 mΩ by interpolation. Using the same Eq. (2.20) as above:

$$Z_{RF} = 9.9 \ m\Omega \times 3,000/900 = 33 \ m\Omega$$

Here again, the RF impedance will govern. A 30,000 A lightning current will cause a transient voltage difference of $30{,}000 \times 0.033 = 990$ V.

For poles and towers made of steel beams, several calculation methods have been devised to simplify the engineer's task when $l/p > 10$; that is, when the ground plane approach does not apply. For instance, in the case of a tower made of four main beams arranged in a square shape (Fig. 2.19), the whole tower behaves approximately as a single cylinder with diameter d given by:

$$d = 1.83 \ D^4 \ \sqrt{d'/D} \qquad\qquad (2.22)$$

where,

$\quad$ d' = equivalent diameter of a single beam

$$= \sqrt{\frac{4A}{\pi}} \ \text{ if A is the cross section of that single beam}$$

$\quad$ D = distance between main beams

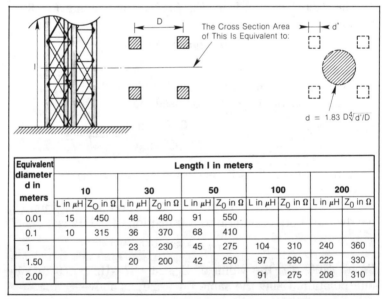

Equivalent diameter d in meters	Length l in meters									
	10		30		50		100		200	
	L in μH	Z_0 in Ω	L in μH	Z_0 in Ω	L in μH	Z_0 in Ω	L in μH	Z_0 in Ω	L in μH	Z_0 in Ω
0.01	15	450	48	480	91	550				
0.1	10	315	36	370	68	410				
1			23	230	45	275	104	310	240	360
1.50			20	200	42	250	97	290	222	330
2.00							91	275	208	310

Figure 2.19—Inductance L and Characteristic Impedance Z_0 of Long Metallic Structures

Using d, the self-inductance of any segment of the tower can be calculated from the simple inductance formula of a round wire:

$$L = 0.2 \times l \left(\ln \frac{4l}{d} \right) \ \mu H$$

for l and d in meters.

Figure 2.19 and its associated table show the inductance for metallic towers and poles with lengths from 10 m to 200 m and equivalent diameters d from 1 cm to 2 m. Notice that the l/d ratio is always >10, so the external inductance behaves like that of a filar element.

Illustrative Example 2.3

What is the inductance of a metallic structure having the cross section shown in Fig. 2.20 and a length of 10 m? What is its impedance for a 1 μs rising front of current?
From Eq. (2.22),

$$d = 1.83 \times 0.30^4 \ \sqrt{d'/D}$$

$$\text{with d'} = \sqrt{\frac{4 \times 30 \text{ cm}^2}{\pi}} = 6.18 \text{ cm}$$

So,
$$d = 0.37 \text{ m}$$

$$L = 0.2 \times 10 \ln \left(\frac{4 \times 10 \text{ m}}{0.37} \right) = 9.36 \ \mu H$$

For a 1 μs rise time, the dynamic impedance will be:

$$L/dt = \frac{9.36 \times 10^{-6} \text{ H}}{10^{-6} \text{ s}} = 9.36 \ \Omega$$

Figure 2.19 also shows the characteristic impedance (also called **wave impedance**) offered by these structures. This value is to be used when the rise time of the current equals or exceeds the propagation delay over the structure length, i.e., the beams have to be treated as transmission lines.

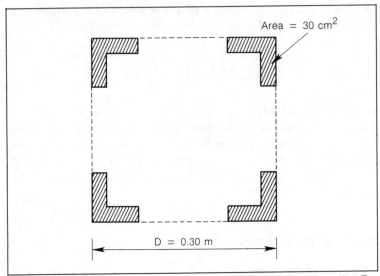

Figure 2.20—Cross Section of the Metallic Structure for Illustrative Example 2.3

2.6 Ground Grids and Wire Meshes

Although a homogeneous metal plane is by far the best RF ground, in many cases construction, practicability and cost considerations dictate the use of a gridded ground such as reinforced concrete rebars, buried ground mesh, wire mesh, raised metal floor grid, etc. The exact calculation of the impedance of such structures is quite complex, especially considering that this impedance will depend on the orientation of the current flow, i.e., the location of the two points between which the impedance is to be defined. Finally, it depends on the aspect ratio (length-to-width) of the grid and its elementary cells.

A good data base of recent measurements made on ground grids exists. When impedance is measured on a limited area near the center, edge effects and resonance are less pronounced. Some essential results are shown in Fig. 2.21[3] for various types of grid nets (square mesh cells, rectangular mesh cells, etc.) and different locations of the measuring points. Typical values for individual segments are:

60 cm copper AWG 2 wire (6.5mm dia): $R_{dc} = 500\ \mu\Omega$, $L \approx 0.6\ \mu H$

60 cm aluminum stringer: $R_{dc} = 60\ \mu\Omega$, $L \approx 0.4\ \mu H$

Details are discussed in the next section.

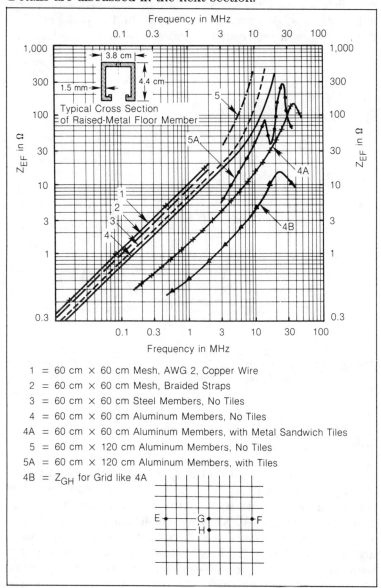

1 = 60 cm × 60 cm Mesh, AWG 2, Copper Wire
2 = 60 cm × 60 cm Mesh, Braided Straps
3 = 60 cm × 60 cm Steel Members, No Tiles
4 = 60 cm × 60 cm Aluminum Members, No Tiles
4A = 60 cm × 60 cm Aluminum Members, with Metal Sandwich Tiles
5 = 60 cm × 120 cm Aluminum Members, No Tiles
5A = 60 cm × 120 cm Aluminum Members, with Tiles
4B = Z_{GH} for Grid like 4A

Figure 2.21—HF Impedance of Some Gridded Floor Configurations

Finally, Fig. 2.22 shows the enormous advantage of using a ground grid (even imperfect) instead of a ground wire, especially when the length of the ground path is not a negligible fraction of wavelength. In the example shown, 60 m corresponds to $\lambda/4$ for 1.25 MHz, which is exactly what the measured data indicates. By comparison, the ground impedance via a ground grid will not resonate until several tens of megahertz.

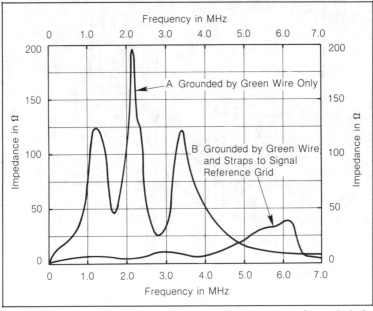

Figure 2.22—Grounding Impedance of a Cabinet when Grounded via 60 m of Green Wire (A) vs. Grounded to a Metal Grid by 75 cm Braid Straps

2.6.1 Square Grids

The calculation based on the resistance only is straightforward (although tedious), using network theory and tee-to-wye transformations. Some essential results are shown in Figs. 2.23 and 2.24 for a square-mesh type. Calculation of HF impedance is more complex because it includes both effects of skin depth and self-inductance. Earlier calculations found in literature were pessimistic. More recent data, backed up by actual measurements, show that: [3]

1. **At very low frequencies** up to few hundred hertz, the grid impedance calculation based on the resistance r of one single element is satisfactory.
2. **At medium frequencies**, from few hundred hertz up to the frequency where the perimeter of one single loop in the mesh approaches $\lambda/10$, the grid impedance calculation can be made by replacing r with the inductive reactance X_L of one single element.
3. **At high frequencies**, i.e., above the $\lambda/10$ limit for one loop, the inductance and capacitance of grid members can no longer be considered as lumped elements. At a given instant, the current distribution is not constant in a given mesh loop, and peaks and nulls occur at every integer multiple of $\lambda/4$.

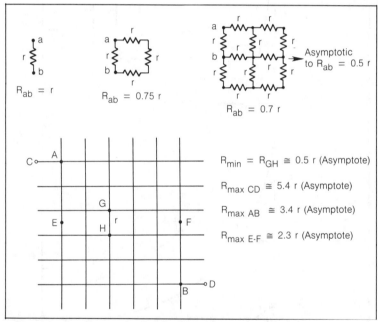

Figure 2.23—Equivalent Resistances of a Square Mesh Grid

From Fig. 2.23 one can see that, given the resistance r (or medium- frequency impedance Z_m) of a single bar of a mesh cell, the impedance of the whole grid, depending which two points are used for reference, cannot be lower than 0.5r (or Z_m) nor greater than 5.4r (or Z_m). So as a rule of thumb (or default), we could say that on the average, the impedance between two points anywhere on the grid corresponds to about 3 times that of one single bar or wire segment. It is interesting to note that there is a significant difference between the impedances Z_{CD} and Z_{AB} due the addition of twice Z_m caused by the segments CA and BD. So, trying to make grounding connections at a node instead of a wire end will roughly divide the impedance by two.

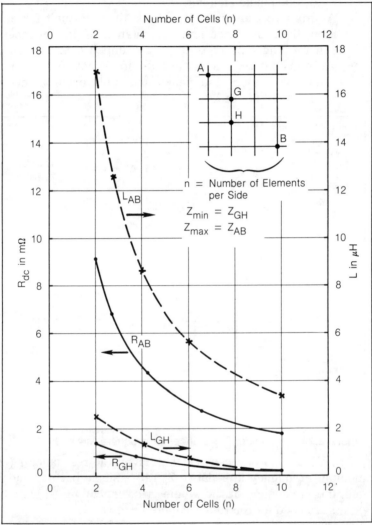

Figure 2.24—Resistance and Inductance of a 100 m² Square Grid Made of AWG 2 (Dia. 6.5 mm) Copper Wire as a Function of the Number Cells. Parameters are, for individual wire: R_{dc} at 20°C ≅ .8 mΩ/m
$$L ≅ 1 \ \mu H/m$$

2.6.2 Rectangular Grid with Square Mesh Cells

The impedance of such a grid can be derived from the previous square grid case. The following approach is used (Fig. 2.25):

If k is the aspect ratio length/width and Z_{sq} the impedance of a whole square grid made with the same type of square cells, the impedance will be:

  a.   Along the longest dimension:
      $Z = k \times Z_{sq}$
  b.   Along the shortest dimension:
      At dc and very low frequencies,
      $Z = Z_{sq}/k$
      At medium frequencies and higher,
      $Z \approx Z_{sq}$

since between the two reference points, the current will not spread using the whole span of the grid, due to the highest reactance of the remote sides.

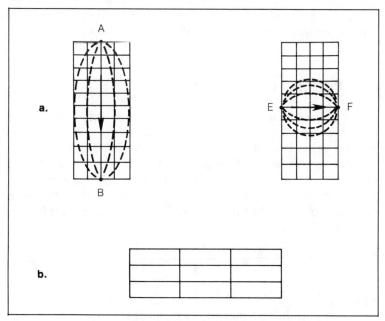

Figure 2.25—Various Configurations of Other-Than Square Grids

2.6.3 Grids with Rectangular Mesh Cells

From Refs. 4 and 5 we can derive that for a two-to-one mesh cell, the minimum impedance between two nodes, which was 0.5 Z_m with square cell, is now 2/3 Z_m. This is a 33 percent increase.

The impedance accross the grid is shown in Fig. 2.21 for a two-to-one square grid, using the elementary resistance r of the smaller member (identical to the one used for a square grid) as a reference.

2.6.4 Effects of Metal Panels

In the case of a grid used for a raised metal floor, many false floors incorporate metal clad or metal sandwich panels which significantly reduce the total impedance, even if these panels are making poor or no electrical contact with the grid members. In a sense, they act as the shorted turn put around power transformer windings to neutralize magnetic leakages, i.e., they decrease the external self- inductance of each individual grid loop. Consequently they will reduce resonance effects.

2.7 Earth Impedance

The ground resistance of any type of electrode that may be used to connect a reference circuit, structure, etc. to earth is directly proportional to the resistivity of the soil. Consider a metallic hemisphere which is buried flush with the surface of the earth. If the resistance of the electrode itself is neglected, the resistance of the earth connection will be that offered to the current flow through the soil volume immediately surrounding the electrode:

$$R = \rho \int_a^\infty \frac{dx}{2\pi \, x^2} = \frac{\rho}{2\pi a} \tag{2.23}$$

where,

a = radius of metallic hemisphere
ρ = earth resistivity

Therefore, if any of the grounding conductors previously described (wires, beams, planes, grids) are to be earthed, the knowledge of earth resistance and impedance is important since it may govern the total impedance and efficiency of the earthing path. Earth resistivity is variable as a function of soil type, temperature and moisture content. Figure 2.26 and Table 2.8 show data related to soil type. From this table it is noted that a grounding system which is entirely adequate in clay soil will be almost worthless in sandy soil.

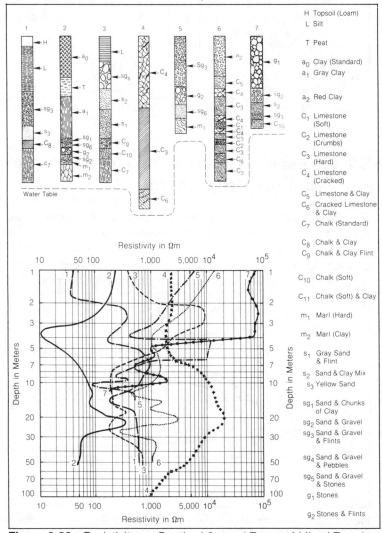

Figure 2.26—Resistivity vs. Depth of Several Types of Mixed Terrains, Measured in Low-Moisture Conditions

2.37

Table 2.8—Earth Resistivity of Different Soils Measured per Three-Point Method

R & ρ / Soil Fills	Resistance* in Ω 16 mm (5/8") × 1.5 m (5') rods			Resistivity in Ω/cm³ or Ωcm		
	Avg.	Min.	Max.	Avg.	Min.	Max.
Ashes, Cinders, Brine Waste	14	3.5	41	2,370	500	7,000
Clay, Shale, Gumbo, Loam	24	2	98	4,060	340	16,300
Same, with Varying Proportions of Sand & Gravel	93	6	800	15,800	1,020	135,000
Gravel, Sand, Stones with Clay or Loam	554	35	2,700	94,000	39,000	458,000

*National Bureau of Standards Technical Report No. 108

2.7.1 Resistivity Variations as a Function of Moisture Content

Soils that are relatively good conductors with normal moisture content become good insulators when such content is low. Figure 2.27 shows the variation of soil resistivity with moisture content for various soil types. For most soil types, moisture content of 30 percent will result in a sufficiently low resistivity.

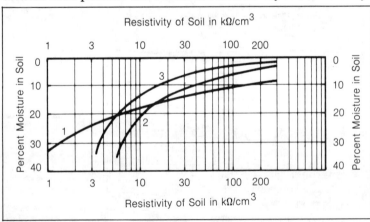

Figure 2.27—Resistivity of (1) Clay, (2) Topsoil and (3) Sandy Loam as a Function of Moisture Content

2.7.2 Resistivity Variations as a Function of Temperature

Soils that have sufficient moisture content to be good conductors at normal temperatures will become ineffective below freezing due to increased resistivity. This is illustrated in Fig. 2.28.

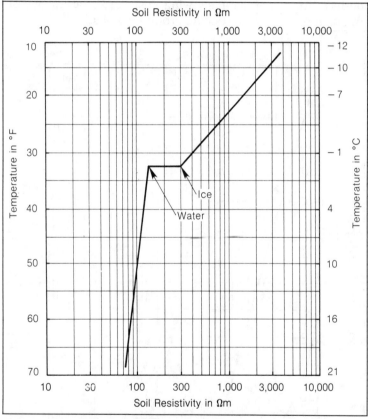

Figure 2.28—Variations of Soil Resistivity with Temperature, for an Average Soil (Sandy Loam). Resistivity ρ is in Ωm, since $\rho = R \times A/l$. Also, 1 Ωm $\equiv$ 100 Ωm

2.7.3 Resistivity Variations Due to Salt Content

Soil resistivity varies as a function of the salt content of the soil. Figure 2.29 shows the effect of salt content in reducing the resistivity of various types of soil. Soil can be artificially treated with salt to increase the conductivity. Figure 2.30 is derived from test data showing resistance variations as a function of time for a specific ground connection.

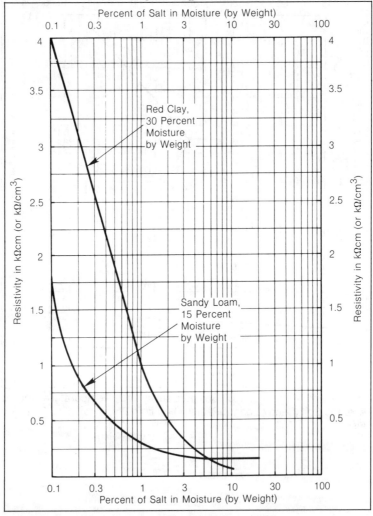

Figure 2.29—Effect of Salt (NaCl) Addition on Soil Resistivity

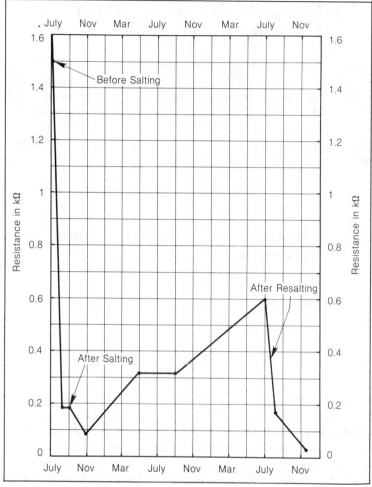

Figure 2.30—Changes in Resistance of a Ground Connection vs. Salt Treatment

For all structures requiring a low-resistance earth grounding system which cannot be obtained by use of rods or grids due to soil considerations, the following techniques may be used:

1. Artificial salting of soil
2. Immersion in nearby water source of grid or plate connected to the structure to be grounded
3. Use of available underground piping systems or metallic well casing

2.7.4 Design of Grounding System Utilizing Ground Rods

Ground resistances are computed either by application of the concepts of field theory or by the average-potential method. Although the latter method is not exact from the standpoint of applied physics, it furnishes fairly accurate results and is readily adaptable to the problems at hand. In recent years it has been accepted as the only practical means of solving problems of a more involved nature.

2.7.4.1 Resistance to Earth of Single Electrodes

The earthing resistance of a single rod of length L and radius a is given by:

$$R = \frac{\rho}{2\pi L} \left(\ln \frac{4L}{a} - 1 \right) \tag{2.24}$$

Earth is inherently a rather poor conductor, with resistivities in the range of 10^8 to 10^9 times that of copper. Therefore, the conductivity of the metal constituting the earthing rod does not matter much because the whole resistance of the earth connection will be dominated by the earth resistance itself. Figure 2.31 shows that even a thick, deep-driven rod in a good, average soil barely reaches 20 Ω of earthing resistance.

The earthing resistance can be pictured as the collective resistance of a series of equally thick, concentric shells of earth around the electrode. The inner ring represents the largest increment of resistance, since the resistance is proportional to 1/r. Thus, the central small-diameter shell of earth makes the bulk of the earthing resistance. For instance, with a 3 m rod, 16 mm in diameter, half of the resistance is contained within a cylinder of 0.12 m radius around the rod (see Fig. 2.32).

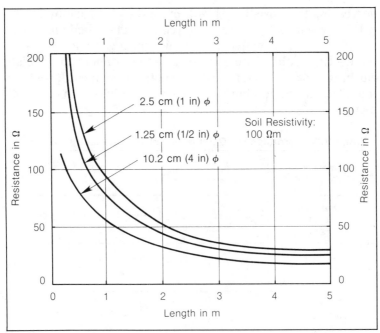

Figure 2.31—Variations of Earthing Resistance of Rod Electrodes of Different Diameter with Length (British Code Earthing)

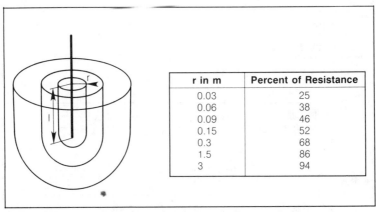

r in m	Percent of Resistance
0.03	25
0.06	38
0.09	46
0.15	52
0.3	68
1.5	86
3	94

Figure 2.32—Conceptual View of Earthing Resistance

As the distance r increases, so do the cross-sectional areas of the individual shells, and their resistance decreases accordingly. This shows why, in locations with high soil resistivity, decreasing this resistivity just around the electrode by chemical treatment or by using reinforced concrete pods improves significantly the effectiveness of the earthing. Table 2.9 (called the **Dwight Table**, from Ref. 6) gives the formulas to calculate earthing resistances of various electrode shapes. Resistivity must be entered in ohm-centimeters and dimensions in centimeters.

Table 2.9—Formulas for Calculation of Resistances to Ground

Shape	Formula
Hemisphere radius a	$R = \dfrac{\rho}{2\pi a}$
One ground rod length L, radius a	$R = \dfrac{\rho}{2\pi L}\left(\ln\dfrac{4L}{a} - 1\right)$
Two ground rods spacing s > L	$R = \dfrac{\rho}{4\pi L}\left(\ln\dfrac{4L}{a} - 1\right) + \dfrac{\rho}{4\pi s}\left(1 - \dfrac{L^2}{3s^2} + \dfrac{2L^4}{5s^4}\right)$
Two ground rods spacing s < L	$R = \dfrac{\rho}{4\pi L}\left(\ln\dfrac{4L}{a} + \ln\dfrac{4L}{s} - 2 + \dfrac{s}{2L} - \dfrac{s^2}{16L^2} + \dfrac{s^4}{512L^4}\right)$
Buried horizontal wire length 2 L, depth s/2	$R = \dfrac{\rho}{4\pi L}\left(\ln\dfrac{4L}{a} + \ln\dfrac{4L}{s} - 2 + \dfrac{s}{2L} - \dfrac{s^2}{16L^2} + \dfrac{s^4}{512L^4}\right)$
Right-angle turn of wire length or arm L, depth s/2	$R = \dfrac{\rho}{4\pi L}\left(\ln\dfrac{2L}{a} + \ln\dfrac{2L}{s} - 0.2373 + 0.2146\dfrac{s}{L} + 0.1035\dfrac{s^2}{L^2} - 0.0424\dfrac{s^4}{L^4}\right)$
Three-point star length of arm L, depth s/2	$R = \dfrac{\rho}{6\pi L}\left(\ln\dfrac{2L}{a} + \ln\dfrac{2L}{s} + 1.071 - 0.209\dfrac{s}{L} + 0.238\dfrac{s^2}{L^2} - 0.054\dfrac{s^4}{L^4}\right)$

Table 2.9 (Continued)

$+$	Four-point star length of arm L, depth s/2	$R = \dfrac{\rho}{8\pi L}\left(\ln\dfrac{2L}{a} + \ln\dfrac{2L}{s} + 2.912 - 1.071\dfrac{s}{L} + 0.645\dfrac{s^2}{L^2} - 0.145\dfrac{s^4}{L^4}\right)$
$\divideontimes$	Six-point star length of arm L, depth s/2	$R = \dfrac{\rho}{12\pi L}\left(\ln\dfrac{2L}{a} + \ln\dfrac{2L}{s} + 6.851 - 3.128\dfrac{s}{L} + 1.758\dfrac{s^2}{L^2} - 0.490\dfrac{s^4}{L^4}\right)$
$\ast$	Eight-point star length of arm L, depth s/2	$R = \dfrac{\rho}{16\pi L}\left(\ln\dfrac{2L}{a} + \ln\dfrac{2L}{s} + 10.98 - 5.51\dfrac{s}{L} + 3.26\dfrac{s^2}{L^2} - 1.17\dfrac{s^4}{L^4}\right)$
$\bigcirc$	Ring of Wire Diameter of Ring D, Diameter of Wire d, depth s/2	$R = \dfrac{\rho}{2\pi^2 D}\left(\ln\dfrac{8D}{d} + \ln\dfrac{4D}{s}\right)$
—	Buried horizontal strip length 2L, section a by b, depth s/2, b< a/8	$R = \dfrac{\rho}{4\pi L}\left(\ln\dfrac{4L}{a} + \dfrac{a^2 - \pi ab}{2(a + b)^2} + \ln\dfrac{4L}{s} - 1 + \dfrac{s}{2L} - \dfrac{s^2}{16L^2} + \dfrac{s^4}{512L^4}\right)$
⊘	Buried horizontal round plate radius a, depth s/2	$R = \dfrac{\rho}{8a} + \dfrac{\rho}{4\pi s}\left(1 - \dfrac{7a^2}{12s^2} + \dfrac{33a^2}{40s^4}\right)$
	Buried vertical round plate radius a, depth s/2	$R = \dfrac{\rho}{8a} + \dfrac{\rho}{4\pi s}\left(1 + \dfrac{7a^2}{24s^2} + \dfrac{99a^4}{320s^4}\right)$

*Approximate formulas, including effects of images. Dimensions must be in centimeters to give resistance in ohms.

ρ = resistivity of earth in ohm-centimeters.

For 10 ft (3 m) rods of 1/2, 5/8, and 3/4 in (12.7, 15.88, and 19.05 mm) diameters, the grounding resistance may be quickly determined by dividing the soil resistivity ρ, $\Omega \bullet$ cm, by 292, 302, and 311, respectively.

2.7.4.2 Multiple Electrodes

Adding more electrodes reduces the earthing resistance, but the final resistance is higher than the value which would be simply obtained by dividing the resistance of one single rod by the number of parallel rods (unless they are separated by an impractically great distance). An approached value of the reducing factor is given in Table 2.10. For instance, a single 3 m rod, 16 mm in diameter, driven into soil with 10,000 Ωcm (100 Ωm) average resistivity will have an average earthing resistance of 30 Ω. Using 12 rods in parallel, placed one rod length apart in a line triangle or circle, will give a final resistance equal to 30 Ω × 0.15 = 4.5 Ω. A more accurate value of the grounding resistance of many closely-spaced parallel ground rods is expressed as:

$$R = \frac{\rho}{2\pi nL} \left[\ln \frac{4L}{a} - 1 + \frac{2kL}{\sqrt{A}} (\sqrt{n} - 1)^2 \right] \Omega \qquad (2.25)$$

where, R = grounding resistance in ohms
ρ = soil resistivity in ohm-centimeters
L = length of each rod in cm
a = radius of rods in cm
n = number of equally-spaced rods within area A
A = area of rod coverage in cm^2
k = coefficient explained below
$\ln$ = natural logarithm

Table 2.10—Resistance Coefficient for Multiple Rods

Number of Rods	k
2	0.58
3	0.43
4	0.34
8	0.21
12	0.15
16	0.12
20	0.10
24	0.09

The coefficient k in Eq. (2.25) is obtained from the expression $R_p = (\rho/\pi)(k/\sqrt{A})$ for the resistance of a horizontal thin plate. When L approaches infinity, Eq. (2.25) approaches this value R_p. The coefficients k, for square and rectangular plates at each surface, are plotted as curve A in Fig. 2.33.

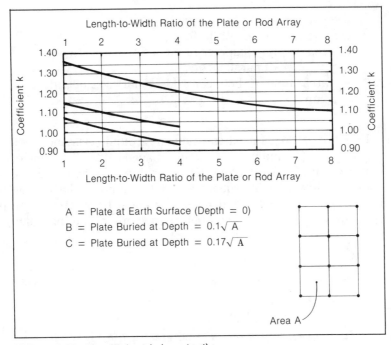

Figure 2.33—Coefficient k (see text).

In most practical cases, grids or rod beds are buried to depths much less than $\sqrt{A}$ so that the coefficients k for the surface level hold with sufficient accuracy. The determination of soil resistivity as a function of measurement locality and depth of ground-rod penetration cannot be practically realized with a high degree of accuracy. The effect of various terrain considerations upon soil resistivity and the accuracy of various methods of measuring soil resistivity are discussed in Section 10.3.

Rearranging Eq. (2.25) into English units yields:

$$R = \frac{0.52\,\rho}{nL}\ [\ln\left(\frac{2L}{3b}\right) - 1\ \frac{2kL}{\sqrt{A}}\ (\sqrt{n} - 1)^2]\ \Omega \qquad (2.25A)$$

where,

ρ = soil resistivity in ohm-meter
L = rod or pipe length in feet
b = rod or pipe diameter in inches
n = number of parallel rods
A = area in sq. ft. between rods at farthest outside position

Equation (2.25) is used to calculate ground resistance as a function of (1) number of evenly-spaced rods, (2) area of coverage and (3) depth of earth penetration. Resultant data are shown in Fig. 2.34 for square areas. Calculations have been based upon a value of soil resistivity equal to 50 Ωm. Earth resistance resulting from soil resistivities other than this value are:

$$R_1 = R\,\frac{\rho'}{50} \qquad (2.26)$$

where,

R = grounding resistance obtained from Fig. 2.34
ρ' = measured value of soil resistivity in ohm-meters

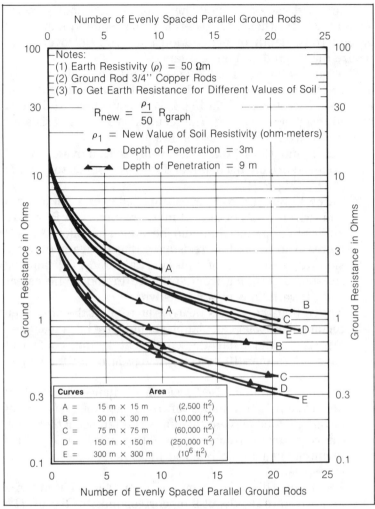

Figure 2.34—Ground Resistance vs. Number of Evenly-Spaced Parallel Ground Rods for Various Areas of Coverage and Depths of Earth Penetration (Valid for Approximately Square Areas) (continued next page)

Illustrative Example 2.4

A low-resistance earth grounding system is required for a proposed building with foundation dimensions of 30 m × 25 m. Terrain considerations allow penetration of long ground rods, and a soil resistivity of 25 Ωm was measured at a depth of 5 m.

The intended use of the building requires a grounding resistance no greater than 1 Ω. Determine the required number of ground rods, depth of penetration and area of coverage to realize the desired ground resistance.

The foundation area is $30 \times 25 = 750$ m². The soil resistivity, ρ, is 25 Ωm, or one-half the value used for calculating data in Fig. 2.34. Therefore, 2 Ω in Fig. 2.34 is equivalent to the 1 Ω ground resistance required. The required grounding resistance is obtained from Fig. 2.34 as follows:

1. Ten 19 mm (0.75") dia. rods, evenly spaced over a 750 m² area and driven to a depth of 3 m, corresponds to R ≈ 1 Ω (2 Ω in Fig. 2.34).

2. Three 19 mm dia. rods, evenly spaced over a 750 m² area and driven to a depth of 9 m, corresponds to R = 1 Ω. Sufficient tolerances should be added to allow for (1) increase in grounding resistance due to age and corrosion, (2) resistance of rods and tie-cables, (3) bonding resistance resulting from structure to rod or tie cables and (4) variations in soil resistivity.

   Notice that the area is nearly square. Had the area been rectangular, exact calculation should have been made per Eq. (2.25) and using the coefficient k: this coefficient causes less than 10 percent change in result for length/width ≤ 3.

   To obtain the decreased resistance, change (1) depth of penetration, (2) number of rods, and/or (3) area of coverage. A 50 percent tolerance is often used; therefore, the resultant resistance requirement will be 0.5 Ω. This requirement may be realized by either of the following examples.

3. Ten 19 mm dia. rods, evenly spaced over a 750 m² area and driven to depths of 9 m, corresponds to R ≈ 0.5 Ω.

4. Seven 19 mm rods, evenly spaced over a 1,200 m² area and driven to depths of 9 m, corresponds to R ≈ 0.5 Ω.

Illustrative Example 2.5

Consider a building identical to that of Illustrative Example 2.4. except that the building is intended to house critical instrumentation facilities, and the ground resistance is required to be ≤ 0.25 Ω. Such resistance should be practically constant with seasonal change and temperature fluctuations. Since ground resistance is critical, a tolerance of 50 percent is again allowed to ensure consistent compliance with requirements. Resistance fluctuations might be expected due to factors stipulated in Example 2.4. To ensure constant ground resistance as a function of climatic changes, rods should be driven to the permanent water level if possible.

The required ground resistance is 0.25 × 50 percent = 0.125 Ω. Since ρ_1 = 25 Ωm, we can use 0.25 Ω for R in Fig. 2.34. Only areas of coverage in excess of 2,325 m^2 (250,000 ft^2) and using 30 evenly-spaced rods driven to a depth of 9.14 m (30 ft) will result in the specified grounding resistance. This approach is impractical due to both the extensive area of coverage and large number of ground rods required. Thus, ground rods alone cannot be used to obtain a satisfactory solution to the problem.

The goal is to reduce the resistance to specified limits at a reasonable cost, and Eq. (2.25) is used to calculate the results of various resistance-reduction factors. For example, if rods could be driven to the permanent water level, where the soil resistivity may be 12.5 Ωm, the extra length of rod penetration would reduce the required area of coverage and number of rods to practical values. In lieu of this approach, a ground grid may be used in conjunction with ground rods to obtain the desired ground resistance. A discussion of ground grids is presented in a later section.

2.7.5 Materials to be Used in Ground Rods and Coatings

Copper ground rods are commonly used for grounding purposes due to their high conductivity and high corrosion resistance properties. Figure 2.35 illustrates the physical make-up of existing ground rods that have proven both effective and capable of being driven to substantial depths. Such rods come in a variety of sizes, but the 19 mm (0.75″) dia. rod appears to be the most compatible with electrical and mechanical requirements.

These effects of corrosion must be considered in the selection of compatible ground rods:

1. In most cases, both water and oxygen are necessary for corrosion.
2. The initial rate of corrosion is comparatively rapid, slowing as protective films form.
3. Surface films are important in controlling the rate and distribution of corrosion.
4. Increased rate of motion increases corrosion in water.
5. Dissimilar metals in contact accelerate corrosion of whichever metal is higher in the electrochemical series.

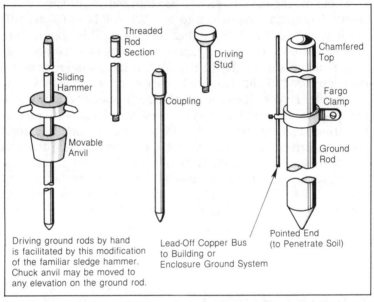

Figure 2.35—Physical Characteristics of Typical Grounding Rods

While copper is reasonably corrosion resistant, it is anodic (higher in the electrochemical series) to some metals used underground for piping and construction purposes. To reduce copper rod corrosion, it is therefore desirable to coat copper grounding rods with a material that is less anodic to metallic objects in the near vicinity, has high electrical conductivity and high corrosion resistance and is galvanically compatible with the base metal.

Tin coatings on copper and copper alloys are normally anodic to the base metal, as indicated in Table 2.11. The tin-copper alloy layer, formed in coating by hot dipping, is cathodic to tin and may be slightly cathodic to copper. Pores in the coating are not usually sites of corrosion attack on copper, and in general the corrosion of tinned copper is essentially corrosion of the tin. The function of tin coatings is usually to provide, between copper and the material in question, a layer which if corroded at all will yield as innocuous a corrosion product as possible.

Table 2.11—Metal Corrosivity as a Function of Soil Resistivity

Resistivity in Ωcm	Severity of Galvanic Effects
Less than 400	Extremely Severe
400-900	Very Severe
900-1,500	Severe
1,500-3,500	Moderate
3,500-8,000	Mild
8,000-20,000	Slight

The advantage obtained from deep-driven ground rods is realized due to the decreased soil resistivity and increased volume of earth associated with deep rods. However, as indicated in Table 2.11, metal corrositivity increases as soil resistivity decreases, which imposes more stringent requirements on the corrosion-resistant properties of ground rods. Two promising groups of alloys which may be valuable in the prevention of galvanic corrosion are the austenitic irons (SDTMA-439, Type D2) and austenitic stainless steel of the 18 percent chromium and 8 percent nickel variety. However, additional research is required to evaluate the effectiveness of such materials for use in conjunction with grounding.

2.7.6 Design of Earthing System Utilizing Ground-Grid Mesh

Ground-grid meshes are often required to complement rod beds or to be used separately when deep-driven rods are impractical due to soil and terrain considerations. The following formula is used to calculate the ground resistance of an earth ground grid mesh:

$$R = \frac{\rho}{\pi L} \left[\ln \left(\frac{L}{az} \right) + k_1 \frac{L}{\sqrt{A}} - k_2 \right] \Omega \qquad (2.27)$$

where,

ρ = soil resistivity in ohm-centimeters
L = total length of all connected conductors, in cm
z = depth of burial (if conductors are flush on earth surface, use $a \times z = a$)
a = conductor radius in cm
A = area covered by conductors, in cm^2
k_1, k_2 = coefficients explained below

The coefficient k_1 is the same as k used in Eq. (2.25). Coefficient k_2 has been calculated for loops encircling areas of the same shape and depth as used for calculating k_1 (see Fig. 2.33). Calculated results are shown in Fig. 2.36.

Equation (2.27) is rearranged into English units:

$$R = \frac{1.045 \, \rho}{L} \left[\ln \left(\frac{2L}{a} \right) + K_1 \frac{L}{\sqrt{A}} - k_2 \right] \Omega \qquad (2.27A)$$

where,

a = conductor diameter in inches $\times$ depth in feet
L = rod length in feet
ρ = soil resistivity in ohm-meters

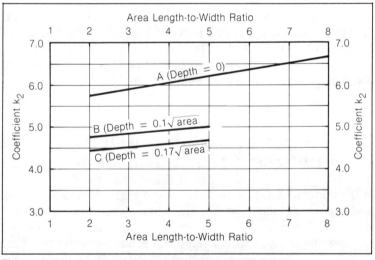

Figure 2.36—Coefficient k_2 vs. Area Shape and Depth

Resistance has been calculated as a function of foundation or area of grid coverage and number of grids per side using AWG# 4/0 (11.7 mm dia.) copper cable. The resistivity of the earth was assumed to be 5,000 Ωcm for calculation purposes. Coefficients k_1 and k_2 vary only slightly with area, and the error introduced by using calculated data for both square and rectangular grids is negligible. Calculated data is presented graphically in Fig. 2.37. Grounding resistance afforded by buried grid meshes can be reduced significantly by increasing both the number of grids and the area of grid coverage. Data has been extrapolated from Fig. 2.37 and replotted in Fig. 2.38 to show ground resistance as a function of the area of grid mesh coverage, for single and 30 grids per side.

Various factors in developing optimum design criteria for earth grid meshes are illustrated by such graphic presentations:

1. A far greater reduction in ground resistance is realized by using increased areas of grid coverage up to approximately 5,000 m^2.
2. Beyond 5,000 m^2, maximum ground resistance reduction is realized by the use of number of grids.
3. The average reduction of ground resistance resulting from additional grids is approximately 0.2 Ω.

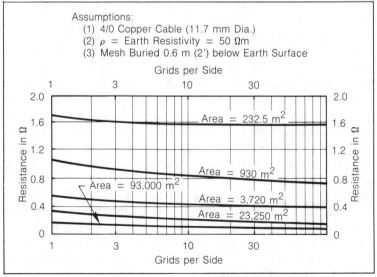

Figure 2.37—Ground Resistance vs. Number of Grids in Mesh as a Function of Total Mesh Area

2.55

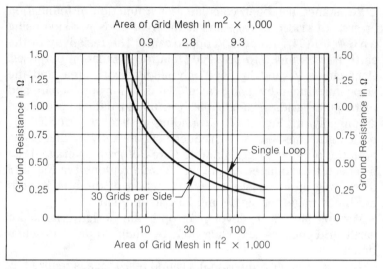

Figure 2.38—Ground Resistance vs. Grid mesh

Illustrative Example 2.6

An earth ground grid mesh is to be installed under a building to be located in an area that is not prone to severe climatic fluctuations. The foundation area of the structure is to be approximately 15×15 m (50×50 ft), or 225 m^2 (2,500 ft^2). A grounding resistance of approximately one $1\ \Omega$ is required.

Measurements indicate that a soil resistivity of 50 Ωm exists at a depth of 1 m (3 ft) below the earth's surface, and rocky soil precludes measurements at greater depths. As previously remarked, a ground resistance tolerance of approximately 50 percent should be allowed in design procedures to account for possible fluctuations in earth resistivity and bond impedance due to age and wear. Therefore, the design resistance should be approximately 0.5 Ω. Since the value of soil resistivity is the same as that used for calculating data for Figs. 2.37 and 2.38, graphical values may be used directly. Figure 2.37 indicates that the required grounding resistance cannot be realized using a number of meshes over an area of 232.5 m^2 (2,500 ft^2). An area of coverage of approximately 50×50 m (175×175 ft) or 2,500 m^2 (30,000 ft^2) using approximately 10 grids per side will yield the required grounding resistance.

Figure 2.37 indicates that either an increased area of coverage or grids per side beyond these amounts will yield a relatively small reduction in ground resistance. Thus, it is recommended that 4/0 copper cable be used to construct a grid mesh 50 × 50 m (175 × 175 ft) having 10 grids per side and buried 1 m below the surface of the earth. In lieu of the above, the required area of coverage can be reduced considerably, if the earth is artificially treated to reduce the soil resistivity.

2.7.7 Method for Approximating Combined Ground Resistance of Mesh and Ground Rods

In many cases it may be necessary to use a combination of ground rods and a grid mesh below ground to obtain a sufficiently low ground resistance. Fig. 2.39 illustrates how a combination of a grid mesh and ground rods might be physically implemented. The mutual resistance between the two grounding systems can be approximated by the following equation:

$$R_{12} = R_{21} = \frac{\rho}{\pi L} \left[\ln \left(\frac{2L}{L_1} \right) + k_1 \frac{L}{\sqrt{A}} - k_2 + 1 \right] \Omega \qquad (2.28)$$

where,
$R_{12} = R_{21}$ = mutual resistance of both systems
L, L_1 = length of rod and total developed grid length, respectively

The remaining parameters are equivalent to those used in either equations for rod and mesh resistances.

The combined rod bed and grid resistance is:[7]

$$R = \frac{R_{11}R_{22} - R_{12}^2}{R_{11} + R_{22} - 2R_{12}} \qquad (2.29)$$

where,
R_{11} = resistance of grid alone as presented in Section 2.7.6
R_{22} = resistance of rod bed alone as presented in Section 2.7.4
R_{12} = mutual resistance between systems
R = combined resistance

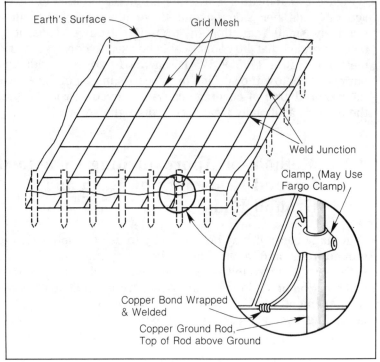

Figure 2.39—Typical Combination of Ground Rods and Grid Mesh

If it were only to decrease the grounding resistance, the eduction achieved by adding rods to a grid would hardly warrant the extra cost. Yet there are points in favor of such an arrangement:

1. It ensures practically constant ground resistance near the earth's surface where soil resistivity may fluctuate due to extreme climatic conditions.
2. The rods provide a reliable ground source, and the grid equalizes fault potentials over the earth's surface. This provides an extra measure of safety.

In this section, ground rod and grid mesh criteria have been developed on the assumption that a sufficiently low earth resistivity can be realized for effective implementation. In extremely rocky or frozen soil, deep penetration of ground rods is impractical. In such cases ground grids might be used, but earth resistivity will vary considerably in regions subjected to extreme climatic variations. This will cause resistance changes in shallowly buried grid meshes. In various localities such as dry, sandy soils, earth resistivity may be extremely high regardless of the depth of ground rod penetration. In situations such as these, other techniques may be employed to obtain the required low ground resistance:

1. Impregnation of soil with salt solution
2. Immersion of grid or plate in nearby water sources and connection of such grounding media to structures to be grounded
3. Utilization of available underground piping systems

2.7.8 Combined Soil and Rod or Grid System Impedance

Although characterization of earthing is generally done at dc or at ac mains frequency, it could be interesting to know how earthing impedance varies with frequency. The few data which have been published can be summarized as follows:[4,8,9]

1. Up to a few kilohertz, earthing is mostly resistive.
2. Above a few kilohertz, a capacitive reactance appears whose effect depends on the shape of the electrode and the resistivity of the soil.
3. The "shunting" effect of the electrode capacitance to the surrounding earth is more pronounced when the resistivity is higher (see Fig. 2.40).
4. Above a few hundred kilohertz (depending on shape and length of the electrode), self-inductance and skin effects both appear (see Table 2.12), which tends to balance the impedance falloff created by the capacitance. Therefore, the earth impedance appears more or less constant.

With regard to the fourth observation, it must be remarked that all the HF measurements are made by a current injection between two or more electrodes (see Chapter 10), which are representative of the cases of electronic systems grounding but do not accurately represent the conditions of a lightning stroke. In a lightning stroke the energy is generated between cloud and earth, the circuit dimensions are in the range of kilometers and the electron transfer is not confined between two rods.

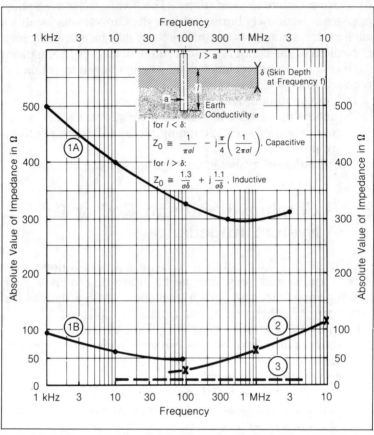

Figure 2.40—Impedance vs. Frequency of Several Ground Electrodes.
1A = 3 m Rod, $\sigma = 10^{-3}$ mho/m. 1B = Same, after NaCl Treatment
2 = 3m Rod, $\sigma = 10^{-2}$ mho/m. 3 = Hemisphere, $\sigma = 10^{-2}$ mho/m.

For earth resistivities of 100 to 1,000 mho/m, the HF impedance of vertical rods can be approximated by the following
formulas, derived from Vance.[8]
For l < δ:

$$Z_o \simeq \frac{1}{\Pi\sigma l} - j\frac{\Pi}{4}\left(\frac{1}{2\Pi\sigma l}\right), \text{ mostly capacitive} \qquad (2.30)$$

For l > δ:

$$Z_o \simeq \frac{1.3}{\sigma\delta} + j\frac{1.1}{\sigma\delta}, \text{ mostly inductive} \qquad (2.31)$$

Example: Find the impedance of a 5 m rod, driven into soil with resistivity $\rho = 300$ Ωm.

For $\rho = 300$ Ωm, $\sigma = 3.10^{-3}$.

Table 2.12 shows that skin depth δ at 100 kHz in a poorly conductive soil is > 16 m.

Therefore =

$$Z_0 \simeq \frac{1}{\Pi \times 3.10^{-3} \times 5} - j\frac{\Pi}{4}\left(\frac{1}{2\Pi \times 3.10^{-3} \times 5}\right)$$

$$= 21.2\ \Omega - j\ 8.3\ \Omega$$

Table 2.12—Skin Depth for Different Soils at Different Frequencies
Assuming that current is driven from the surface, the skin depth is the layer where 63 percent of this current (or $I - 1/e$) will concentrate, and only 27 percent will penetrate deeper. The attenuation is 8.7 dB per skin depth.

F	Sand $\rho \simeq 100$ Ωm	Aver. Land $\rho \simeq 30$ Ωm	Marsh $\rho \simeq 10$ Ωm	Sea Water $\rho \simeq 0.2$ Ωm
50-60 Hz	700 m	390 m	220 m	30 m
400 Hz	250 m	140 m	80 m	11 m
1 kHz	160 m	90 m	50 m	7 m
100 kHz	16 m	9 m	5 m	70 cm
10 MHz	1.6 m	90 cm	50 cm	7 cm
1 GHz	16 cm	9 cm	5 cm	7 mm

Finally, earthing behaves as a lossy line whose HF impedance will be less than the dc resistance for high-resistivity earthings (capacitive effect dominates for a steep wavefront) and more than the dc resistance for low-resistivity earthings inductive effect dominates). Figure 2.41 represents the transient impedance, i.e., the behavior of the earthing resistance when a step function is applied.

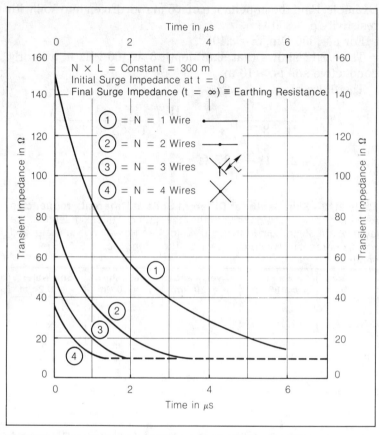

Figure 2.41—Transient Impedance of 300 m of Buried Wire as Function of Wire Arrangement (Low-Resistivity Earthing)

2.7.9 Summary of Earthing Resistance Aspects

To summarize the previous sections, the following can be enumerated:

1. Given that practical soil resistivities range from 10 to 1,000 Ωm, earthing resistances of 10 to 30 Ω are achievable with single rods. For less resistance, rod arrays, grids or both are necessary. These can provide earthing resistances inferior to 0.5 Ω.

2. Resistance of grounding grids decreases with an increase in:
   a. The enclosed area
   b. The wire diameter
   c. The burial depth
   d. The number of crisscrossings
   However, more than 16 to 20 meshes per side does not bring a worthwhile improvement.
3. Crossings must be durably bonded (brazing, welding etc.).
4. Concrete (or reinforced concrete) footings are a good intermediate medium between metal structures and soil.
5. The diameter of wires and rods is an important factor, so tubing may be advantageous.
6. Buried grids are always better. Machines which can plow several hundred meters of cable per hour in 0.50 to 0.75 m trenches are available.
7. Grid systems may have to extend beyond the actual installation. This also improves people's safety by reducing touch voltage exposure from outside the building.
8. A good earthing net is also an asset (and most often mandatory) for radio antenna counterpoise.

2.8 References

1. Denny, H.W., *Grounding, Bonding and Shielding Practices, Vol. 1*, (Atlanta, GA: Engineering Exp. Station, Georgia Institute of Technology, December, 1975).
2. Terman, F.E., *Radio Engineer's Handbook*, (New York: McGraw Hill, 1943).
3. Olin, R.P., Hoolihan, D., and Romano, D., "Computer System Grounding," (CDC Publication 1501300, June, 1979).
4. Ianovici, M., *Compatibilite Electro Magnetique*, (Ecole Poytechnique Federale Lausanne, 1983).
5. Golde, R.H., *Lightning Protection*, (London:Edward Arnold Publ. Ltd., 1973).
6. "Grounding of Industrial and Commercial Power Systems," *IEEE Std. 142–1982*.
7. Schwartz, S.J., "Analytical Expressions for the Resistance of Grounding Systems," (*Proceedings of AIEE*, August, 1954).

8. Vance, E., *Coupling to Shielded Cables* (Wiley InterScience, 1978).
9. Kouteynikoff, P., "HF Impedance in Semi-Conducting Space," 1983 EMC Symposium, Tregastel, France.

2.9 Bibliography

1. Higgs, P.J., "Investigation of Earthing Resistances," (*IEEE Journal*, Feb. 1930).
2. Bodier, G., *Protection Contre la Foudre*, (France: Rapport ORTF, 1970).
3. Henry, J., *Interconnexions en Electronique*, (Paris: Masson Ed., 1970).
4. *Military Handbook 419*.

Chapter 3

Electrical Bonding

Electrical bonding refers to the process by which parts of an assembly, equipments or subsystems are electrically connected by their joints or any low-impedance media. The purpose is to make the structures homogenous with respect to the flow of RF currents. This mitigates electrical potential differences which can produce EMI among metallic parts.

3.1 Purpose of Bonding

With regard to EMI, an ideal system would be one in which everything requiring isolation from chassis or reference ground could be "floating" forever via an infinite impedance, and everything which had to be connected to chassis or reference ground would do so via a null impedance at all frequencies. Since physics do not permit such conditions, the engineer has to accommodate reality and devise bonding techniques which create connecting resistances and impedances below an acceptable limit within the frequency range of concern.

Bonding is also important to the performance of cable shields, shielded housings and shielded rooms. For example, adequate bonding of connector shells to equipment enclosures is essential to the maintenance of the integrity of cable shields and to the retention of the low-loss transmission properties of the cables. The careful bonding of seams and joints in enclosures and covers is essential to the achievement of a high degree of shielding effectiveness.

3.2 Effects of Poor Bonds

Poor bonds lead to a variety of hazardous and interference-producing situations. For example, loose connections in ac power lines may cause heat to be generated in the joint and damage the insulation of the wires or loosen the contact pressure. Loose or high-impedance joints in signal lines are particularly annoying because of intermittent signal behavior such as decreases in signal amplitude, increases in noise level or both. Degradations in system performance from high noise levels are frequently traceable to poorly bonded joints in circuit returns and signal referencing networks.

An example of the importance of bonding to reduce EMI is shown in Fig. 3.1a in which the effectiveness of a filter can be nullified by improper bonding. In that example, the contact resistance of a poor bond does not provide the low-impedance path necessary for shunting interference currents coming from the power mains. This current now flows through the filter capacitors, shunting the blocking inductor, and reaches the equipment which had to be protected. In Fig. 3.1b, the receiver is not well bonded to a common ground plane reference for both the antenna and the power mains return. Thus, RF

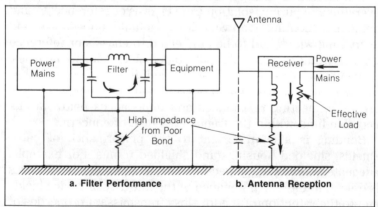

Figure 3.1—Two Effects of Poor Bonding

currents existing on the power mains share a common impedance path at the bond with RF signals picked up by the
antenna. As a result, the low-level signal delivered between the
antenna and its reference ground plane combines with the RF
voltage drop caused by the power return currents. Thus, the
radio signal is modulated by the on-board noise. In the
presence of high-ambient fields, poor bonds also behave as
nonlinear junctions and can produce audio rectification (parasitic detection) as explained in the Volume 5, Chapter 4 of this
EMC handbook series.

3.3 Bond Equivalent Circuits, Resistance and Impedance

A primary requirement for effective bonding is that a low-
resistance path be established between two joined objects. A
bonding resistance of 1 mΩ indicates a high-quality junction.
Experience shows that 1 mΩ can be achieved if surfaces are
properly cleaned and adequate pressure is maintained between
the mating surfaces. **There is little need to strive for a
junction resistance that is appreciably less than the
intrinsic resistance of the conductors being joined.**

A similarly low value of resistance between widely separated
points on a ground reference plane or network ensures that all
junctions are well made and that adequate quantities of
conductors are provided throughout the plane or network. In
this way, resistive voltage drops are minimized which enhance
noise control.

It should be recognized that a low dc bond resistance is not a
reliable indicator of the performance of the bond at high
frequencies. Inherent conductor inductance and stray capacitance, along with associated standing wave effects and path
resonances, will determine the impedance of the bond. Thus, in
RF bonds, these factors must be considered along with the dc
resistance.

A low-impedance path is possible only when the separation
of the bonded members is small compared to a wavelength of
the EMI being considered, and the bond is a good conductor.
This was discussed in Chapter 2. At high frequencies, structural
members behave as transmission lines whose impedance can

be inductive or capacitive in varying magnitudes (depending upon geometrical shape and frequency) in a manner similar to that explained in connection with Eq. (2.7).

Figure 3.2 shows the equivalent electrical circuit of a bond strap. The circuit contains resistance due to the finite conductance of the strap in series with the self inductance of the bond. Shunt capacitance exists due to the residual capacity of the strap and its mounting. This capacitance and self-inductance form a parallel antiresonant circuit, resulting in the adverse impedance response shown in the figure.

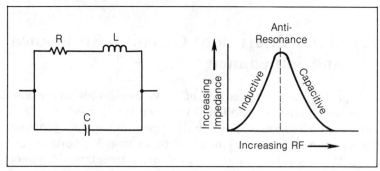

Figure 3.2—Equivalent Circuit of Bond Strap and Its Impedance

The value of the first resonance frequency can be found from Fig. 3.3, provided L and C are known. To find the resonant frequency, enter the strap parasitic inductance L and follow the slope until crossing with the parasitic capacitance C. L can be computed as shown in Section 2.3. A default value for typical flat straps is 7 nH/cm of length. If several straps exist in parallel, the value of L decreases accordingly, provided they are sufficiently far from each other (at least one strap length).

There is little correlation between the dc resistance of a bond and its RF impedance. The measured RF impedance of artificial bonds, per se, such as jumpers, straps, rivets, etc., is not a reliable indication of the bonding effectiveness in an actual installation. Here, the artificial bond is in parallel with the members to be bonded, and the total impedance includes various parallel paths over which RF conductive or displacement currents may flow. Thus, a bond strap of low inductance combines with the capacitance of the installation as shown in Fig. 3.4 to form a high-impedance antiresonant circuit at some frequency. The bibliography contains a number of sources presenting math models of various bond configurations.

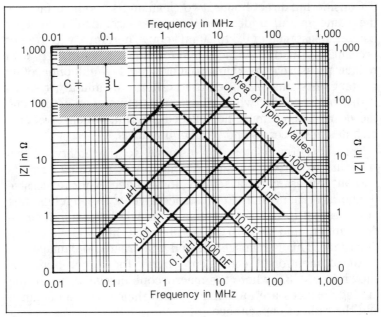

Figure 3.3—Resonant Frequency Chart for Bonding Straps

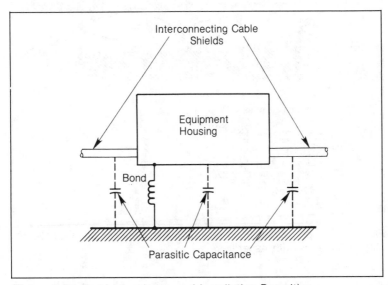

Figure 3.4—Bond Impedance and Installation Parasitics

Considering direct bonds, two clean and smooth surfaces of the same metal, under sufficient pressure, can have a dc contact resistance of 0.5 to 50 mΩ/cm^2. Therefore, with proper precautions, mating surfaces of a few square centimeters with regular pressure can exhibit no more than few milliohms of dc contact resistance. An often used criteria for military systems is that between the two most extreme points of an equipment, the dc resistance must not exceed 2.5 Ωm, which of course includes many series and parallel bondings.

This criterion relates, for instance, to the ability of this structure to carry thousands of amperes of lightning currents without excessive heat (from Joule effect) nor excessive temporary ground shift. For instance, given a 10,000 A lightning pulse lasting 100 μs, an aluminum skin will behave in a quasi-dc manner, and the 2.5 mΩ will result in a 25 V ground difference. This is manageable and will create no damage.

An oft-mentioned equivalent circuit for direct bonds is shown in Fig. 3.5 where the macroscopic irregularities of the mating surfaces are modeled by both their series inductance and their shunt capacitance.

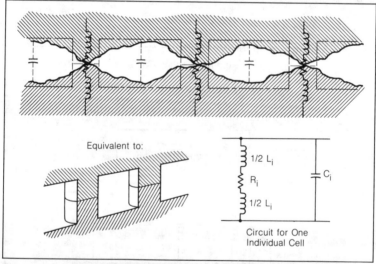

Figure 3.5—Approximate Equivalent Circuit for Bond Impedance between Mating Surfaces with Asperities

On a microscopic scale, metal-to-metal contact is made of many peak-to-peak contacts. These contacts have both an ohmic resistance and the series inductance of the peak "stud" which can be averaged as a cylinder. Each one of these R, L elements is paralleled by the capacitance of the cavity. Each contact cell (peak and cavity) is thus made of R_c, R_i, L_i, C_i:

R_c = contact resistance, depending on metal, pressure, etc.

$$R_i = \rho \frac{l_i}{a_i} \; \Omega$$

$$L_i \approx 0.2 \ln \left(\frac{4l_i}{d} \right) 10^{-9} \; \text{H/mm} \qquad \text{(from Eq. 2.12A)}$$

$$= 0.2 \, l_i \, [\ln(2 \, l_i \, \sqrt{\frac{\pi}{a_i}} \,)] \, 10^{-9} \; \text{H} \qquad (3.1)$$

$$\approx 0.2 \text{ to } 1 \text{ nH/mm for typical asperities}$$

$$C_i = \frac{1}{n} \frac{\varepsilon_0 \, (A - n \, a_i)}{l_i} = \frac{8.8 \, (A - n \times a_i)}{n \times l_i} \times 10^{-15} \; \text{F}$$

where, R_i = individual bond element resistance
  L_i = individual bond element inductance
  C_1 = individual bond element capacitance
  A = total contact area of the bond in mm^2
  a_i = averaged cross section of one individual contact point in mm^2
  l_i = total bond element length in mm
  n = number of individual cells

Thus the total impedance of one bond cell is:

$$Z_i = (R_c + R_i + j\omega \, L_i) \; // \; (1/j \; \omega C_i)$$

and the total impedance of the bond is:

$$Z = \frac{Z_i}{n}$$

Application of this simplified model and comparison with actual measurements give the following results:

The number and dimensions of bond cells can be estimated from the machining method. For example, aluminum surfaces with a surface roughness of 3.2 microns (125 μin) rms, or 11.6 microns (455 μin) peak-to-peak can be produced by milling. The grooves in the metal have a slope approximately equal to the angle of the cutter, i.e. 10° for aluminum and 5° for steel. The number of grooves per unit can be found from:

$$n_g \simeq \frac{\tan \theta}{2S} = \frac{\tan \theta}{l_i}$$

where S is the peak-to-peak surface roughness, in the same unit as n.

Then, the number of bond elements will be the product of n_g (grooves per cm or mm) in each of the two mating surface by the total contact area:

$$n = n_{g(1)} \times n_{g(2)} \times A$$

Curves on Fig. 3.6, from Ref. 1, show measured contact impedance, while Table 3.1 shows some parameters, calculated by the former model, that can be compared to measured data.

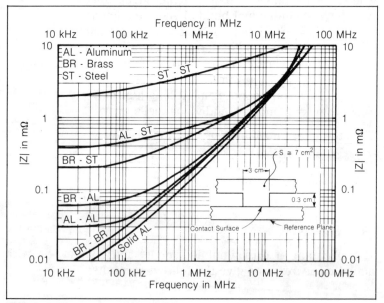

Figure 3.6—Measured Bond Impedance of Several Bond Pairs

Figure 3.6 also shows a dependency of contact impedance with frequency starting as low as 10 kHz for most metals. This is presumed to be the skin effect, causing a current concentration on the edges of the bond area, thus increasing the apparent contact resistance as described in Fig. 3.7.

Table 3.1—Example of Bond Impedance Calculated Parameters for a 7 cm² Sample of Al - Al Bonding

$$R_{dc} = 26 \text{ m}\Omega$$
$$R_i = 2.6 \ \Omega$$
$$n = 100.10^3 \text{ Contact Points}$$
$$a_i = 10^{-7} \text{ mm}^2$$
$$l_i = 10.10^{-3} \text{ mm}$$
$$L_i = 2 \text{ pH}$$
$$C_i = 6.10^{-15} \text{ F}$$

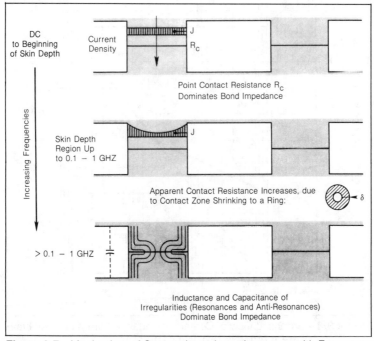

Figure 3.7—Mechanism of Contact Impedance Increases with Frequency

The skin effect for a given bond pad of area A causes the current to leave the center of the pad. For instance, in Denny's experiment of Ref. 1, a radius of 1.5 cm will reach skin depth at about 30 Hz, for aluminum. Beyond that point, the radial dimension of the actual contact zone shrinks like $1/\sqrt{F}$. As a result:

1. Contact **area** shrinks like $(1/\sqrt{F})^2 = 1/F$.
2. C_{TOT} of the number of small cavities being paralleled decreases like F.

Therefore, while ωL_T increases like $F \times F$ or F^2, $1/C\omega$ varies like F/F or 1, i.e., the capacitive contribution stays flat above 30 Hz. This is shown conceptually in Fig. 3.8.

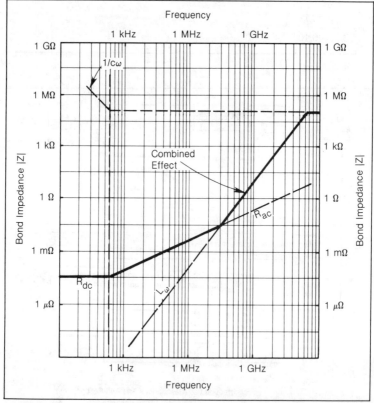

Figure 3.8—Graphical View of Contact Impedance Parameter Combination. R_{dc}, R_{ac} are the purely resistive parts of $|Z|$.

3.4 Direct Bonds

Direct bonding is where specific portions of the surface areas of the members are placed in direct contact. Electrical continuity is obtained by establishing a fused metal bridge across the junction by welding, brazing or soldering or by maintaining a high-pressure contact between the mating surfaces with bolts, rivets or clamps. Properly constructed direct bonds exhibit a low dc resistance and provide an RF impedance as low as the configuration of the bond members will permit. Direct bonding is always preferred, but it can be used only when the two members can be connected together without an intervening conductor and can remain so without relative movement.

Direct bonds may be either permanent or semipermanent in nature. Permanent bonds may be defined as those intended to remain in place for the expected life of the installation and not required to be disassembled for inspection, maintenance, or system modifications. Joints which are inaccessible by virtue of their locations should be permanently bonded, and appropriate steps should be taken to protect the bonds against deterioration.

Many bonded junctions must retain the capability of being disconnected without destroying or significantly altering the bonded members. Junctions which should not be permanently bonded include those which may be broken for system modifications, for network noise measurements, for resistance measurements and for other related reasons. In addition, many joints cannot be permanently bonded for reasons of costs.

All such connections not permanently joined are defined as semipermanent bonds. Semipermanent bonds include those which use bolts, screws, rivets, clamps or other auxiliary fastening devices.

3.4.1 Screws and Bolts

In many applications, permanent bonds are not desired. The most common semipermanent bond is the bolted connection (or one held in place with machine screws, lag bolts or other threaded fasteners) because this type of bond provides the flexibility and accessibility. The bolt or screw should serve only as a fastener to provide the necessary force to maintain the 85 to 110 kg/cm^2 (1,200 to 1,500 psi) pressure required between the contact surfaces for satisfactory bonding. Except for the fact that metals are generally required to provide tensile strength, the fastener does not have to be conductive.

Star or lock washers or lock nuts should be used to ensure the continuing tightness of a semipermanent bond but preferably not directly on the mating surfaces. Figure 3.9a shows one recommended arrangement. Star washers are sometimes relied on for cutting through protective and insulating coatings on metal such as anodized aluminum, and unintentional oxides and grease films developed during periods between maintenance. But this can cause long-term corrosion under the washer teeth.

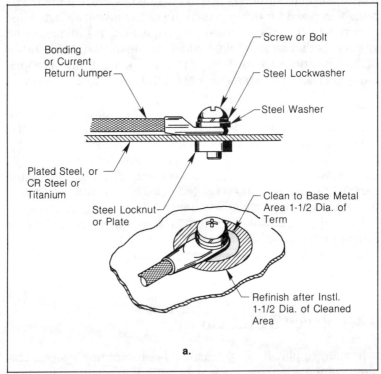

Figure 3.9—Bonding Connections (courtesy AFSC Deisgn Handbook DH 1-4 EMC) (continued next page)

Joints that are press-fitted or joined by self-tapping or sheet-metal screws cannot provide reliable low-impedance RF paths. Among other considerations, these screws are made on screw machines which employ jets of coolant oil.

The threads may retain some residual oil in spite of a degreasing bath. Often there is a need for relative motion between members that should be bonded, as in the case of shock mounts. In this case, a flexible metal strap can be used as a bonding agent as shown in Fig. 3.9b.

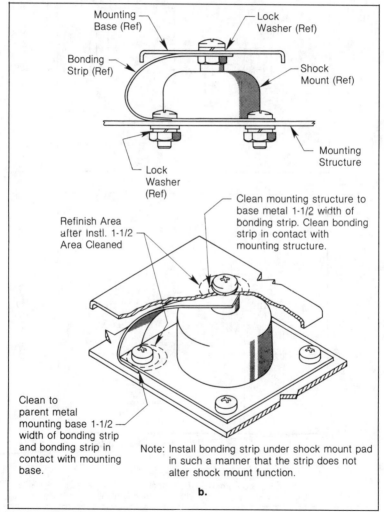

Figure 3.9—(continued)

3.13

Figure 3.10 shows the impedance range for various treatments for pop and percussion riveted aluminum alloys L70 (Fig. 3.10a) and L72 (Fig. 3.10b). Impedances were measured up to 50 MHz using Dr. Denny's method of "T shunt."

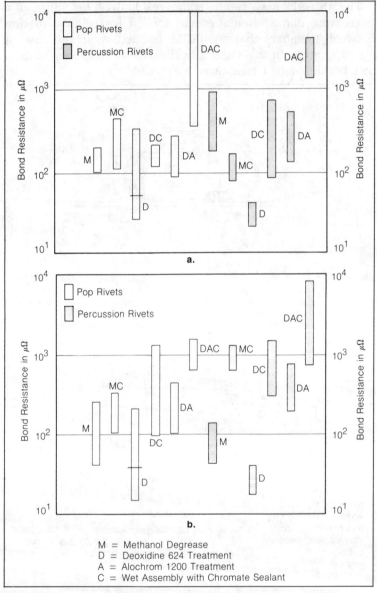

Figure 3.10—Range of Impedance for Various Treatments for Pop and Percussion Riveted Aluminum Alloys L70 (a) and L72 (b)

Figure 3.11 is a plot of applied torque to resistance for several lug types. The anomaly on curve 6 is due to the shank of the lug making contact first (giving an abnormally low reading) then finally bending as torque increases.

Figure 3.12, from Ref. 2, provides an examination of an old grounding connection after a lifetime of service from a Canberra bomber.

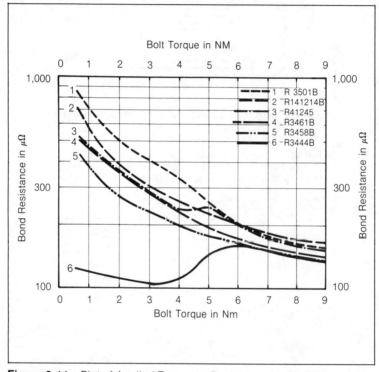

Figure 3.11—Plot of Applied Torque to Resistance for Six Different Lug Types onto a Deoxidined L65 Bar, 8 mm Thick, Using 6.35 mm (1/4'') UNF Bolts

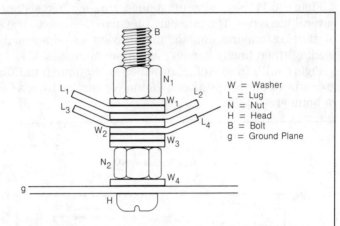

2 Amp passed down L_4 and into Aluminum Ground Plane.

Net Resistance of Bond + Wire.

R total = 5.75 mΩ (11.5 mV)
R Wire Alone = 4.75 mΩ (9.5 mV)
R for L_4 to g = 1.00 mΩ (2 mV)

Potential Drops Between Each Adjacent

Component	Potential	Types of Interface
BN_1	43 μV	Threaded Joint
N_1W_1	45	Cd/Cd
W_1L_1	14	Cd/Sn
L_1L_2	5	Sn/Sn
L_2L_3	6.5	Sn/Sn
L_3L_4	13	Sn/Sn
L_4N_2	29	Sn/Cd
W_2W_3	300	Cd/Cd
W_3N_2	115	Cd/Cd
N_2W_4	120	Cd/Cd
W_4g	1450	Cd/Al
gH	1750	Al/Cd

N.B. 1. The wire resistance was a continuous one with a shallow potential gradient.

2. The interface or connection resistance was 1 mΩ with a high potential gradient.

3. The sum of the intervening component potentials equals 2.01 mV (cf. 2.0 mV for the overall P.D.).

Figure 3.12—Examination of an Old Grounding Connection After a Lifetime of Service (from a Scrap Canberra Bomber)

3.4.2 Soft Solder

Soft solder is attractive because of the ease with which it can be applied. Properly applied to compatible materials, the bond provided by solder is nearly as low in resistance as one formed by welding or brazing. Because of its low melting point, however, soft solder should not be used as the primary bonding material where high currents may be present, as in power fault or lightning discharge paths.

3.4.3 Brazing

Brazing (also including silver soldering) is another metal flow process for permanent bonding. As with welds, the resistance of the brazed joint is essentially zero. Since brazing frequently involves the use of a metal different from the primary bond members, precaution must be taken to protect the bond from deterioration through corrosion.

3.4.4 Welding

In terms of electrical performance, welding is the ideal bonding method. The intense heat involved is sufficient to boil away contaminating films and foreign substances. A continuous metallic bridge is formed across the joint; the conductivity of this bridge approximates that of the primary members. The net resistance of the bond is essentially zero because the bridge is very short relative to the length of the bond members. The mechanical strength of the bond is high; the strength of a welded bond can approach or exceed the strength of the bond members themselves. Since no moisture or contaminants can penetrate the weld, bond corrosion is minimized.

3.4.5 Cadweld Joints

A cadweld joint is obtained by bringing the two surfaces together at a high temperature and fusing them with a metallic powder which is ignited by a special cartridge. The process is extremely dependable and noncorrodible. It is specially recommended for bondings subjected to harsh climatic or corrosive ambients. Figure 3.13 shows the essentials of this process.

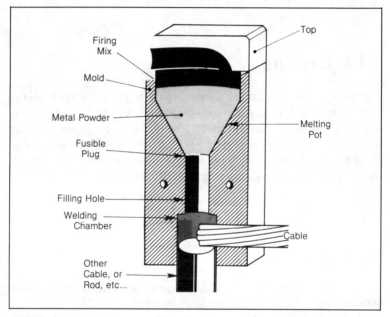

Figure 3.13—The Cadweld Process and the Different Bondings that are Obtainable (continued next two pages)

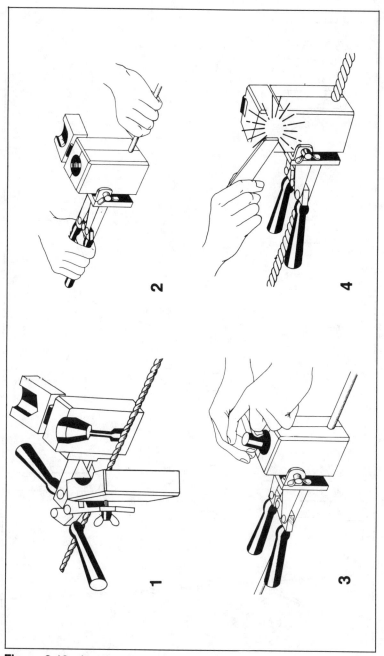

Figure 3.13—(continued)

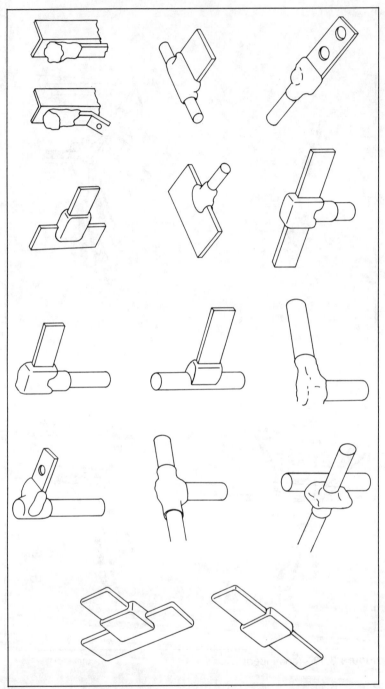

Figure 3.13—(continued)

3.4.6 Conductive Adhesive, Caulking and Grease

Direct bonds between two surfaces can be made with a high viscosity conductive cement. Depending on strength, cost and application or curing constraints, they are alternatives to soldered or mechanical joints. Most commercially available materials are based on epoxy resins, either as two-component, low-temperature curing, or one component oven curing formulas. As for any homogeneous material, the resistance of the joint is given by

$$R = \frac{\rho L}{A}$$

where,

R = resistance of the joint, in ohms
ρ = resistivity of the conductive compound, once dry, in ohm centimeters (Ωcm)
A = cross section in cm^2
L = length in cm

Conductive adhesives, including the epoxy resin, the conductive filler, catalyst, solvent, etc., have resistivities in the following ranges:

Carbon loaded = 10 Ωcm or more
Silver and gold loaded = 6×10^{-3} to 20×10^{-6} Ωcm

As a rule, the greater the metal content, the better the conductivity but the lesser the adhesion. The best tradeoff seems to be 60 to 70 percent metal by weight. The best shear strength value claimed is about 300 kg/cm^2 (4,100 psi), for a resistivity of 2×10^{-3} cm. Conductive caulking and sealing paste are used for semipermanent joints like pipe and conduit threads, shielded enclosure seams, etc. Therefore, they require no mechanical strength. Instead, the binder serves as weather sealant or thermal bond in addition to providing electrical conductivity. Unless silicones or special epoxy are used, continuous operation is limited to below 300°C.

Conductive grease is used to provide electrical bonding between two parts which have relative motion such as sliding, rotation, etc. It is usually a low-resistivity, silver-silicone grease. Applications include:

1. Switches blades (knife type) and insulator suspensions in power substations. This reduces arcing, pitting and EMI noise and prevents sticking by corrosion or arcing.
2. Ball bearings used with nonconductive pulleys, belts, tires, etc. This reduces the constant microscopic arcs caused by static charging.
3. Potentiometers and rotary switches shafts. This restores shield integrity at shaft penetration through the enclosure wall.

Typical greases have a volume resistivity of 0.02 Ωcm. Their time and temperature stability is excellent. However, people using them in equipment containing printed circuit boards, connectors, etc., must be extremely careful about cleanliness since even a minuscule film of grease can create a short between traces, pins, etc.

Conductive epoxy, pastes and grease are also discussed in Volume 3, *Shielding*, of this handbook series, as they relate to shielding effectiveness.

3.4.7 Bonding of Composite Materials and Conductive Plastics

Composite materials like carbon or boron fibers used in aeronautics pose serious problems for electrical bonding (see Figs. 3.14 and 3.15[4]). The first problem lies with the material itself. Carbon fiber composite (CFC), for instance, is made of layers of carbon fibers embedded in nonconductive layers, at different angles. The media is both nonisotropic and nonhomogeneous. Resistivity of CFC, depending on the number of plies and their weaving angle, ranges from 3 mΩcm to more than 100 mΩcm. This is three or four orders of magnitude larger than copper or aluminum. Therefore it is pointless to try to achieve dc bonding resistances much below 1 Ω since they will be overridden by the material's poor conductivity anyway.

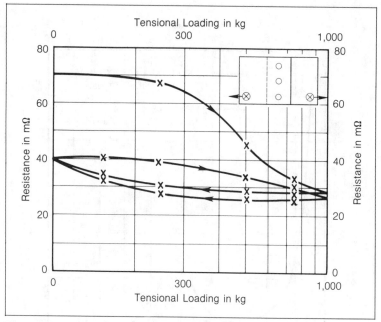

Figure 3.14—Resistance vs. Tensional Loading for a Carbon Fiber Joint. Inset shows the points of loading necessitated by the available chucks. The various curves are the effects of repeated mechanical cycles.

Figure 3.16, from Ref. 3, shows another method of achieving bonds with such nonhomogeneous materials like honeycomb by using an intermediate edge piece of solid metal. The conduction can be improved by removing the epoxy-rich surface layer. This is done by a slight countersink under the bolt or nut heads or an abrasion of the mating surfaces.

A better approach is to coat the composite material with a thin layer of conductive film like zinc spray, copper or silver paint, etc. This will not add much weight penalty and can create surface resistances of 5 to 100 mΩ/sq, far superior to the composite material itself as far as RF bonding and shielding effectiveness are concerned.

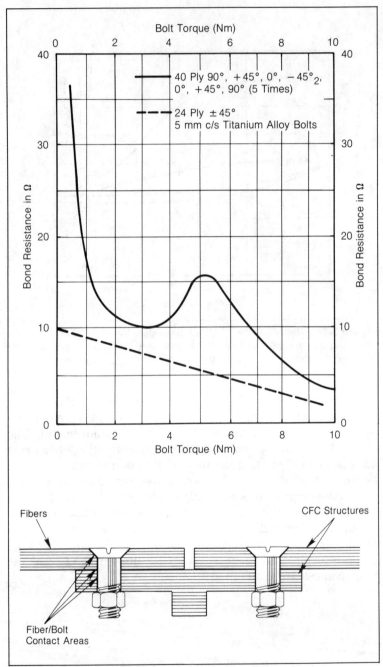

Figure 3.15—Resistance vs. Torque of Some Bolted CFC Joints

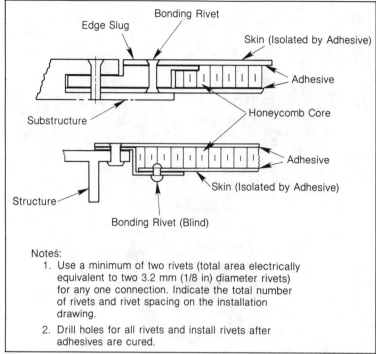

Figure 3.16—Bonding Method for Nonhomogeneous Structures (Honeycombs, etc.)

Conductive coatings are widely used, too, in commercial and consumer equipment since the enforcement of national and international RFI limits. They, as well, pose the problem of making simple inexpensive RF bonds: making a low resistance and long-term reliable electrical contact between a ground lug, a filter case, etc. with a sufficient pressure is not so easy on a thin film, especially if the underlying material is simply plastic. Figure 3.17 shows some alternative solutions to this problem.

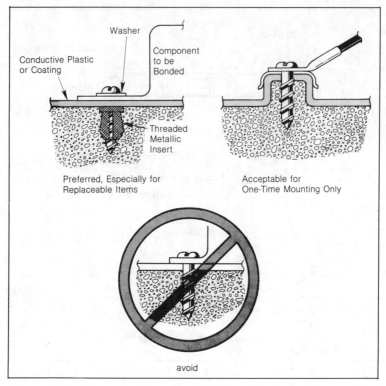

Figure 3.17—Direct Bonding over Metallized Plastics or Composites

3.5 Indirect Bonds

Operational requirements or equipment locations often preclude direct bonding. Many times, the metal-to-metal contact provided by the mechanical fixture is not dependable electrically, such as in the case of parts that have relative motion, are exposed to corrosion or removed frequently. In such cases, it becomes necessary to dissociate the electrical function from the mechanical one. When physical separation is necessary between the elements of an equipment complex or between the complex and its reference, auxiliary conductors such as bonding straps or jumpers must be incorporated. Such straps are commonly used for bonding of shock-mounted equipment to the structural ground reference. They are also used for bypassing structural elements such as the hinges on distribution box covers and equipment covers to eliminate the wideband noise generated by those elements when illuminated by intense radiated fields or when carrying high level currents. Bond straps or cables are also used to prevent static charge buildup and to connect metal objects to lightning down-conductors to prevent flashover.

3.5.1 Jumpers and Bond Straps

Bonding jumpers are short, round, braided or stranded conductors used in applications where EMI currents exist at frequencies below about 10 MHz. They are frequently used in low-frequency devices to prevent the development of static charges. They are also used to provide good electrical continuity across tubing members and associated clamps such as shown in Fig. 3.18. The clamp itself should not be relied upon for continuity because it is affected by tubing finishes, grease films and oxides.

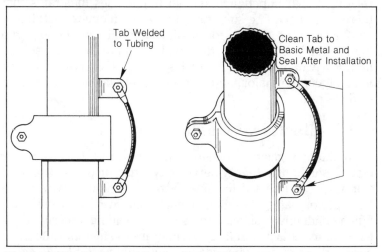

Figure 3.18—Bonding of Tubing Across Clamps

To provide a low-impedance path at radio frequencies, one must minimize both the self-inductance and residual capacitance of a bond to maximize the parasitic resonant frequency. Since it is difficult to change the residual capacitance of the strap and mounting, self-inductance becomes the main controllable variable. Thus, flat straps are preferable to round wires of equivalent cross sectional areas.

Bond straps are either solid, flat metallic conductors or of a woven braid configuration where many conductors are effectively in parallel. Solid metal straps are generally preferred for the majority of applications. Braided or stranded bond straps are not generally recommended because of several undesirable characteristics. Oxides may form on each strand of unprotected wire and cause corrosion. Because such corrosion is not uniform, the cross-sectional area of each strand of wire will vary throughout its length.

The nonuniform cross-sectional areas (and possible broken strands of wire) may lead to generation of EMI within the cable or strap. Broken strands may act as efficient antennas at high frequencies, and interference may be generated by intermittent contact between strands. Solid bond straps are also preferable to stranded types because of lower self-inductance. The direct influence of bond-strap construction on RF impedance was shown previously in Fig. 2.1, where the impedance of bonding straps and wire were compared as a function of frequency. The relatively high impedance at high frequencies illustrates that there is no adequate substitute for direct metal-to-metal contact. A rule of thumb for achieving minimum bond strap inductance is that the length-to-width ratio of the strap should be a low value, such as 5:1 or less. This ratio determines the inductance, the major factor in the high-frequency impedance of the strap.

3.5.2 Electrical Gaskets

Conductive gaskets traditionally are used to ensure or restore shielding integrity between two mating parts. By extension they can be used for any electrical conductivity purpose (except for safety bonding, where their use is prohibited). When conductive gaskets are used for shielding integrity, their figure of merit is generally given in terms of shielding effectiveness (SE) or transfer impedance (see Volume 3, *Shielding*, of this handbook series). If a conductive gasket is required for high-current sinking, another predominant factor becomes the maximum peak current density the gasket can handle for a certain duration without damage or pitting.

3.5.3 FARGO® Clamps and Other Hardware

A variety of hardware types have been developed to electrically secure grounding straps, ground wires, ground rods, grids, etc. This is particularly true for mating odd shapes such as round-to-round, round-to-plate, etc. Figure 3.19 shows a few of these pieces. Although they appear quite trivial, one should consider these parts as important links in a whole grounding and bonding system since they are **in series in the electrical path**. They are made of (or plated with) noncorrodible metal like brass, galvanized steel, etc. When they have toothed grips, a sealant can be applied after tightening the bolts to prevent moisture penetration.

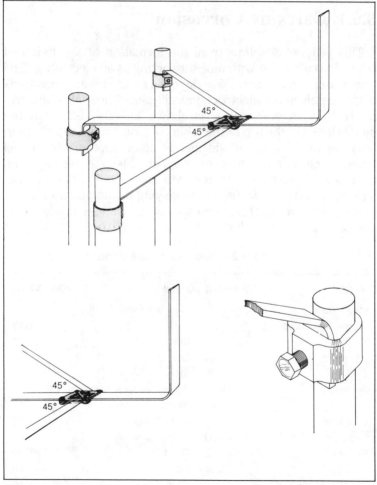

Figure 3.19—Examples of Clamping Hardware Used for Structural Bonds (Lightning, etc.)

3.6 Corrosion and Its Control

An important side effect of bonding is corrosion. This section discusses the problem and how to deal with it. When two metals are in contact (bonded) in the presence of moisture, corrosion may take place through either of two chemical processes: galvanic or electrolytic corrosion.

3.6.1 Galvanic Corrosion

This process develops from the formation of a voltaic cell between the metals, with moisture acting as an electrolyte. The degree of resultant corrosion depends on the relative positions of the metals in the electrochemical (sometimes called electromotive) series. This series is shown in Table 3.2, with the metals listed at the top of the table corroding more rapidly than those at the bottom. If the metals differ appreciably in this series, such as aluminum and copper (2.00 V difference) the resulting electromotive force will cause a continuous ion stream with a significant accompanying decomposition of the more active metal (higher in the series or less noble) as it gradually goes into solution.

Table 3.2—Electrochemical Series

Metal	EMF (Volts)	Metal	EMF (Volts)
Magnesium	+2.37	Stainless Steel (10-18)	*
Magnesium Alloys	+0.95	Lead	+0.13
Beryllium	+1.85	Brass	*
Aluminum	+1.66	Copper	-0.34
Zinc	+0.76	Bronze	*
Chromium	+0.74	Copper-Nickel Allows	-0.35
Iron or Steel	+0.44	Monel	*
Cast Iron	*	Silver Solder	-0.45
Cadmium	+0.40	Silver	-0.80
Nickel	+0.25	Graphite	-0.50
Tin	+0.14	Platinum	-1.20
Lead-Tin Solders		Gold	-1.50

*Reliable Values N/A

Corrosion caused by electrochemical action between dissimilar metals is minimized if the combined potential does not exceed approximately 0.6 V. Using 0.6 V as a maximum permissible EMF, Table 3.3 shows the allowable combinations of mating metal parts. Combinations above the dividing line (in the shaded area) should be avoided.

Table 3.3—Electrochemical Corrosion Table

Legend:
Ag = Silver · Al = Aluminum · Cr = Chromium · Cd = Cadmium · Cu = Copper · Mg = Magnesium · Ni = Nickel · Rh = Rhodium · Zn = Zinc

	Magnesium, Mg Alloys	Zinc, Zinc Alloys	80 Tin/20 Zn on Steel, Zn on Iron or Steel	Aluminum	Cd on Steel	Al/Mg Alloy	Mild Steel	Duralumin	Lead	Cr on Steel, Soft Solder	Cr on Ni on Steel, Tin on Steel, 12% Cr Stainless Steel	High Cr Stainless Steel	Copper, Copper Alloys	Silver Solder, Austenitic Stainless Steel	Ni on Steel	Silver	Rh on Ag on Cu, Silver/Gold Alloy	Carbon	Gold, Platinum
Gold, Platinum	1.75	1.70	1.20	1.05	0.95	0.90	0.85	0.75	0.70	0.65	0.60	0.50	0.40	0.35	0.30	0.15	0.10	0.05	0
Carbon	1.70	1.65	1.15	1.00	0.90	0.85	0.80	0.70	0.65	0.60	0.55	0.45	0.35	0.30	0.25	0.10	0.05	0	
Rh on Ag on Cu, Silver/Gold Alloy	1.65	1.60	1.10	0.95	0.85	0.80	0.75	0.65	0.60	0.55	0.50	0.40	0.30	0.25	0.20	0.05	0		
Silver	1.60	1.55	1.05	0.90	0.80	0.75	0.70	0.60	0.55	0.50	0.45	0.35	0.25	0.20	0.15	0			
Ni on Steel	1.45	1.40	0.90	0.75	0.65	0.60	0.55	0.45	0.40	0.35	0.30	0.20	0.10	0.05	0				
Silver Solder, Austenitic Stainless Steel	1.40	1.35	0.85	0.70	0.60	0.55	0.50	0.40	0.35	0.30	0.25	0.15	0.05	0					
Copper, Copper Alloys	1.35	1.30	0.80	0.65	0.55	0.50	0.45	0.35	0.30	0.25	0.20	0.10	0						
High Cr Stainless Steel	1.25	1.20	0.70	0.55	0.45	0.40	0.35	0.25	0.20	0.15	0.10	0							
Cr on Ni on Steel, Tin on Steel, 12% Cr Stainless Steel	1.15	1.10	0.60	0.45	0.35	0.30	0.25	0.15	0.10	0.05	0								
Cr on Steel, Soft Solder	1.10	1.05	0.55	0.40	0.30	0.25	0.20	0.10	0.05	0									
Lead	1.05	1.00	0.50	0.35	0.25	0.20	0.15	0.05	0										
Duralumin	1.00	0.95	0.45	0.30	0.20	0.15	0.10	0											
Mild Steel	0.90	0.85	0.35	0.20	0.10	0.05	0												
Al/Mg Alloy	0.85	0.80	0.30	0.15	0.05	0													
Cd on Steel	0.80	0.75	0.25	0.10	0														
Aluminum	0.70	0.65	0.15	0															
80 Tin/20 Zn on Steel, Zn on Iron or Steel	0.55	0.50	0																
Zinc, Zinc Alloys	0.05	0																	
Magnesium, Magnesium Alloys	0																		

3.6.2 Electrolytic Corrosion

While this second process also requires two metals to be in contact through an electrolyte, the metals need not have different electrochemical activity, i.e., they can be the same material. In this case, decomposition is attributed to the presence of local electrical currents which may be flowing as a result of using a structure as a power system ground return.

3.6.3 Finishes

Since mating bare metal to bare metal is essential for a satisfactory bond, a frequent conflict arises between bonding and finishing specifications. Oxides which form on metal are, as a rule, nonconductors. For this reason, it is desirable that they be softer than the base metal and as thin as possible. Melting temperatures of various metals and their oxides, which track closely with their hardness, are shown in Table 3.4. It appears that oxides of common structure materials like aluminum are much harder than the base metal (higher melting point). So an ideal contact for bonding would consist of plating the contact area with one of the metals given in the right-hand column of the table. However, corrosive or salt-spray ambients may exist, so this factor usually prevails, and exposed surfaces are given a protective finish.

**Table 3.4—Melting Temperatures
of Common Contact Materials and Their Oxides**

Material	Temperature °C	Material	Temperature °C
Aluminum	660	Copper	1,083
Al_2O_3	2,050	CuO	1,026
Magnesium	651	Gold	1,063
MgO	2,800	Au_2O	205
Beryllium	1,350	Molybdenum	2,620
BeO	2,570	MoO_3	795
Chromium	1,615	Palladium	1,550
CR_2O_3	1,990	PdO	750
Cobalt	1,480	Platinum	1,773
CoO	1,935	PtO	550

For EMI control, it is preferable to remove the finish where bonding effectiveness would be otherwise compromised. Certain conductive coatings such as alodine, irridite and Dow #1, or protective metal platings such as cadmium, tin or silver generally need not be removed. Most other coatings, however, are nonconductive and destroy the concept of a bond offering a low-impedance RF path. For example, anodized aluminum appears to the eye to be a good conductive surface for bonding, but in reality it is an insulated coating. Figure 3.20 and Table 3.5 show the effect of various protective coatings on the electric field shielding effectiveness of aluminum and magnesium. In the figure, 0 dB on the scale means there is no change in surface resistance once the finish has been applied. The shielding effectiveness is a function of the coating conductivity. The superiority of bare metal over a 12 octave frequency range is evident.

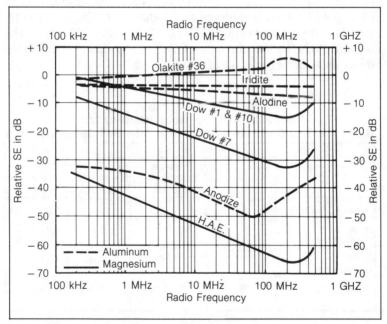

Figure 3.20—Effect of Various Finishes on Shielding Effectiveness of Aluminum and Magnesium

**Table 3.5—DC Contact Resistance for
Aluminum Test Specimens Under Different Pressure**

Treatment	Electrical Resistance	
	700 g/cm² (10 psi) Pressure	7,000g/cm²(100 psi) Pressure
Cleaned Aluminum	1,500 $\mu\Omega$	500 $\mu\Omega$
Aluminum plus Iridite No. 14	8,000 $\mu\Omega$	1,900 $\mu\Omega$
Aluminum Plus Anodizing	Over 88 Ω	Over 88 Ω

For RF bonding, iridite #14 is the best tradeoff. Unlike many other treatments, iridite is neither an oxide nor a phosphate but a complex chromium-chromate, and the film becomes an integral part of the metal itself. It produce a clear yellow, corrosion-resistant finish without alteration of dc or RF contact resistance. Table 3.6 shows resistance measurements of treated and untreated aluminum. Alodine 1200 also has acceptable electrical properties. Figures 3.21 and 3.22 show the benefit of the iridite chromate finish in stabilizing the surface RF resistance before and after salt spray.

**Table 3.6—DC Contact Resistance for
Aluminum Test Specimens Before and After Salt Spray Exposure**

Finish	Before Salt Spray		After Salt Spray	
	Number of Readings	Average Resistance in microhms	Number of Readings	Average Resistance in microhms
Clean Aluminum	75	96	60	$6,085 \times 10^3$
Iridite 2-Minute Dip	75	2,018	60	$3,366 \times 10^3$
Iridite 3-Minute Dip	75	2,675	60	10,577
Silver Plated	75	All Specimens less than 4 $\mu\Omega$	-----	-----

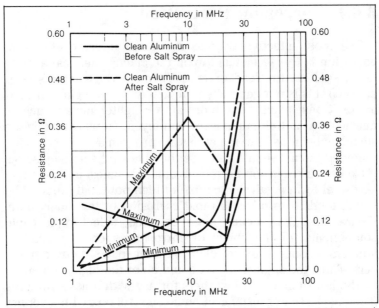

Figure 3.21—Values of Equivalent Series RF Resistance of Uncoated Aluminum Sections before and after 64-Hour Salt Spray Test

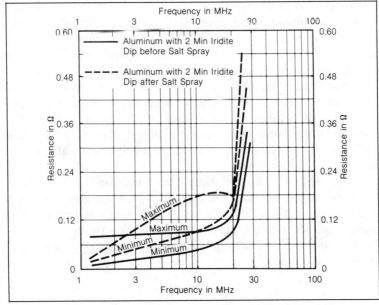

Figure 3.22—Values of Equivalent Series RF Resistance of Chromate-Treated Aluminum Sections before and after 64-Hour Salt Spray Test

3.6.4 Corrosion Protection

The most effective way to avoid the adverse effects of corrosion is to use metals low in the electrochemical activity table, such as tin, lead or copper. In many structures (e.g., aircraft) this is not generally practical due to weight considerations. Consequently, the more active, lighter metals such as magnesium and aluminum are employed. However, stainless steel has been used in many missile programs.

Joined metals should be close together in the activity series if excessive corrosion is to be avoided. Magnesium and stainless steel form a galvanic couple of high potential (about 3 V) which tends to produce a rapid corrosion of the magnesium. Where dissimilar metals must be used, select replaceable components for the object of corrosion, such as grounding jumpers, washers, bolts or clamps rather than structural members. Thus, the smaller mass should be of the higher potential (cathode), such as steel washers for use with brass structures (see Fig. 3.23). For instance, bonding a steel box with a copper strap will result in minimal corrosion due to reduced cathode surface. Also, the part which deteriorates (losing its mass) will be the replaceable one.

When members of the electrolytic couple are widely separated in the activity table, it is often practical to use a plating such as cadmium or tin to help reduce the dissimilarity. Sometimes it is possible to electrically insulate metals with organic and electrolytic finishes and seal the joint against moisture to avoid corrosion. However, this is an unacceptable practice for EMI control. One solution to electrolytic corrosion is to avoid the use of the structure or housing for power ground return. Any anticipated corrosion should occur in easily replaceable items, as previously mentioned.

Joints should also be kept tight and well coated after bonding to prevent the entrance of liquids or gases, since a galvanic cell cannot function without moisture. With dissimilar metal contact, coating just one of the "electrodes" is insufficient (see Fig. 3.24). Complete coating, or at least edge sealing, is required.

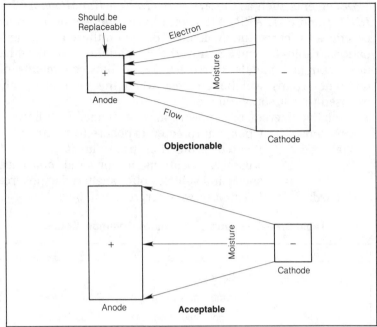

Figure 3.23—With dissimilar metals, the smaller mass should be of higher potential.

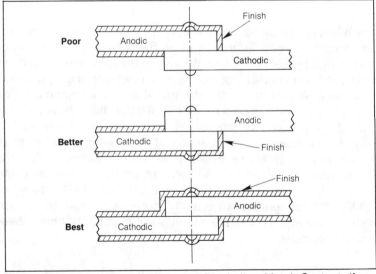

Figure 3.24—Coating Methods for Dissimilar Metal Contact (from AFSC-DH/1-4)

3.37

Documents such as the *Air Force Design HandBook AFSC-DH/1-4* and SAE ARP-1481 give accurate details on bonding practices for corrosion avoidance. Based on these recommendations, Tables 3.7 and 3.8 show the compatible grouping of the most common metals. Corrosive action between metals of different groups will be greatest when the joint is openly exposed to salt spray, rain, etc.

The relative degrees of exposure may be defined as follows:

Exposed:	Open, unprotected exposure to weather
Sheltered:	Limited protection from direct action of weather. Locations in louvered housings, sheds and vehicles offer sheltered exposure.
Housed:	Located in weatherproof buildings

Table 3.7—Compatible Groups of Common Metals

Group	Metals
I	Magnesium
II	Aluminum, Aluminum Alloys, Zinc, Cadmium
III	Carbon Steel, Iron, Lead, Tin, Lead-Tin Solder
IV	Nickel, Chromium, Stainless Steel
V	Copper, Silver, Gold, Platinum, Titanium

When bonds under these different exposure conditions must be made between different groups, they should be protected as indicated by Table 3.8. Condition A in the table means that the couple (joint) must have a protective finish applied after metal-to-metal contact has been established so that no liquid film can bridge the two elements of the couple. Condition B means that the two metals may be joined with bare metal exposed at junction surfaces. The remainder of the bond must be given an appropriate protective finish. Condition C indicates that the combination cannot be used except under very unusual circumstances where short life expectancy can be tolerated or when the equipment is normally stored and exposed for any short intervals. Protective coatings are mandatory under these circumstances.

Table 3.8—Bond Protection Requirements (*Groups as per Table 3.7)

Condition of Exposure	Anode*				Cathode*
	I	II	III	IV	
Exposed	A	A			II
Sheltered	A	A			
Housed	A	A			
Exposed	C	A	B		III
Sheltered	A	B	B		
Housed	A	B	B		
Exposed	C	A	B	B	IV
Sheltered	A	A	B	B	
Housed	A	B	B		
Exposed	C	C	C	A	V
Sheltered	A	A	A	B	
Housed	A	B	B	B	

A. Protective finish applied after metal-to-metal contact: any liquid film cannot bridge the two elements of the couple.

B. Two metals may be joined with bare metal exposed at the junction surfaces. The remainder of the bond must be given a protective finish.

C. The combination cannot be used except under rare circumstances where short life expectancy can be tolerated. Protective coatings are mandatory.

3.7 Workmanship and Maintenance

Whichever bonding method is determined to be the best for a given situation, the mating surfaces must be cleaned of all foreign material and substances which would preclude the establishment of a low resistance connection. Next, the bond members must be carefully joined employing techniques appropriate to the specific method of bonding. Finally, the joint must be finished with a protective coating to ensure continued integrity of the bond. The quality of the junction depends upon the thoroughness and care with which these three steps are performed.

Personnel making bonds must be carefully trained in the techniques and procedures required. Where bonds are to be welded, for example, work should be performed only by qualified welders. No additional training should be necessary because standard welding techniques appropriate for construction purposes are generally sufficient for establishing electrical bonds. Qualified welders should also be used where brazed connections are to be made.

Pressure bonds utilizing bolts, screws or clamps must be given special attention. Routine construction practices do not require the surface preparation and bolt tightening necessary for an effective and reliable electrical bond. Therefore, force beyond what would be required for strictly mechanical strength is necessary.

Bonds of this type must be checked rigorously to see that the mating surfaces are carefully cleaned, that the bond members are properly joined, and that the completed bond is adequately protected against corrosion. Specific recommendations are:

1. Utilize welding whenever possible for permanent bonds. The welds must be adequate to support the mechanical load demands on the bonded members.

2. Use brazing (or silver soldering) for permanently bonding copper and brass.

3. Do not use soft-soldered connections in fault protection grounding networks or for any connection in the lightning protection system.

4. The mating surfaces of bolted and other compression-type bonds require careful cleaning. The basic cleaning requirements are:

   a. All nonconductive material must be removed. Such materials include paints, adhesives and other organic finishes; anodizing films; oxide and sulfide films; and oil, grease and other petroleum products.

   b. All corrosive agents must be removed. Such agents include water, acids, strong alkalies, and any other materials which provide conductive electrolytic paths. For instance, a chemically cleaned surface can have its conductivity severely degraded if touched with fingers or perspiration.

   c. All solid matter which would interfere with the low-resistance path across the bond or which forms a wedge or barrier allowing the entrance of corrosive materials or agents must be removed. Such solid materials include dust, dirt, sand, metal filings and corrosion by-products.

5. The proper order of assembly for bolted bonds is illustrated in Fig. 3.25. Position load distribution washers directly underneath the bolt head or under the nut next to the primary member. Lock washers may be placed between the nut and any load distribution washers. **Toothed lock washers should not be placed between the primary bonded members.**

6. Once the mating surfaces have been cleaned of all nonconductive material, join the bond members together as soon as possible. If delays beyond two hours are necessary in corrosive environments, the cleaned surfaces must be protected with an appropriate coating which, of course, must be removed before completing the bond.

7. Alligator clips and other spring loaded clamps are to be employed only as temporary bonds. Use them primarily to ensure that personnel are not inadvertently exposed to hazardous voltages when performing repair work on equipment or on facility wiring.

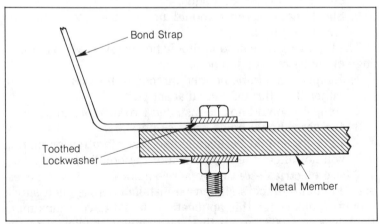

Figure 3.25—Order of Assembly for Bolted Connection

3.8 Equipment Bonding Practices

This section presents design and construction guidelines for effective bonding of equipment circuits, equipment enclosures and cabling. These guidelines are not intended as step-by-step procedures for meeting EMC specifications. Rather they are aimed at focusing attention on those principles and techniques which lead to increased compatibility between circuits, assemblies and equipments:

1. Welded seams should be used wherever possible because they are permanent, offer a low-impedance bond, and provide the highest degree of RF shielding.
2. Spot welds may be used where RF tightness is not necessary. Spot welding is less desirable than continuous welding because of the tendency for buckling and the possibility of corrosion occurring between welds.
3. Soldering should not be used where high mechanical strength is required. If mechanical strength is required, the solder should be supplemented with fasteners such as screws or bolts.
4. Fasteners such as rivets, "Philips" screws and other self-tapping screws for sheet metal should not be relied upon to provide the primary current path through a joint.
5. Rivets should be used primarily to provide mechanical strength to soldered bonds.
6. Sheet metal screws should not be used to secure an electrical bond.

The following precautions should be observed when employing bonding straps or jumpers:

1. Jumpers should be bonded directly to the basic structure rather than through an adjacent part.
2. Jumpers should not be installed two or more in series.
3. Jumpers should be as short as possible.
4. Jumpers should be installed so that vibration or motion will not affect the impedance of the bonding path.

Where electrical continuity across shock mounts is necessary, bonding jumpers should be installed across each shock mount. Jumpers for this application should have a maximum thickness of 0.063 cm so that the damping efficiency of the mount is not impaired. In severe shock and vibration environments, solid straps may be corrugated, or flexible wire braid may be used.

Where RF shielding is required and welded joints cannot be used, the bond surfaces must be machined smooth to establish a high degree of surface contact throughout the joint area. Fasteners must be positioned to maintain uniform pressure throughout the bond area. Chassis-mounted subassemblies should utilize the full mounting area for the bond as illustrated in Figs. 3.26 and 3.27. Separate jumpers should not be used for this purpose.

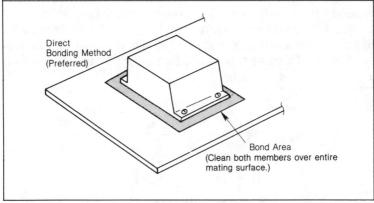

Figure 3.26—Bonding of Subassemblies to Equipment Chassis

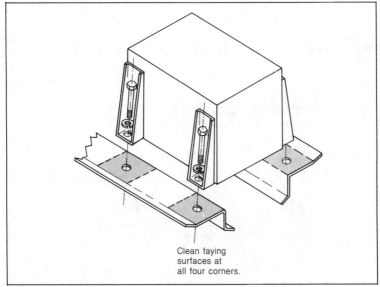

Figure 3.27—Bonding of Equipment to Mounting Members

Equipment racks (19″ and other sizes) provide a convenient means of maintaining electrical continuity between such items as rack-mounted chassis, panels and ground planes. They also provide an electrical interconnection for cable trays. A typical equipment cabinet, with the necessary modifications to provide such bonding, is shown in Figs. 3.28 through 3.30. Bonding between equipment chassis and rack is achieved through equipment front panel and rack right-angle brackets. These brackets are grounded to the unistrut horizontal slide that is welded to the rack frame. The lower surfaces of the rack are treated with a conductive protective finish to facilitate bonding to a ground-plane mat. The ground stud at the top of the rack is used to bond a cable tray, if used, to the rack structure, which is of welded construction.

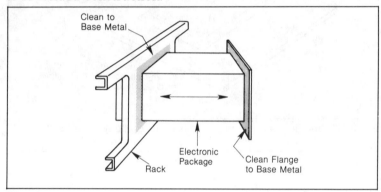

Figure 3.28—Typical Method of Bonding Equipment Flanges to Frame or Rack

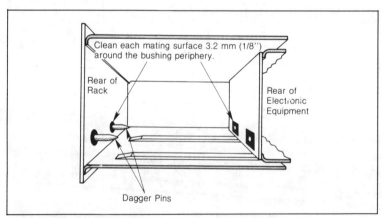

Figure 3.29—Bonding of Rack-Mounted Equipment Employing Dagger Pins

3.44

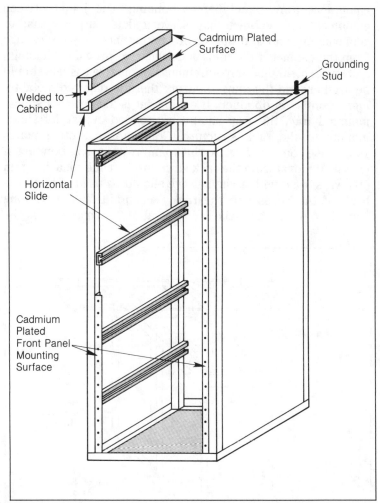

Cadmium Plated
Surface

Grounding
Stud

Welded to
Cabinet

Horizontal
Slide

Cadmium
Plated
Front Panel
Mounting
Surface

Figure 3.30—Recommended Practices for Effective Bonding in Cabinets

Figure 3.31 illustrates a typical bonding scheme of a whole cabinet for very severe EMC requirements. Cable trays are bonded together and the cable tray is bonded to the cable chute. The cable chute is bonded to the top of the cabinet; the cabinet is bonded to the flush-mounted grounding insert (which is welded to the ground grid); and the front panel of the equipment is bonded to the rack or cabinet front-panel mounting surface. Nonconductive finishes are removed from the equipment front panel before bonding. The joint between equipment and cabinet may serve a dual purpose: that of achieving a bond and that of preventing interference leakage from the cabinet if the joint is designed to provide shielding.

If such shielding is a requirement, conductive gaskets should be used around the joint to ensure that the required metal-to-metal contact is obtained. If equipment is located in a shock-mounted tray, the tray should be bonded across its shock mounts to the rack structure. Connector mounting plates should use conductive gasketing to improve chassis bonding. If chassis removal from the rack structure is required, a 25.4 mm (1″) wide braid with a vinyl sleeve should be used to bond the back of the chassis to the rack. The braid should be long enough to permit a partial withdrawal of the chassis from the rack.

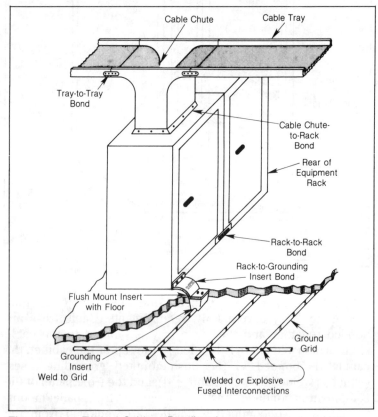

Figure 3.31—Typical Cabinet Bonding Arrangements

3.9 Summary of Bonding Principles

1. Bonding does not "happen." Bonds must be designed as components of the grounding system because they affect the system's overall performance.

2. Electrical continuity and mechanical fastening are two different functions, never to be mixed. Fasteners, spring washers, threads, etc. are strictly to apply mechanical pressure; then, the current can flow through base metal mating surfaces.

3. Bonding must achieve and maintain intimate contact between metal surfaces. The surfaces must be smooth, clean and free of nonconductive finishes. Fasteners must exert sufficient pressure to hold the surfaces in contact in the presence of the deforming stresses, shocks and vibrations associated with the equipment and its environment.

4. The effectiveness of the bond depends upon its construction, the frequency and magnitude of the currents flowing through it, and the environmental conditions to which it is subjected.

5. Bonding jumpers are only a substitute for direct bonds. If the jumpers are kept as short as possible, have a low resistance, low length-to width ratio, and are not higher in the electromechanical series than the bonded members, they can be reasonable substitutes.

6. Bonds are always best made by joining similar metals. If this is not possible, attention must be paid to bond corrosion through the choice of the materials to be bonded, the selection of supplementary components (such as washers) to assure that corrosion will affect replaceable elements only, and the use of protective finishes.

7. Even if metals are similar, a protective overcoat must be provided if moisture or contaminants are expected.

8. Finally, throughout the lifetime of the equipment, system or facility, the bonds must be inspected, tested and maintained.

3.10 References

1. Denny, H., "RF Characteristics of Bonding Systems," (*IEEE Transactions on EMC*, Feb., 1969).
2. Brettle, J., and Baskerville, M., "Electrical Bonding in Aircrafts," (IEEE EMC Symposium, 1981).
3. *AFSC-DH/1-4*, March 1984.
4. Brettle, J., and Lodge, K.J., "Carbon Fibre Composite Joints for EMC," (IEEE EMC Symposium, Univ. of Surrey, U.K., 1982).

3.11 Bibliography

1. Moyer, D., and Lubar, D., "Electrical Bond Contact Impedance," (IEEE EMC Symposium, 1982).

Chapter 4

Grounding for Safety and Fault Protection

Fault protection is an integral part of ground network design. Frequently, signal grounds are commoned with fault protection paths, particularly where structural elements of a building are involved. Traditional practices as well as personnel and structural protection requirements strongly favor that priority be placed on fault protection needs over EMI needs. Therefore, it is likely that signal ground networks must be designed to be compatible with fault protection networks. Occasionally, fault protection requirements will force compromises in signal ground design and implementation. The following discussion presents an overview of the design principles behind fault protection systems.

4.1 Electric Shock

Electric shock occurs when the human body becomes a part of an electric circuit. It most commonly occurs when people come in contact with energized devices or circuits while touching a grounded object or while standing on a damp floor. The effects of an electric current on the body are principally determined by the magnitude of current and duration of the shock. Current is determined by the open-circuit voltage of the source and total path resistance including internal source resistance and human body resistance.

In power circuits, internal source resistance is usually negligible in comparison with that of the body. In such cases, the voltage level V is the important factor in determining if a shock hazard exists. At commercial frequencies of 50/60 Hz and voltages of 120/140 V, the contact resistance of the body primarily determines the current through the body. This resistance may decrease by as much as a factor of 100 between a completely dry condition and a wet condition. For estimation purposes, the lower range of the skin resistance is usually somewhere between 500 and 1,500 Ω.

An electric current through the body can produce varying effects, including death, depending upon the magnitude of current. For example, the **perception current** is the smallest current that might cause an unexpected involuntary reaction and produce an accident as a secondary effect. **Shock currents** greater than the perception current produce an increasingly severe muscular reaction. Above a certain level, the shock victim becomes unable to release the conductor. The maximum current at which a person can still release a conductor by using the muscles directly stimulated by that current is called the **let-go current**. Shock currents above the let-go level can begin to cause chest muscles to contract and breathing to stop. If the current is interrupted quickly enough, breathing will resume. At a still higher level, electric shock currents can cause an effect on the heart called **ventricular fibrillation.** Under this condition, heart action usually stops. Various current levels for 60 Hz and for dc are summarized in Table 4.1.

At frequencies above 300 Hz, the current levels required to produce the above effects begin to increase due to skin effect. For example, the perception current is approximately 100 mA at 70 kHz. Above 100 to 200 kHz, the sensation of shock changes from tingling to heat. It is believed that heat and burns are the only effects of shock above these frequencies. There is also some nonlinearity in human body resistance, as is evident in Fig. 4.1. Figure 4.2 shows what percentage of the total resistance is contributed by each body part.

Table 4.1—Effect of Electrical Current to Human Body

Alternating Current (60 Hz)	Direct Currents	Effects
(mA)	(mA)	
0.5-1	0-4	Perception
1-3	4-15	Surprise (Reaction Current)
3-21	15-80	Reflex Action (Let-Go Current)
21-40	80-160	Muscular Inhibition
40-100	160-300	Respiratory Block
Over 100	Over 300	Usually Fatal

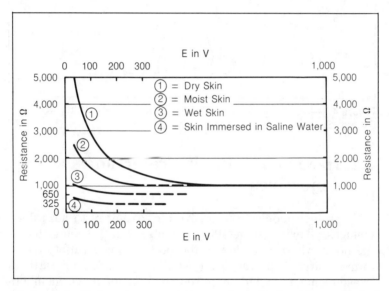

Figure 4.1—Various Aspects of Human Body Resistance vs. Applied Voltage (Measured Hand-to-Hand or Hand-to-Foot)

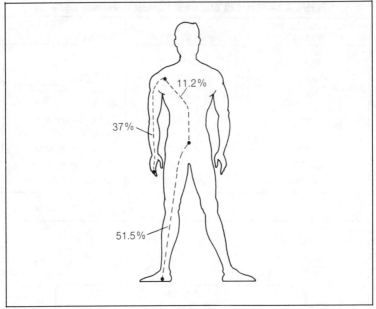

Figure 4.2—Distribution by Percentage of Internal Body Resistance (Skin Excluded)

4.2 Hazard and Fault Protection Objectives

To protect people from inadvertent exposure to hazardous voltages, all exposed metallic elements should be connected to the point where one side of the power source (utility transformer, aircraft power plant, etc.) is grounded or earthed. These elements include exposed equipments, metal members of the building, plumbing fixtures and any other metallic structures likely to be at a different (hazardous) potential in the event of a fault. Then, if accidental contact occurs between energized conductors and chassis, frame or cabinet through human error, insulation failure or component failure, a direct low-resistance path will exist between the fault and the energy source (usually a transformer). In this situation, fuses will blow or breakers will trip and thus quickly remove the hazard.

The previously noted dependence of shock effects upon frequency suggests that the danger from electric shock is related to the duration of exposure (see Fig. 4.3). C.F. Dalziel, in an article titled "Electrical Shock Hazard," (*IEEE Spectrum*, Feb. 1972), indicates that the current levels required to produce a given effect are inversely proportional to the square root of the time of exposure. Thus, one objective of the fault protection system (network) is to reduce the time of exposure to a minimum. Another reason for achieving rapid fault clearance is to limit temperature rise in the faulted conductor and thus minimize fire hazard.

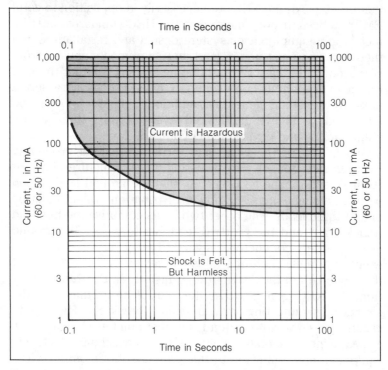

Figure 4.3—Safe/Unsafe Currents vs. Duration of Exposure

4.3 U.S.A. National Standard for Safety Ground

The National Electrical Code (NEC) is issued by the National Fire Protection Association as NFPA 70 and is updated every three years. This code has been adopted by the American National Standards Institute as ANSI C1, and it is rapidly gaining universal acceptance. It has become, in effect, a federal standard with its incorporation into the Occupational Safety and Health Administration (OSHA) requirements. When viewed from the perspective of EMI and noise control, it should be remembered that the primary objectives of the NEC are fire and shock hazard protection and not the achievement of electromagnetic compatibility. However, this does not mean that practices of the NEC are necessarily in opposition to good EMI practices. It does mean that the NEC standards must be met in any equipment or system design and installation, and therefore one must understand its requirements and incorporate them within any EMI grounding system. Another thing to realize is that simply conforming to the NEC does not assure a noise-free system; generally, additional measures must be employed to achieve the desired level of total system (equipment, facility and environment) compatibility.

Article 250 of the NEC sets forth the general grounding requirements for electrical wiring in a structure. Present requirements of the NEC specify that the ground lead (green wire) in a single-phase ac power distribution system must be one of three leads. The other two leads comprise the **hot** lead (black wire) and the **neutral** lead (white wire). The ground lead is a safety conductor designed to carry current only in the event of a fault. The **hot** lead is connected to the high side of the secondary of the distribution transformer. For fault protection, the NEC specifies that the neutral be grounded at the service disconnecting means (main breaker). The safety ground (green wire) is grounded at that point as shown in Fig. 4.4. All exposed metallic elements of electrical and electronic equipment are connected to this ground with the green wire.

Grounding of a three-phase wye power distribution system is done similarly to the single-phase system. The connections for a typical system are shown in Fig. 4.5. The neutral lead, as in single-phase systems, is grounded for fault protection at the service disconnecting means. The NEC specifies that the neutral should never be grounded at any point on the load side of the service entrance on either single-phase or three-phase systems.

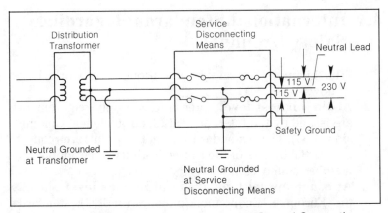

Figure 4.4—Single-Phase 115/230 Vac Power Ground Connections

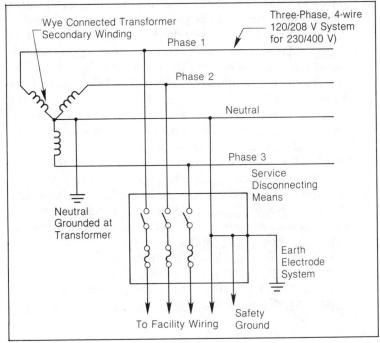

Figure 4.5—Three-Phase 120/208 Vac Power System Ground Connections

4.4 International Standards Regarding Safety Ground

The hierarchy of safety rules around the world is as follows:

1. **At the highest level**, international safety requirements are issued by the International Electrotechnical Commission (IEC). These standards are not rules but are requested, per the bylaws of the United Nations, to be adopted by member countries.

2. **At commonwealth or group of nations level**, such as the European Economic Community (EEC), standards are becoming directives whose adoption guarantees uniformity of safety requirements and approval procedures within this group. This helps to remove trade barriers.

3. **At a national level**, standards are incorporated into national laws, decrees or codes whose application is mandatory and eventually imposed by all means of law enforcement. Examples of this are CSA, VDE, etc. In some cases, e.g. the U.S.A., the requirements are set by the National Electrical Code, but its application is more or less under the eyes of Underwriter's Laboratories, an independent organization that acts as a technical inspector. The IEC, being made up of representatives from many countries worldwide, publishes specifications which are based on a national consensus. Then, IEC recommendations are generally reflected in each country's national rules. The most relevant IEC publications with regard to safety and grounding topics are:

   IEC-65, Consumer Electronic Equipment
   IEC-380, Electrical Safety of Office Machines
   IEC-435, Safety of Data Processing Equipment
   IEC-601, Safety of Medical Electrical Equipment

4.4.1 Highlights of IEC Standards

The IEC essential points are:
1. Safe and Unsafe Voltages
   The standards establish a level of SELV (Safety Extra Low Voltages) at 42.4 V peak or dc. All voltages above are

deemed hazardous. To qualify for this, a circuit must be so designed that under **normal and single-fault** condition the SELV level is not exceeded.

2. Power Distribution Grounding and Earthing
   The standards distinguish between:
   a. TN system: power source with one point (generally the neutral) directly earthed, all the exposed conductive parts (i.e., touchable) being connected to that point by protective earth (PE) wires
   b. TT system: power distribution with one point directly earthed, all exposed conductive parts being earthed via individual electrodes
   c. IT system: power distribution with isolated (non-earthed) neutral (or return), all exposed conductive parts being earthed. The neutral is either totally floated or earthed through an impedance (generally 1,000 Ω).

3. Protection Against Electric Shock
   All conductive parts of a machine which contains higher than SELV-level circuits must be unaccessible to operator's body or otherwise connected to the earthing conductor. This includes any conductive part which is separated from a hazardous voltage area by a basic insulation only.

For Class II (double insulation) equipment, capacitors with hazardous voltages shall not be connected to accessible conductive parts. Pluggable equipment shall be designed such that there is no risk of shock from charged capacitors when touching the pins of the plug 1 s after the equipment is disconnected. (Any residual voltage after 1 s should not exceed 34 V peak between the pins of the plug.)

Protective earthing shall contain no switches or fuses and shall be such that the disconnection of earthing conductor in one assembly does not break the earthing link in other assemblies. Screwless terminals are not allowed.

Resistance between earthing terminals of a machine and the parts to be earthed shall not exceed 0.1 Ω when measured under 12 V, 50 or 60 Hz. In a case of an earth fault (short to case, etc.), a protective device must be inserted in all supply conductors (neutral is exempted if the neutral pin of the power plug is reliably identified and cannot be reversed). The protective device must trip just above the safe current rating of the circuit but also be capable of breaking the maximum fault current which may flow.

4.4.2 Class I and II Equipments

With regard to safety, the standard describes two general categories:

1. **Class I** equipment, in which there are accessible metal (or conductive) parts that enclose, or could be related to, hazardous voltages. Such parts must be connected to the protective earthing. Simply said, in a Class I equipment, safety relies on earthing.

2. **Class II** equipment, in which protection against electrical shock relies on reinforced insulation (double insulation) such that no conductive part containing a hazardous voltage can be directly touched. In most cases, such equipment does not need an earthing (green/yellow) conductor.

A special third class, **Class III** equipment is also defined where only ELV (less than 42.4 V) is used.

Aside from these insulation versus grounding aspects, Classes I and II dictate different leakage current limits which in turn affect the design of EMI filters.

4.5 Permissible Leakage Current

In most electrical safety requirements, a maximum permissible ground leakage current is stipulated. This clause guarantees that, besides dielectric strength (checked by high-potential tests) and electrical creepage (checked by minimum spacing requirements), insulation between live parts and earth is such that no objectionable current will flow in the user's body under the following conditions:

1. Normal condition (machine "on," at maximum input voltage tolerances)
2. Any combination of switch positions, blown fuses, tripped circuit breakers, etc.
3. Any single fault (damaged insulation, loose terminals, broken ground, etc.)

Note that a catastrophic combination of conditions 2 and 3 is not contemplated.

Leakage currents are measured at 50/60 Hz or whatever is the rated frequency of the device under test. The limits differ depending on equipment class and, to some extent, national agencies.

4.5.1. Leakage Current for Nonmedical Apparatus

The maximum permissible leakage currents for nonmedical apparatus are as follow:
> Class II equipment: 0.25 mA (IEC and UL requirements)
> Class I hand-held equipment: 0.75 mA
> Class I movable equipment and pluggable stationary equipment: 3.5 mA (5 mA for UL 478)
> Class I stationary equipment, permanently connected: 3.5 mA, with a waiver allowing up to 5 percent of equipment input current, provided the following warning label is affixed visibly near the power input connection:

HIGH LEAKAGE CURRENT, EARTH CONNECTION
IS ESSENTIAL BEFORE CONNECTING SUPPLY

To measure the leakage current, an ammeter in series with a 1,500 Ω resistor (simulating the human body) is used. The measuring set is shunted by a 150 nF capacitor to desensitize the meter above 600 Hz, corresponding to the lesser sensitivity of the human body to HF currents. Then,

For Class I equipment:
> The safety ground connection is removed and the measuring set is inserted between the equipment case and the earth reference, or the equipment is powered through an isolation transformer and the leakage is measured between each supply lead and the casing.

For Class II equipment:
> Since there is generally no earth wire, the leakage current is measured between each supply lead and any accessible metal (or conductive part), or it is measured between each supply lead and a metal foil which is wrapped around the insulating body of the equipment.

4.11

4.5.2 Leakage Current for Medical Equipment (Microshock Hazard)

During the three decades following World War II, as great advances were made in medical practice and techniques, there was corresponding advancement in medical electronics technology. Growth in this field was phenomenal, and pioneering work in medical electronics was essentially free of outside regulation, resulting in both positive and negative consequences.

However, during the 1970s, the situation changed rapidly. Reports began to circulate which asserted that hospital patients were being electrocuted by the very equipment that was used in their treatment. Such reports were difficult to confirm or deny during that period because few hospitals had staff engineers with the training or background to investigate such incidents. These reports, together with those which only intimated that electricity was a possible cause of injury or death, added to the growing turmoil.

Inevitable consequences of this situation included rapid acceleration of biomedical engineering, which until this time concerned itself primarily with research. It stimulated awareness that some control had to be exercised for protection of the patient. In response, the IEC issued its document IEC-601, "Safety of Medical Electrical Equipment."

In the U.S.A., the two organizations most involved with electrical safety are the National Fire Protection Association (NFPA) and the Association for the Advancement of Medical Instrumentation (AAMI). AAMI differs from NFPA in several respects; however, the primary difference is that AAMI concerns itself primarily with activities related to medical devices, whereas the NFPA concerns itself primarily with facility planning and life safety regulations. Accordingly, AAMI is extremely active in the areas of medical device standards and patient electrical safety standards. The electrical safety requirements presented in this section are primarily those of AAMI.

The application of electrical safety to medical equipment involves various risk values for hospital patients, depending upon the nature and condition of the illness, treatment and equipment used and the electrical susceptibility of the patient. Of particular concern are electrical safety considerations pertaining to lead leakage and chassis leakage currents.

4.5.2.1 Categories of Risk

Electrical safety in hospitals can be expressed in three categories of risks as they relate to different respective grades of patients. For example, the first and most severe risk (with a correspondingly strict limit) concerns the patient with an inserted catheter or other conductive pathway to the heart. Such a person may be especially vulnerable to fibrillation because of a debilitating condition or drugs which tend to "irritate" the cardiac musculature. This type of patient is usually referred to as an electrically susceptible patient (ESP). The second category involves the largest number of patients: those who are bedridden but are not considered to be electrically susceptible. The third category embraces ambulatory patients and the hospital staff, i.e., those who have little or no involvement with electrically powered equipment.

The primary concern of designers under these risk conditions is the electrically susceptible patient. Any monitoring device which cannot be used on the electrically susceptible patient is of limited use and, in terms of economics, a marketing risk.

A monitoring device used on an electrically susceptible patient will be subjected periodically to electrical safety checks described in Section 4.4. Thus, the patient-connected preamplifier of these devices will be periodically subjected to voltage overload, a consideration that demands early design attention.

4.5.2.2 Power Distribution Conventions

It is appropriate to review some fundamentals of commercial power distribution systems as they relate to hospitals. Non-American readers should consult applicable codes to correlate information to their particular circumstances.

Almost all hospital areas supply commercial line power to wall receptacles which employ parallel-bladed connectors with a ground blade, as illustrated in Fig. 4.6. The only exceptions to this generalization are operating rooms and cardiac catheterization laboratories, which require isolated power transformers, line isolation monitors and special "twist-lock" receptacles. In the U.S.A., the commercial power distribution wiring generally will be color coded as shown in Fig. 4.6, with the hot conductor black, the neutral conductor white (used with a taller slot in more recent installations) and the ground conductor green.

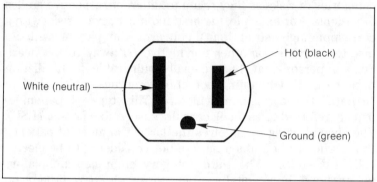

Figure 4.6—Power Distribution Designations and Color Codes (U.S.A.)

Those familiar with power distribution wiring will note that the neutral (white) wire is actually grounded at some point. In effect, the power to the load is provided between the hot and neutral wires, while the ground wire is added as a safety device which is used in the event of a wiring fault or equipment malfunction. Hence, a distinction must be preserved between the neutral (white) and the ground (green) leads.

In modern facilities, areas which are designed to accommodate electrically susceptible patients will be designed to provide an equipotential ground. This means that all exposed metallic surfaces are connected to a central room grounding point, along with all ground leads from the wall wiring. In this way, all grounds are at the same potential (equipotential), which eliminates hazards due to potential differences caused by currents circulating in ground loops. All room grounding points are likewise connected to the grounding bus on the branch circuit distribution panel and ultimately connected to earth ground in the transformer vault. Therefore, while the hot and neutral leads may be part of a power distribution system serving several rooms, the ground lead represents a well-defined point to which all measurements may be referenced. For this reason, all electrical safety measurements are made with respect to room ground.

4.5.2.3 Patient Lead Leakage Current

The primary concern in electrical safety considerations is lead leakage. Patient lead leakage is defined as the amount of current passing through the patient to room ground when the patient lead is connected directly to the hot lead of the commercial power line (115 Vac in the U.S.A.). This situation is illustrated in Fig. 4.7. The term **lead** refers to any physical connection to the patient, thus, conductive respirator tubing could conceivably exceed the patient lead leakage current limit. At this time, the allowable patient lead leakage current for equipment used on electrically susceptible patients is 20 μA rms in the U.S., while IEC-601 stipulates a maximum of 10 μA under normal conditions. In most cases, medical devices will be electronic, and more than one patient lead will be present, usually in the form of electrode leads. In such cases, the patient lead leakage of each individual lead to ground must not exceed 20 μA rms.

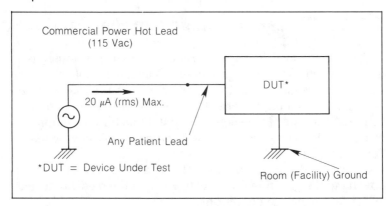

Figure 4.7—Measurement of Patient Lead Leakage

In the case of electrocardiogram (ECG or EKG) equipment, the definition of patient lead leakage includes the current seeking ground through each patient under the prescribed circumstances, as well as the current seeking ground when one patient lead is in contact with commercial power while the other patient leads are grounded. An ECG monitor must meet the patient lead leakage current limits for all possible combinations of patient leads in which one lead contacts commercial power, and a path to ground exists through any other lead. This is shown schematically in Fig. 4.8.

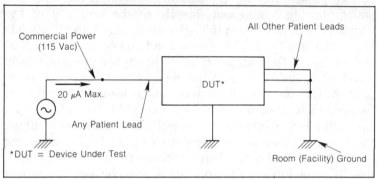

Figure 4.8—Lead-Leakage Measurement for Electrocardiographs

4.5.2.4 Chassis Leakage Current Limits

The patient lead leakage current discussed previously is a universal limit. That is, if patient lead leakage is applicable to a particular design, and if that equipment is to be used on an electrically susceptible patient, there is really only one limit to be met. There are also leakage current limits for the equipment chassis which correspond to the degrees of risk mentioned in Section 4.5.2.1.

Chassis leakage current is defined as the largest current flowing in the ground wire (green wire), of the medical device, under four separate conditions:

1. Device power "on," hot and neutral wires normal
2. Device power "on," hot and neutral wires reversed
3. Device power "off," hot and neutral wires normal
4. Device power "off," hot and neutral wires reversed

The maximum current arising from these four separate conditions is then applied to the appropriate current limit for that equipment type. The chassis leakage current is the maximum current which will flow to any ground at any time as a result of contact with the equipment chassis. The appropriate chassis leakage current limits for the three categories of risk are given in Table 4.2.

Table 4.2—Chassis Leakage Current Limits

Risk	Category	Leakage Limit (rms)
1	General	500 μA
2	High Risk	100 μA
3	Extreme Risk (ESP)	100 μA

4.5.2.5 Derivation of Leakage Current Limits

If a designer is not familiar with the history of the electrical safety issue, definition of patient lead leakage and chassis leakage currents may seem extremely heuristic. In fact, they arise directly from experience in critical care situations and from analysis of tragic accidents. A short explanation is offered here by way of illustration. The most familiar ECG tracing presents the variation of potential between the left and right arms while using the right leg as reference potential. It was common practice to make the right leg lead a direct connection to ground, thereby simplifying design of the front-end differential amplifier. This situation is safe only as long as the patient remains electrically isolated from any other electrical connection.

Unfortunately, it is practically impossible to guarantee this level of patient isolation. An electrical connection can be established in any number of ways, e.g., contact with bed frames having wiring faults, equipment having high leakage currents or an electrical source through touching an attending nurse or physician. Even though the resulting currents may be exceedingly small, the amount of current required to interfere with normal heart rhythm in an electrically susceptible or seriously debilitated patient is only tens of microamperes.

4.5.2.6 Simulated Patient Load

The simulated patient load shown as Fig. 4.9 is of most importance to the designer for several reasons. First, it may be used to determine whether a design meets established electrical safety standards with a realistic load. Second, it will assist the design effort by representing a fairly accurate impedance model of the human body. This patient load model is seen to simplify to the 1 kΩ skin impedance discussed in Section 4.1 as long as the frequency is kept below 1 kHz. While the patient load model of Fig. 4.9 is fairly accurate in representing the impedance of the human body in the general case, the reader should be aware that other, more specific, models exist for specific applications. For example, a patient load may be necessary to verify device performance in compliance testing. In such cases, the patient load model of Fig. 4.9 should be used only if no other model is specified by the controlling authority.

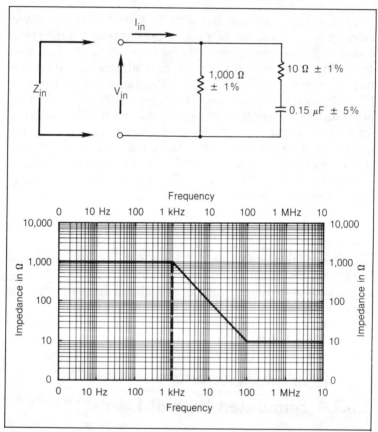

Figure 4.9—AAMI Patient Load Model

4.5.2.7 Extension of Electrical Safety Limits

The limits discussed so far were developed primarily to ensure the safety of the electrically susceptible patient. Accordingly, they apply primarily to those equipment types which may be used in the routine monitoring of a seriously ill or electrically susceptible patient.

Even so, the need to ensure patient safety has caused electrical safety limits to be applied to any type of equipment which may monitor an intensive-care patient. Presently, the strictness of application and interpretation of these electrical safety limits is rather subjective and varies according to the hospital involved.

In general, the chassis leakage current limits will be applicable and rigorously applied to almost all patient-connected equipment whether or not it will be used in an intensive-care setting. This is largely due to the safety element which is afforded to the patient as well as the hospital staff.

For some equipment, the patient lead leakage current limit is regarded as performance criteria to be approximated. For example, a defibrillator may contain an ECG-processing section which enables the unit to fire synchronously with the QRS complex of the electrocardiogram. In most cases, the ECG is sensed through the defibrillator needles themselves. Consequently, the function of the ECG is not to present ECG information for diagnostic purposes, but rather to enable the defibrillator to fire at the proper point in time to restore the heart to its normal rhythm. In such circumstances, the ECG isolation may be excused from complying with the 20 μA patient leakage limit as long as it comes reasonably close. In this situation, "reasonably close" will be defined by each individual institution.

It is anticipated that device-specific FDA legislation will address the patient lead leakage limits for specific items of equipment. For example, there is a tendency to regard electro-encephalography and hemodialysis as having characteristics of an intensive-care area. Under these conditions, it is reasonable to assume that the electrical safety limits already described may eventually be applied to equipment such as electroencephalograph (EEG) units.

4.5.2.8 Verification Procedures

The designer should be aware that patient-connected equipment will be investigated periodically by hospital or shared-service technicians as part of a required preventive maintenance program. Certain devices, ECG monitors in particular, will be investigated every other month to ensure their compliance with the patient lead leakage limit. Although this maintenance is routine, it will regularly impose line voltage on the patient leads. Design of the patient-connected preamplifier should be executed with this in mind.

The basic test configuration was given in Fig. 4.7. In practice, patient leads are not connected directly to the commercial power line, but instead are connected in series with a 1 kΩ resistor or with the patient load model given in Fig. 4.9. This load serves both as a current limiter and artificial patient, and it does not affect validity of the patient leakage current reading if the ECG monitor is functioning properly. The actual test configuration is indicated in Fig. 4.10.

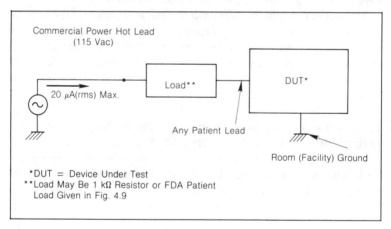

Figure 4.10—Actual Lead-Leakage Measurement with Current-Limiting Load in Series

4.5.2.9 Relationship of Medical Electrical Safety to EMC

The preceding sections were intended to provide equipment designer with an understanding of electrical safety requirements which must be satisfied for some types of medical devices. It will now be shown how these limits relate to the problem of meeting the EMC guidelines established by the FDA.

A common technique to protect active linear devices from EMI is to provide capacitive bypassing to ground, or zero-voltage reference. While this technique is usually preferred for a variety of reasons, it will be of little use in the design of a patient-connected preamplifier. If we consider that a leakage current of 20 μA, produced during an electrical safety test, is caused only by capacitive effects in the preamplifier and patient leads, then the maximum allowable shunt capacitance for the preamplifier may be computed by:

$$I = \frac{V}{X_c} = 2\pi fCV$$

$$C = \frac{I}{2\pi fV}$$

In this example,

$$I = 20 \times 10^{-6} \text{ A rms}$$
$$f = 60 \text{ Hz}$$
$$V = 115 \text{ V rms}$$

Solving for C, we find than an equivalent shunt capacitance of only approximately 460 pF is responsible for 20 μA rms leakage current even under the assumption that the resistive component of the preamplifier impedance was infinite.

As a practical matter, 460 pF is a strict capacitance limit. If the path from the patient electrodes to the actual device input for a typical EEG unit were traced, the following sources of capacitance would be found:

1. Individual electrode leads, typically 1 m long
2. Capacitance of connector pins joining individual electrode leads to patient cable
3. Patient cable, typically 1 m long
4. Capacitance of connector pins joining patient cable to ECG unit panel
5. Wiring from panel to circuit board
6. Capacitance of overvoltage protection circuit (needed to prevent damage from accidents and electrical safety test)
7. Capacitance of circuit board traces
8. Capacitance of active device input
9. Capacitors in a power line filter (as discussed in Section 4.5.3)

When one considers that a simple 1 m (3 ft) long section of patient cable alone is capable of contributing some tens of picofarads, exclusive of connector capacitance, it may be appreciated that a 460 pF limit for all sources of capacitance in the preamplifier of a typical ECG is a fairly tight design specification in itself. Unfortunately, this leaves little or no capacitance for bypassing to meet EMI/EMC criteria.

Even if there were no capacitance associated with the preamplifier input, it would still be necessary to maintain a minimum impedance of 6 MΩ to comply with the 20 μA leakage current limit. In practice, the impedance must be much higher because capacitance is present. As a consequence, shielded patient cables are not a solution to an EMI problem.

Shielded cables have characteristic impedances that rarely exceed several hundred ohms: they cannot be terminated in their characteristic impedance if the preamplifier is to maintain its input impedance for safety requirements. Therefore, it is evident that the 20 μA patient lead-leakage limit severely restricts the designer, and the conflict between electrical safety and EMI "hardening" may not be easily resolved. Unless new technology and new techniques become available, or the leakage limits may be relaxed at a future date, the problem defies a simple solution.

In the event of a conflict between electrical safety requirements and EMC guidelines, concern for patient safety will certainly be the overriding consideration. If compliance with both the electrical safety requirements and the EMC guidelines is impossible for valid technical reasons, the FDA should be petitioned to waive the EMC guideline requirements.

4.5.3 Impact on EMI Filters

As explained in Section 1.4, leakage current limits put a severe constraint on the filtering capacitors which are used between each line and ground, i.e. common-mode capacitors, since their 50 or 60 Hz current will be seen during the measurement. For example, looking at Fig. 4.11, one sees that the leakage current via the filter capacitor is not simply V/X_c, since the leakage is measured **in any possible configuration of the switches**, including the one where the on-off switch is a single-pole one and the phase and neutral prongs have been reversed in the plug, or one fuse has blown. Therefore, if $C_1 = C_2$, for single-phase machines (U.S. uses 115 Vac/60 Hz, Europe uses 230 Vac/50 Hz):

$$C_{max} = \frac{1}{2} \times \frac{I_{leakage}}{V \times 2\pi \times F} = \frac{I_{leakage}}{87 \times 10^3} \text{ in the U.S.A.}$$

$$= \frac{I_{leakage}}{144 \times 10^3} \text{ in Europe}$$

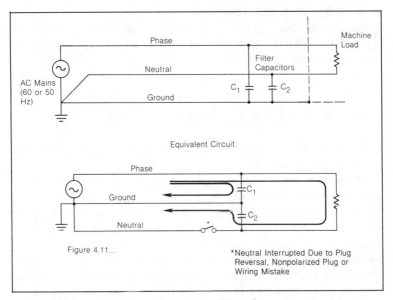

Figure 4.11...

*Neutral Interrupted Due to Plug Reversal, Nonpolarized Plug or Wiring Mistake

Figure 4.11—Safety Issue Created by Filter Capacitors Leakage

Because paper capacitors of this type usually have tolerances of −0 to +20 percent, and because ac main voltages can have steady values of +10 percent above nominal, the usual safety conservatism will dictate values of C_{max} about **30 percent lower**.

Considering for instance UL 114 (now part of UL 478) for portable equipment in the U.S.A.:

$$I_{leak\ max} = 0.25 \text{ mA}$$

gives:

$$C_{max} \simeq 2 \text{ nF}_{..}$$

In a similar manner, considering a Class I stationary equipment limit of 3.5 mA would give $C_{max} \simeq 17$ nF in Europe. The fact that most filter manufacturers limit C to less than 5 nF is either to:

1. Make their product comply to the most severe constraint, i.e., portable equipment, or
2. Take into account that in a mini-system configuration, the host unit will drain the leakages of several tributary peripherals.

Military specifications, too, put a limit on the size of these capacitors, although there the concern is more of ground "cleanliness" than people's safety. Except for special exemptions, MIL-STD-461 demands that line-to-ground filter capacitors be limited to 100 nF maximum.

4.6 Ground Fault Interruptors

Power systems are grounded via either low-resistance paths (the most common scheme) or impedant-neutral paths, when continuity of service is of prime importance. More details on power distribution grounding will be given in Chapter 5. However, as far as safety is concerned, the circulation of an abnormal current (i.e., above the permitted ground leakage limits) in the safety earth wire corresponds to a potential hazard. With low-resistance grounding systems ("solidly" grounded neutral), a single phase-to-chassis short normally trips a fuse or circuit breaker. However, the short may be a "calibrated" short, like an insulation degradation midway between a real short and a good insulation. Or, the short circuit current may in fact be limited by some device's resistance.

In either case, this calibrated short may not permit enough current flow to operate the fuse or circuit breaker, and yet it may pose a safety hazard. So a ground fault detection system is recommended. With impedant grounding system (impedant neutral, etc.), even a single solid short to ground (first fault) would not operate the fuses. In this case a potential safety hazard may exist as long as the faulted circuit has not been located, isolated and repaired. In this latter case, a ground fault alarm, interrupter or both must be used. Three systems are generally used for ground fault detection and warning (see Fig. 4.12, parts a, b and c).

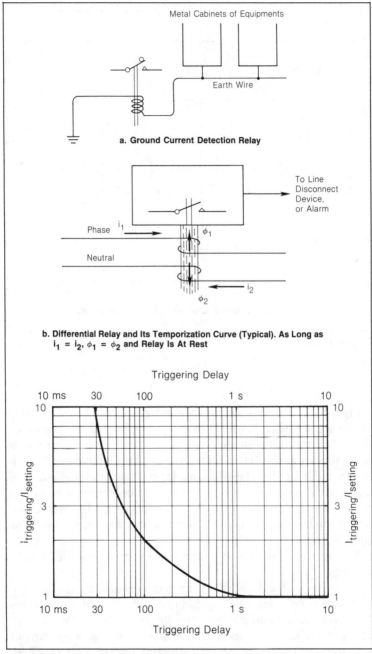

a. Ground Current Detection Relay

b. Differential Relay and Its Temporization Curve (Typical). As Long as $i_1 = i_2$, $\phi_1 = \phi_2$ and Relay Is At Rest

Figure 4.12—Various Types of Ground Fault (or Isolation Failure) Detectors (continued next page)

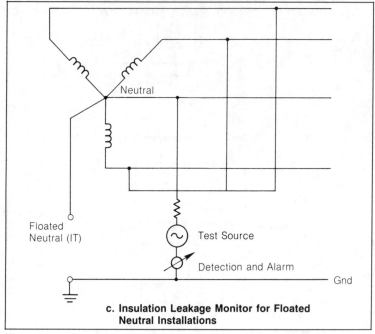

c. Insulation Leakage Monitor for Floated
Neutral Installations

Figure 4.12—(continued)

Figure 4.12a shows an overcurrent relay connected directly
to the ground wire, with a sensitivity set such that "resistive"
shorts to ground will activate the relay. The sensitivity is
generally set in the 100 mA range or so. This simple device will
detect most of the classical insulation breakdowns, etc. The
relay may then actuate, via an associated contactor, a complete
power-down of the installation or of the specific branch circuit
where the fault occurred. Or the relay may activate a visible or
audible alarm.

This system falls short of preventing two kinds of safety
hazards:

1. In case of a broken or missing ground in one of the
   supposedly earthed equipments, the condition may remain unnoticed for months or years. If a ground fault
   occurs, this equipment will not cause any ground current
   to flow. Therefore, an unsuspecting user can get shocked,

and even during this shock the relay will not detect anything. On the other hand, one may object that this scenario is a **double-fault** situation which generally is not considered in ordinary installations.

2. Those relays are usually of a quite rugged type with mediocre accuracy. So with aging and other factors, the actual sensitivity may be only 200 or 300 mA; that is, a "calibrated" phase-to-chassis short may behave as a 200 mA current source to a person's body and be a fatal risk while not yet activating the relay.

Figure 4.12b depicts a differential relay. This is sometimes mechanically coupled with a circuit-breaker, thus making a differential circuit breaker. With this relay, all phase wires (for three-phase system) or phase and neutral (for single-phase system) are wound on the bobbin in the same direction. Normally, all the current which goes to the load returns to the source, so fluxes cancel out and the relay is not excited. If a ground leakage exists, the sum of the currents in and out is no longer null, and a flux exists proportional to the difference (hence the term **differential**).

Actual detectors of this type can be made more sophisticated than the simplistic sketch of Fig. 4.12b: the wires are actually wound on a toroid to increase flux concentration and setting accuracy, and the differential flux is in fact picked by an additional auxiliary winding. These relays can be set as low as 30 mA of sensitivity; that is, low enough to prevent safety hazard. They overcome the disadvantage of the simple ground wire relay type by actually checking that "all the current coming in comes out." If any difference exists, **even though that difference is not flowing in the ground wire**, it is still flowing somewhere, like through a person's body.

A problem arises with the sensitivity of the device: during turn-on of equipment with some capacitance to ground (like those equipped with EMI filters), the differential relay may be triggered just because of the high CdV/dt current leaking to ground during a short period. This condition is harmless but would cause many false alarms and triggering. This phenomenon was once so troublesome that in many installations it caused the maintenance people to remove some EMI filters (the designated culprits). Better differential relays have been designed since, with a temporization curve tracking more or less the human body immunity to short duration current (again, see Fig. 4.12b).

4.27

Figure 4.12c illustrates a typical insulation leakage monitor. In some specific power system schemes (called "IT" in the IEC nomenclature), the neutral is not earthed. Therefore a gradual decay in insulation materials would go unnoticed until it caused a solid short. Or a first ground fault would go unnoticed until a second one appeared. Either situation creates a shock and fire hazard. The same is true with unprotected or insufficiently protected impedant neutral power distribution.

For this reason, another device has been introduced which checks continuously, even during power-on conditions, the quality of the insulation in the whole installation, loads included. The device continuously applies a dc or low-frequency (e.g., 10 Hz) voltage between each hot wire and the earthing point. A detector is set to trigger an alarm when the dc or 10 Hz current exceeds a preset value corresponding to an insulation resistance falling below a safe value. Depending on countries and installations, this value ranges from about 10 to 500 kΩ. When the alarm goes on, maintenance technicians have to search for the fault, isolate the faulty equipment or branch circuit and make the repairs.

4.7 Insulation Breakdown and Fire Control

Many cases of insulation breakdown end up with arcing and burning, causing from severe damage to complete destruction. An arcing fault can occur between phase conductors or between any phase conductor and ground (with solidly grounded systems). The fault arc releases an impressive amount of energy in a very limited volume. The resultant heat can vaporize copper or aluminum, throw out molten metal and generate toxic smoke from burning insulation. Prevention of arcing faults relies upon fast and sensitive detection of the arcing current, followed by an interruption of the faulty circuit within approximately 10 to 20 cycles. In this situation, the ground fault sensors described previously become precious for arcs which are started by a phase-to-ground insulation damage. In fact they may also help for phase-to-phase faults: even these often are accompanied by phase-to-ground insulation damage, which is a precursor of the arc and is detectable before fuses or circuit breakers can react.

Therefore, monitoring the solidly grounded-neutral systems, as well as isolated-neutral ones, for currents in the ground circuits provides an effective means of detecting and clearing destructive arcing faults to ground. The sensitivity and speed of ground fault detection for arc damage prevention can be calibrated selectively to avoid a small sub-feeder or branch fault to shut down an entire installation. This is called "coordinated ground fault protection." It is easier to implement with solidly grounded-neutral systems.

4.8 Lightning

The flow of lightning current into structures causes high voltages between them. It can also cause high voltages between structures and their earthing references if a low enough impedance does not exist. Voltages induced by lightning radiation to the outdoor wires can cause high common-mode voltage to appear on the power wiring. Surge arrestors which divert this energy to ground must do so via a low-impedance path to be effective.

Conversely, if structure bonding and grounding is not correctly done, the surge arrestors can work in reverse; that is, inject into the "protected" wires the high voltage which appears on the structures through which they were supposedly grounded. These aspects of lightning damage protection by grounding are addressed in Chapter 9, Architectural Grounding.

4.9 Bibliography

1. Dalziel, C.F., "Electrical Shock Hazard," (*IEEE Spectrum,* Feb.
   1972).
2. MIL-STD-454C, *Standard Requirements for Electronic Equipment,* Oct. 1970.
3. IEC Standard Publication 435, *Safety of Data Processing Equipment.*
4. AAMI SCL-P 10, *AAMI Safe-Current Limits Standard (Proposed),* (Arlington, Virginia: Association for the Advancement of Medical Instrumentation, 1975).

5. Beausoliel, R. Wetal, *Survey of Ground Fault Circuit Interrupter Usage for Protection Against Hazardous Shock*, (National Bureau of Standards).

6. FDA-MDS-021-0001, Draft No. 4, *Cardiac Defibrillator Minimum Safety and Performance Requirements*, (Rockville, Maryland: U.S. Food and Drug Adminstration, 1975).

7. NFPA 76B-T, *Electricity in Patient Care Facilities*, (Boston, Mass.: National Fire Protection Association, 1973).

8. Specification X-1414, *Biomedical Monitoring Systems (Electro- Biometrics for Intensive Care Units)*, (Washington, D.C.: Veterans Administration, 1970).

9. *Standard for Electrocardiographic Devices*, (Rockville, Maryland: U.S. Food and Drug Administration, 1976).

10. Hill, D.W. and Dolan, A.M., *Intensive Care Instrumentation* (London Academic Press, 1982).

11. IEC-601, "Safety of Medical Electric Equipment."

12. Raftery and Green, "Disturbances in Heart Rhythm Produced by Leakage Currents" (*Cardiovascular Research Journal*).

Chapter 5

Power Grounding

From the high-voltage grid at the substation down to the subscriber's wall outlet, shock hazard, lightning protection and fault clearance are subjects which have dictated power grounding conditions since the early days of power distribution. Except for telephone line noise problems when power and telephone lines are sharing the same poles or conduits, power grounding rules were not set with regard for EMI. As a result, conflicting situations may arise between what is best from an EMC standpoint and what is imposed by power grounding practices. This is not to say that grounding rules are always a problem for the EMC engineer. In fact the power community shows an exemplary attitude of a coordinated approach to power grounding both nationwide and worldwide. Rules are clear and unambiguous to a point which has not yet been reached, or even approached, by the EMC community!

This chapter discusses the various grounding practices used by power utility companies as well as other types of power plants (vehicles, ships, etc.). With respect to EMI, the chapter also discusses how these grounding practices cope with transient phenomena. As an introduction to the subject, Fig. 5.1 shows that even when reduced to simple equivalent circuits, the impedance of a power distribution with respect to ground can exhibit many different aspects.

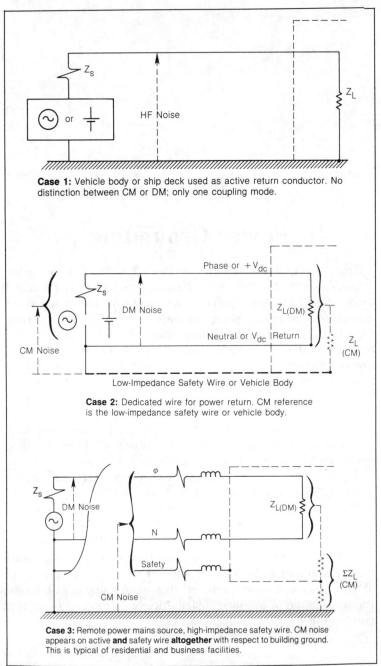

Case 1: Vehicle body or ship deck used as active return conductor. No distinction between CM or DM; only one coupling mode.

Case 2: Dedicated wire for power return. CM reference is the low-impedance safety wire or vehicle body.

Case 3: Remote power mains source, high-impedance safety wire. CM noise appears on active **and** safety wire **altogether** with respect to building ground. This is typical of residential and business facilities.

Figure 5.1—Various Configurations of Power Ground Impedances

5.1 Varieties of Power Distribution Grounding

Following the IEC classifications (adhered to by the U.S. National Electrical Code) which were shown in Section 4.4.1, power sources relative to ground belong to either:

1. **Ungrounded system** (IEC code IT): This refers to a system without an intentional connection to ground (except eventually some high-impedance measuring device). Though called "ungrounded," this type of system is nevertheless coupled to ground through distributed capacitances (see Section 1.3).

2. **Grounded system** (IEC code: TN): This is a system where at least one point (usually a center tap or neutral point of transformer or generator windings) is intentionally grounded, either solidly or through an impedance. Hence, this category contains two subcategories:

   a. Solidly grounded: The system is connected directly to earth via rod, grid or otherwise, with no intentional impedance added in series (see Fig. 5.2, parts a and b). Since one could always find a frequency where this "solid ground" is not so solid due to wire inductance, another term, **effective ground**, is sometimes used.

   The term **effective ground** applies when the reactive part of the impedance of the ground conductor is not larger than its resistive part at the power frequency, provided that the maximum resistance requirements are not exceeded.

   b. Impedance or impedant grounded: This is a system where the mid point or neutral is connected to the earthing terminal via an impedance. This impedance can be primarily resistive or inductive (see Fig. 5.2c).

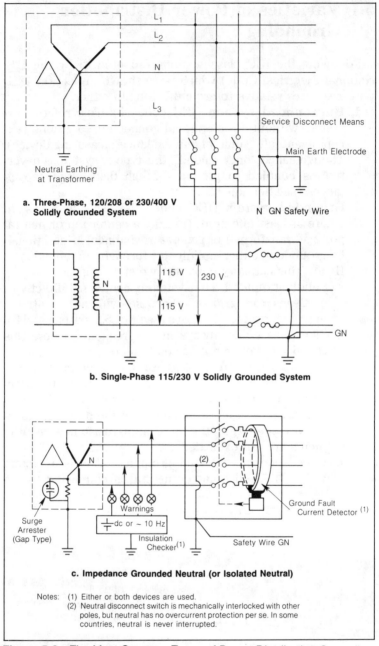

a. Three-Phase, 120/208 or 230/400 V
Solidly Grounded System

b. Single-Phase 115/230 V Solidly Grounded System

c. Impedance Grounded Neutral (or Isolated Neutral)

Notes: (1) Either or both devices are used.
(2) Neutral disconnect switch is mechanically interlocked with other poles, but neutral has no overcurrent protection per se. In some countries, neutral is never interrupted.

Figure 5.2—The Most Common Types of Power Distribution Grounding

5.2 Reasons for Choosing a Grounded or Ungrounded System

Several factors can influence the choice between a solidly grounded, impedance-grounded or ungrounded system. The reasons can be technical issues or safety issues. In either case, the system must be fail-safe in the strict meaning of the term, i.e., "safe when it fails." Under the conditions of a power fault, the system is permitted to evolve only into a status where it is still safe. A subsequent fault condition is generally not considered, provided the first fault has been clearly indicated (fuse blown or breaker tripped, audible or visible warning, etc.).

5.2.1 Service Continuity

For many years a great number of industrial plant distribution systems have been operated ungrounded at one or more voltage levels. In most cases this has been done to gain an additional degree of service continuity. The fact that any contact occurring between one phase of a three-phase system and ground is unlikely to cause an immediate outage to any load may represent an advantage in many plants, varying in its importance according to the type of plant.

Grounded systems in most cases are designed so that circuit protective devices will remove a faulty circuit from the system regardless of the type of fault. A phase-to-ground fault generally results in the immediate isolation of the faulted circuit with the attendant outage of the loads on that circuit. However, experience has shown that in a number of systems, greater service continuity may be obtained with grounded-neutral than with ungrounded-neutral systems.

5.2.2 Multiple Faults to Ground

While a ground fault on one phase of an ungrounded (or impedance-grounded) system generally does not cause a service interruption, the occurrence of a second ground fault on a different phase, before the first fault is cleared, does result in an outage. If both faults are on the same feeder, that feeder will be disconnected from the power source. If the second fault is on a different feeder, both feeders may be de-energized.

The longer a ground fault is allowed to remain uncorrected on an ungrounded system, the greater is the likelihood of another one occurring simultaneously on another phase, resulting in an outage. The advantage of an ungrounded system in not immediately dropping loads upon the occurrence of a ground fault may be largely destroyed by the practice of ignoring a ground fault until a second one occurs and repairs are required to restore service. With an ungrounded system it is extremely important that an organized maintenance program be provided so that ground faults are located and removed as soon as possible after their detection.

An adequate detection system, possibly in conjunction with an audible alarm, is considered essential for operation of an ungrounded (or impedance-grounded) system. In addition, it is advisable in ungrounded systems to employ ground-fault tracing equipment which permits maintenance personnel to locate a ground fault with the system energized and without the necessity of interrupting service on any circuit during the process of fault location.

Experience has shown that multiple ground faults are rarely, if ever, experienced on grounded-neutral systems.

5.2.3 Arcing Fault Burns

Many cases of arcing fault burns have been reported in which severe damage to or complete destruction of electrical equipment was caused by the energy of arcing fault currents. In typical cases, an arcing fault becomes established between two or more phase conductors in an ungrounded system, or between phase conductor(s) and ground in a solidly grounded-neutral system.

It is characteristic of arcing fault burns that the normal phase-overcurrent devices do not operate to remove the initial fault quickly. Arcing fault current levels may be so low that such devices either are not actuated at all (because fault currents are below pickup settings) or are actuated only after a long period of time, too late to prevent burn.

The low-current arcing faults are characteristic of open or covered buses, particularly in switch gear or metal-enclosed switching or motor control equipment. Instances of burn have also occurred in high-capacity buses having relatively wide spacing, served from the utility network at 480/277 V through protective devices rated 2,000 A or larger. Such spacing can limit the current of a single arc to approximately 1,500 A, which is not enough to operate the phase protective devices, so arcing may continue for many minutes.

Thus the solidly and low-resistance grounded-neutral systems provide a basis for easily securing protection against ruinous phase-to-ground arcing faults. (Unfortunately, no comparably reliable and universally applicable means of protection against low-level, line-to-line arcing has been devised.)

5.2.4 Location of Faults

On an ungrounded system, a ground fault does not open the circuit. Some means of detecting the presence of a ground fault on the system should be installed. Lamps connected to indicate the presence of a potential from each phase to ground (lamps are normally lit) will show the presence of a ground fault (lamp will go out) and which phase is involved, but will not show on which feeder the fault has occurred unless a lamp is installed for each feeder. Locating a ground fault on one of the several feeders may require removing from service one feeder at a time until the ground detector indicates that the faulted feeder has been removed.

Should it happen that the same phase of two different feeders becomes faulted to ground at the same time, the faulted feeders cannot be located by removing them from the system one at a time. It may be necessary to remove all feeders and restore them to service one at a time, checking the ground detector as each feeder is restored.

The location of a grounded feeder on an ungrounded system may be facilitated by the use of various types of locating apparatus. For example, a pulsed dc voltage or an audio signal superimposed on the ac line voltage may be applied between the feeder bus and earth, and the return current detected in the grounded feeders. Some locating apparatus do not require de-energizing system feeders. This, of course, has the advantage of permitting the location of ground faults without waiting for light-load periods on the system.

An accidental ground fault on a grounded system is both indicated and at least partially located by an automatic interruption of the accidentally grounded circuit or piece of equipment.

5.2.5 Safety

Many of the hazards to personnel and property existing in some industrial electrical systems are the result of poor or nonexistent grounding of electrical equipment and metallic structures. As explained in Section 1.3, it is important to note here that regardless of whether the power system is grounded, safety considerations require thorough grounding of equipment and structures. Proper grounding of a low-voltage (600 V or less) distribution system may result in less likelihood of accidental harm to personnel than when the system is supposedly left ungrounded. The knowledge that a circuit is grounded will result in greater care on the part of the worker.

It is erroneous to believe that on an ungrounded system a person may contact an energized phase conductor without personal hazard. An ungrounded system with balanced phase-to-ground capacitance has voltage between any phase conductor and ground equal to the line-to-neutral voltage. To accidentally or intentionally contact such a conductor may present a serious, perhaps lethal, shock hazard. If a ground fault occurs on one phase of an ungrounded or impedance-grounded system, personnel contacting one of the other phases and ground will be subjected to the line voltage or 1.73 times the voltage that would be experienced on a solidly neutral-grounded system.

Other hazards of shock and fire may result from inadequate grounding of equipment in either grounded or ungrounded systems. Accidental ground faults are inevitable. The current path to ground for a winding-to-frame insulation breakdown in a motor may include greasy shavings or other materials that can be ignited by sparks or localized heating. Such a high-impedance ground circuit may not permit enough current flow to operate protective devices, with the result that a potential fire and safety hazard may exist for some time. There is hazard of a shock to personnel under such conditions should they bridge all or part of the high-impedance ground path, for example by contacting the frame of the faulty machine.

This hazard is particularly bad because there are more potential victims than in the case where persons familiar with electric systems work on a circuit and are aware of the hazard. On the other hand, the relatively high ground-fault currents associated with solidly grounded systems may present a hazard to exposed workers from hot arc products and flying molten metal, which is not present in ungrounded systems. This problem has become much less serious however, because of the universal use of metal-enclosed equipment.

5.2.6 Abnormal Voltage Hazards and Overstress

The possible overvoltages on the ungrounded system may cause more frequent equipment failures than if the system were grounded. In some cases these overvoltages have caused failures on more than one piece of equipment at a time. These multiple failures are not necessarily confined to one feeder; many involve equipment on several different feeders.

A fault on one phase of an ungrounded or impedance-grounded system places a sustained increased voltage on the insulation of ungrounded phases in a three-phase system. This overvoltage is 1.73 times the voltage normally present on the insulation. This or other sustained overvoltages or the transient overvoltages on the ungrounded system may not immediately cause failure of insulation but may tend to reduce the life of the insulation. By contrast, the reduced overvoltages experienced on grounded systems are less likely to damage equipment or insulation.

A classic (yet widely overlooked or ignored) example is the case of EMI filter capacitors and varistors mounted line to ground. Figure 5.3 shows that with an ungrounded or impedance grounded system, during a phase-to-ground fault of a three-phase system, the voltages on the two other phases rise above ground potential up to the phase-to-phase voltage. All the same, the neutral-to-ground potential rises anywhere from zero to the phase-to-neutral voltage, depending the amplitude of the short circuit current and the total loop impedance.

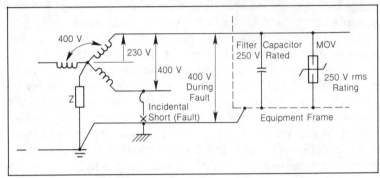

Figure 5.3—Voltage Overstress of EMI and Transient Suppression Components During a Phase-to-Ground Short, in an Impedant-Grounded Neutral Distribution System

If we consider a normal European voltage distribution of 230/400 V, the EMI suppression components mounted line to ground will be normally sized for the phase-to-ground voltage of 230 V; that is, a 250 V rms rating which includes a safety factor. During the fault, filter capacitors and varistors will be stressed by 400 V rms. One might object that filter capacitors should be of the IEC Class Y type and withstand the 1,500 Vac hi-pot testing. But remember that this test lasts one minute, while the actual phase-to-ground fault may last for hours, until the maintenance personnel locates, isolates and disconnects the faulty branch for repair.

A simplistic estimate of the life expectancy of capacitors and varistors based on the Arrhenius model and varistor manufacturers' curves gives the following results:

1. The lifetime of a 250 V capacitor which just passes the 1,500 Vac/1 min test is reduced to few hundred hours when submitted continuously to 400 V rms from a voltage source.

2. The lifetime of a 250 V, 14 mm dia. varistor submitted continuously to 400 V rms from a source having a generator resistance of about $2 \times 0.1\ \Omega$ (the two phases in

series, for instance in a typical 100 kVA power utility transformer) is calculated to be about 10^5 pulses, considering that the varistor will conduct about 5 A for few milliseconds during each positive and negative peak of the 400 V sine wave. The 10^5 pulses at 2×50 pulses per second (pps) represent a life expectancy of about 16.7 min before permanent deterioration occurs. An avalanche of effects will cause the surge suppressor to turn into smoke and char.

This example has happened hundreds times in impedance-grounded distribution, causing explosions of filter capacitors and destruction of varistors. A typical reaction to this would be to blame it on the components, to the point that in some installations EMI engineers discovered that EMI filters or varistors had been permanently removed! We have here another example where grounding schemes adopted for power distribution may conflict with EMI suppression.

5.2.7 Static

Overvoltage buildup on power system conductors due to static charging is not usually a problem in modern plants with properly grounded metal-enclosed circuits and equipment. Static charges on moving belts can build up voltages which can be transmitted to the power system unless motor frames are properly grounded. Overhead open-wire lines may be subject to static overvoltages resulting from certain atmospheric conditions. A system ground connection, even of relatively high resistance, can effectively prevent static voltage buildup.

5.2.8 Contact with a Higher-Voltage System

Contact with a higher-voltage system may be caused by a broken high-voltage conductor falling on a lower-voltage conductor where both lines cross or are carried on the same poles. It may also occur by insulation breakdown between the high- and low-voltage windings of distribution transformers. This may cause other insulation failures, possibly at several points. An effectively grounded low-voltage system, though experiencing high values of fault current for this condition, will hold the system neutral close to ground potential, and thus the overvoltages to ground on the low-voltage system will be greatly reduced.

5.2.9 Resonant Conditions

An ungrounded system may be subjected to resonant overvoltages. With the high intrinsic phase-to-ground capacitance of larger systems, there may be a condition of approximate circuit resonance during a line-to-ground fault through an inductance such as a faulty coil in a motor starter. The voltage to ground of the unfaulted phases will then be considerably in excess of the line-to-line voltage. An overvoltage due to resonant or near-resonant conditions can be encountered on a small system where tuned inductive-capacitive circuits are used for such purposes as the operation of welders. For example, if the welder is equipped with a series capacitor for power factor improvement, the voltages across the capacitor and across the transformer winding are each many times the supply-line-to-line voltage. A fault between the capacitor and the welder transformer imposes this high voltage on the insulation of the ungrounded system. A grounded-neutral system would prevent this overvoltage by holding the phases to their approximate nominal voltages to ground.

5.2.10 Restriking Ground Faults

Field experience and theoretical studies have shown that arcing, restriking or vibrating ground faults on ungrounded systems can, under certain conditions, produce surge voltages as high as six times the normal voltage. The conditions necessary for producing these overvoltages require that the dielectric strength of the arc path build up at higher rate after each extinction of the arc than it did after the preceding extinction.

This phenomenon is unlikely to take place in the open air between stationary contacts because such an arc path is not likely to develop sufficient dielectric recovery strength. It may occur in confined areas where the gas pressure may increase after each conduction period. Neutral grounding is effective in reducing transient voltage buildup from such intermittent ground faults by reducing the neutral potential displacement from ground potential and the destructiveness of any high-frequency voltage oscillations following each arc initiation or restrike.

5.2.11 Cost

The cost difference between grounded and ungrounded neutral systems depends on the method of grounding, the degree of protection desired, and whether a new or an existing system is to be grounded. For the new system in the design stage, power transformers with wye-connected secondaries and wye-connected generators are available as standard options, and there is no cost factor for establishing the system neutral. The additional-cost items are the neutral grounding resistor or reactor if the system is to be impedance grounded, and the cost of ground fault relaying.

To ground an existing ungrounded delta-connected system requires an additional-cost item, namely, the grounding transformer(s) for establishing the system neutral. Also, the existing protective relay schemes may have to be modified to obtain sensitive ground-fault detection. For the existing system, practical considerations may dictate the application of a high-resistance grounding scheme, with alarm annunciation only on the occurrence of a ground fault. This eliminates the requirement of adding sensitive ground-current relays to each feeder circuit.

The decision to convert an existing ungrounded system to grounded operation is usually made for the purpose of limiting transient overvoltages. Systems with older cables and with motor and transformer windings that have degraded insulation levels due to aging, atmospheric conditions, and sustained overvoltages are particularly vulnerable to failure due to transient overvoltages resulting from arcing ground faults. Therefore the cost of converting to grounded operation is small when compared to the cost of possibly having to replace cables or rewind motors or transformers.

5.2.12 Trends in the Application of System Grounding

The basic reasons for system grounding are:
1. To limit the difference in electric potential between all uninsulated conducting objects in a local area
2. To provide isolation of faulted equipment and circuits when a fault occurs
3. To limit overvoltages appearing on the system under various conditions

Many industrial power system operators believe that an ungrounded system offers greater service continuity than a grounded system because a line-to-ground fault does not cause immediate tripping of the faulted circuit. On the other hand, a second ground fault on a different phase of a circuit other than that where the original fault occurred causes a phase-to-phase fault, large short-circuit current flow (with attendant hazards) and tripping of both faulted circuits. Also, the effect of sporadic low-level arcing at the first failure location produced by the capacitive "grounding" currents from the two ungrounded phases, may cause the whole system-to-ground voltage to rise to four or more times normal voltage (to ground), causing severe stress on all of the insulation. It is such an overstress that can cause the failure at a second location, almost concurrent with the first failure.

The various grounding systems eliminate this phenomenon by changing the fault current from entirely capacitive to something nearer a true resistive current. Consequently, a major factor to consider in choosing between a grounded or ungrounded system is the quality of electrical maintenance available. Well-maintained ungrounded systems, in which the first ground fault is promptly located and corrected, probably have greater service continuity than solidly grounded systems. However, many users whose maintenance practices are not quite so extensive feel that a grounded-neutral system gives them more continuous service than an ungrounded system. There has been a trend toward grounding industrial systems to overcome some of the disadvantages attributed to ungrounded operation. In recent years a substantial percentage of new industrial substation transformers have been purchased with wye-connected low-voltage windings, with the insulated neutral brought to external termination suitable for neutral grounding.

In new installations these transformers offer the advantage that they can be operated ungrounded while having the neutral available for grounding, if desired, at some future time.

5.3 Earthing at Points Other Than System Neutral

In some cases low-voltage systems (600 V and less) are grounded at some point other than the system neutral. This has been done to obtain a grounded system at a minimum expense where existing delta transformer connections do not provide access to the system neutral.

5.3.1 Corner-of-the-Delta Grounding

In low-voltage systems, which in the past have nearly all been supplied from transformers with delta-connected secondaries, grounding of one phase, known as **corner-of-the-delta** grounding, has sometimes been used as a means of obtaining a grounded system (see Fig. 5.4a). Its advantages are the following:

1. There is a possible cost advantage over other grounding methods for existing delta systems.
2. There exists the possibility of slightly better protection with two-element motor starters when they are located in the two ungrounded phases; with properly connected circuits, ground-faults in the control circuits will neither start the motor nor prevent stopping the motor by means of the pushbutton.

The disadvantages are:

1. It cannot supply dual-voltage service for lighting and power load.
2. There is the necessity of positive identification of the grounded phase throughout the system to avoid connecting meters, instruments, and relays in the grounded phase.
3. Line-to-ground voltage on two phases is higher than in a neutral-grounded system.
4. There is a possibility of exceeding the interrupting capabilities of marginally applied circuit breakers. Under ground fault conditions, the interrupting duty on the affected circuit breaker pole exceeds the three-phase fault duty. Because of its limitations, this type of grounding has not been widely used in industrial systems.

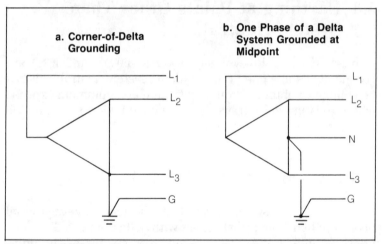

Figure 5.4—Other-Than-Neutral Grounding Connections at Utility Transformer Output

5.3.2 One Phase of a Delta System Grounded at Midpoint

Where existing systems at 600 V or less are supplied by three single-phase transformers with center taps available, it is possible to gain some of the advantages of neutral grounding by grounding the center tap of one phase (see Fig. 5.4b). This method does not provide all of the advantages of system neutral grounding. Such connections are also used to obtain a limited amount of 240/120 V single-phase power in a three-phase 240 V system.

5.4 Grounding Transformers

System neutrals may not be available, particularly in many old systems of 600 V or less and also in many existing 2,400, 4,800 and 6,900 V systems. When existing delta-connected systems are to be grounded, grounding transformers may be used to derive the neutral.

Grounding transformers may be of either the zigzag, the wye delta, or the T-connected type. One type of grounding transformer commonly used is a three-phase zigzag transformer with no secondary winding. The internal connection of the transformer is illustrated in Fig. 5.5. The impedance of the transformer to balanced three-phase voltages is high, so that when there is no fault on the system, only a small magnetizing current flows in the transformer winding. However, the transformer impedance to zero-sequence currents is low, so that it allows high ground fault currents to flow. The transformer divides the ground fault current into three equal components; these currents are in phase with each other and flow in the three windings of the grounding transformer.

The method of winding is seen from Fig. 5.5 to be such that when these three equal currents flow, the current in one section of the winding of each leg of the core is in a direction opposite to that in the other section of the winding on that leg. This tends to force the ground-fault current to have equal division in the three lines and accounts for the low impedance of the transformer-to-ground currents.

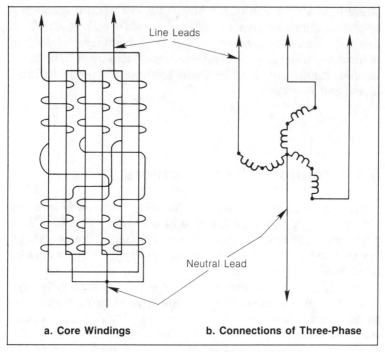

Line Leads

Neutral Lead

a. Core Windings   b. Connections of Three-Phase

Figure 5.5—Zigzag Grounding Transformer (from Ref. 1)

A wye-delta connected three-phase transformer or transformer bank can also be utilized for system grounding. As in the case of the zigzag grounding transformer, the usual application is to accomplish resistance-type grounding of an existing ungrounded system. The delta connection must be closed to provide a path for the zero-sequence current, and the delta voltage rating is selected for any standard value. A resistor inserted between the primary neutral and ground, as shown in Fig. 5.6, provides a means of limiting ground-fault current to a level satisfying the criteria for resistance-grounded systems. For this arrangement, the voltage rating of the wye winding need not be greater than the nominal line-to-neutral system voltage. For high-resistance grounding it is sometimes more practical or economical to apply the limiting resistor in the secondary delta connection. Three single-phase distribution class transformers are used, with the primary wye neutral connected directly to ground. The secondary delta is closed through a resistor which effectively limits the primary ground-fault current to the desired low level.

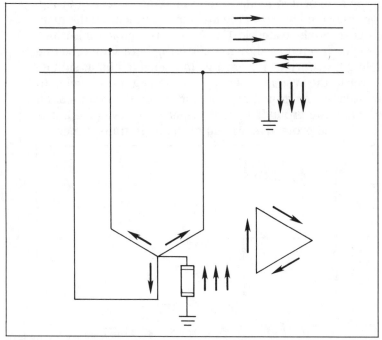

Figure 5.6—Vectors Representing Current Flow in Wye-Delta Transformer Used as Grounding Transformer with Line-to-Ground Fault (from Ref. 1)

For this alternative application, the voltage rating of each of the transformer windings forming the wye primary should not be less than the system line-to-line voltage. The rating of a grounding transformer, in kilovolt amperes, is equal to the rated line-to-neutral voltage in kilovolts times the rated neutral current. Most grounding transformers are designed to carry their rated current for a limited time only, such as 10 s or 1 min. Consequently, they are much smaller in size than an ordinary three-phase continuously rated transformer with the same rating.

It is generally desirable to connect a grounding transformer directly to the main bus of a power system, without intervening circuit breakers or fuses, to prevent the transformer from being inadvertently taken out of service by the operation of the intervening devices. (In this case the transformer is considered part of the bus and is protected by the relaying applied for bus protection.) Alternatively, the grounding transformer should be served by a dedicated feeder circuit breaker, as shown in Fig. 5.7a, or connected between the main transformer and the main switch gear as illustrated in Fig. 5.7b. If the grounding transformer is connected as shown in Fig.5.7b, there should be one grounding transformer for each delta-connected bank supplying power to the system, or enough grounding transformers to assure at least one grounding transformer on the system at all times. When the grounding transformer is so connected, it is included in the protective system of the main transformer.

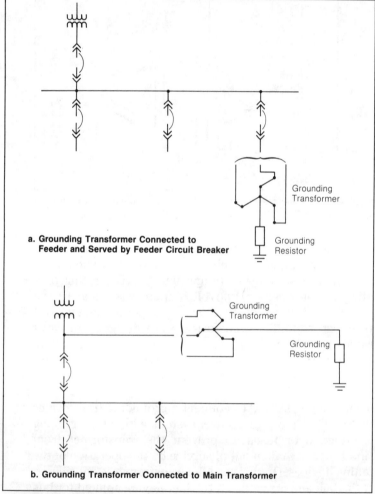

Figure 5.7—Methods of Connecting Grounding Transformer to a Delta-Connected or Ungrounded Power System to Form Neutral for System Grounding (from Ref. 1)

5.5 Grounding at Power Substations

5.5.1 Outdoor Open-Frame Substations

The distributed nature of the typical outdoor open-frame substation (see Fig. 5.8) presents some perplexing grounding problems. It is quite common that various pieces of major apparatus will appear as "island" installations within the substation area. For any single equipment item, the voltage stress imposed on its insulation system will be determined by the voltage difference between its electrical terminals and the frame or metal case which encloses its active parts. The magnitude of electric-shock exposure to an operating or maintenance person within the substation area proper will be a function of the voltage difference between the ground surface on which this person stands and the metal he normally touches, such as apparatus frames or substation structure (see IEEE-Std-80-1976). The magnitude of electric shock voltage exposure to a person approaching the enclosing fence will depend on the character of the earth surface voltage gradient contours adjacent to the fence on the outside of the substation area.

Figure 5.8—A Typical Outdoor Substation

5.5.2 Design of Avenues for Power-Frequency Ground-Fault Current Flow

The ability to carry the ground-fault current from the point where it enters the station to the point where it is to depart is accomplished by supplementing the inherent metallic substation structure with an array of grounding conductors which interconnect the bases of structural columns and are extended to the island installations of apparatus, routed over appropriate paths. Copper cable is generally used for this purpose, with the conductor size ranging from AWG 2/0 (70.1 mm^2) for small stations, for instance, to perhaps 500 kcmil (253.35 mm^2) for large stations. It is appropriate to seek an effective short-time current capability in the grounding-conductor path, which is no less than 25 percent of that possessed by the phase conductor with which it is associated. In any case, it should be capable of accepting the line-to-ground short-circuit current (magnitude and duration) permitted to flow by the overcurrent protection system without thermal distress.

The routing of a grounding conductor should minimize its separation distance from the associated phase conductors. In multibay metal structures, the short-circuited loops created by the bonding grounding conductors between column bases may effectively limit the ground-circuit reactance under seemingly wide spacing conditions.

Grounding conductors sized and routed according to the same rules should be run to those points required for system grounding connections, such as to the neutral terminal of a power transformer which is to be grounded or to the neutral of a grounding transformer. Junctions between sections of grounding conductors, if not exposed, should be made, preferably by cadwelding or brazing. At the exposed junctions and terminations, proper fittings should be used.

If overhead-line ground conductors are terminated at towers along the substation outer boundary and the phase conductors continue out across the station plot, perhaps to a point where they drop down to apparatus terminals, an adequately sized grounding conductor should be strung across the area with a vertical down member to the apparatus frame to establish a path for ground current flow that remains reasonably close to the route of the phase conductors. It is important that the grounding-conductor system extend to and connect with each of the island structures contained within the substation area.

5.5.3 Design of Earthing Connections

The achievement of a prescribed degree of connection to earth will involve a multiplicity of earthing connections (grounding electrodes) distributed about the substation area. If individual grounding electrodes are not kept sufficiently separated physically, their effectiveness is severely impaired (see Section 2.7).

One specific design limitation may be the maximum allowable voltage excursion on the substation structure (relative to mean earth potential) due to a line-to-ground fault or a lightning discharge. All signal and communication circuits that extend from this station to remote locations must be designed to accommodate this voltage excursion without damage. The allowable excursion on the station structure may be limited by the rating of a power circuit entering the station. Consider, for instance, a station whose main circuits operate at 230 kV but which contains outgoing circuits operating at 4.16 kV. A voltage excursion on the station ground mat of 25 kV would not be troublesome to the 230 kV system, but would be disastrous to components of the 4.16 kV system. Even the best of available surge arresters on the 4.16 kV circuits would be destroyed by the excess seal-off voltage present (probably by open circuiting). The allowable maximum voltage excursion on the station ground mat may be set by one of a variety of factors. Once this is set, the design of the station grounding connection systems can proceed.

The effectiveness of reinforcing steel located in below-grade foundation footing as functional grounding electrodes follows the same principles discussed in Section 2.7 and in Chapter 9. All future station design specifications should call for electrical bonding between the metal tower base plate and the reinforcing bars in buried concrete footings. This can be accomplished readily in most instances via the hold-down J bolts.

If the soil at the substation site tends to be an active electrolyte like cinder fill, the use of dissimilar metals (e.g., copper and steel) as grounding electrodes bonded together in the station earthing network may lead to electrolytic deterioration of the buried steel members. With today's knowledge of corrosion control, the avoidance of such trouble may be relatively easy. When the soil is active, the required earthing connection may be obtained using only the buried steel members forming an inherent part of the station. Supplementary electrodes, if needed, should be made of steel. If the soil is not active, the intermix of metals such as copper and steel is permissible.

Lightning masts extending upward from the top structural members of the station can be effective in intercepting lightning strokes and leading the discharged current to earth without insulation flashover at the station. The avoidance of insulation flashover is aided by higher insulation flashover levels between station components. However, these levels may be exceeded by more intense lightning strokes. Even so, an installation which reduces the number of flashover incidents by 60 percent (far short of perfection) can still be a sound economic investment.

5.5.4 Surge-Voltage Protective Equipment

Surge-voltage protective devices intended to deal effectively with fast-front voltage transients must be connected in a close shunt relationship to the apparatus being protected. The presence of an exposed overhead line running to the station but terminating at an open switch or open circuit breaker invites a flashover at the open terminal because of the tendency for a traveling voltage wave to double its voltage upon encountering an open terminal. This type of flashover can be prevented by the installation of line-type surge arresters directly ahead of the open-circuit point on the circuit or by overinsulation (double the nominal value of the approaching line) of the terminal end of the line within the confines of the station, ahead of the point of open circuit.

Note: This increased withstand voltage also applies to the circuit-opening switching device.

5.5.5 Control of Surface Voltage Gradient

The tendency for steeply rising voltage gradients to appear directly around discrete grounding electrodes results in a very nonuniform ground surface potential in the substation area during a ground-fault incident. This can appear as a dangerous electric-shock exposure to the people working in the substation area. It is hardly reasonable to design for a maximum voltage excursion on the station structure low enough to avoid danger.

The alternative approach is to employ a ground mat or mesh grid of relatively small bare conductors located slightly below grade and connected to the station frame. While this will not likely reduce the overall station earthing resistance by very much, it will make all parts of the substation (structure, soil, etc.) equipotential. Only small "scallops" of lesser voltage magnitude will exist between the crisscross conductors of the grid mesh. The possible magnitude of electric shock to maintenance personnel due to earth surface gradients can be reduced to tolerable levels. A surface layer of coarse cracked rock is commonly employed to contribute to reduced contact conductance between the yard surface and the worker's feet.

5.5.6 Surface Voltage Gradients External but Adjacent to the Boundary Fence

The steepness of the surface voltage contour adjacent to but outside the enclosing fence determines whether a person approaching the fence and touching it to the limit of his reach could receive a dangerous electric shock. If the fence were allowed to float, the adjacent voltage gradient would be substantially reduced.

Common practice is to bond the fence to the station ground mat. This is for added security, should a high-voltage wire break and fall on the fence. However, that may create a high voltage gradient between the fence and the exterior.

The present trend seems to favor a solid bond between the boundary fence and the station ground mat. Appropriate potential grading shields are buried below grade adjacent to the fence on the outside of the substation area to control the step voltage and touch potential exposure to acceptable values.

It is very important to avoid a metallic extension from the station structure to some point outside the fenced area which is exposed to contact by people or animals. Such an extension might be a water pipe, an air pipe, a messenger cable, etc., seemingly having no electrical function, but which may convey the potential of the station ground mat to the far end of the metal extension. The earth surface potential drops off fairly rapidly as one moves away from the boundary fence. The 50 percent voltage contour will be reached a short distance away from a small station and in a longer separation distance from a large station. Even a fairly large station will display a 50 percent dropoff in surface potential within 15 m (50 ft). Thus it would be entirely possible for a person standing on earth and touching a pipe extending from the station structure and only 15 m removed from the enclosing fence to be subjected to an electric shock of 50 percent of the ground-mat voltage of the station. A station ground-mat voltage of 5,000 V is not at all unusual for stations operating in the 4.16 to 33 kV range.

5.5.7 Outdoor Unit Substations

While the functional objectives remain unchanged, the concentration of apparatus into a single metal-enclosed package greatly simplifies the equipment grounding system plan. The grounding conductor associated with each electric circuit to and from the substation is continued to the substation proper and terminated on the grounding bus provided there.

The problem of avoiding dangerous electric-shock-voltage exposure to people in proximity to the enclosing fence involves the same considerations as in the case of open-frame substations. Within the confines of many industrial plants, the use of artificially reduced levels of ground-fault current (400 A being a common value) so reduces the voltage gradients around the substation that no fenced enclosure is needed. People can approach and touch the substation enclosure without risk of dangerous electric shock. Of course the grounding bus and enclosure frame of the substation must be connected to the building grounding system, whether or not a local grounding electrode system is installed. If the substation structure is exposed to lightning or contains surge arresters, the installation should include an appropriate grounding electrode. The reinforcing bars contained on the below-grade foundation structure will usually function adequately in this capacity.

5.6 Grounding at Utility Step-Down Transformer and Panel Service Entrance

The facility power is generally obtained through a step-down transformer which may be pole-mounted (rural areas) or ground or underground based (urban areas). The neutral, at the secondary, is connected to earth via a ground rod, and the basic building safety ground (green or green/yellow wire) is derived from there. The basic scheme of Fig. 5.9a applies for small, simple facilities where the transformer and the service entrance (comprising the service disconnect, meter, etc.) are physically close. More often, the transformer and the service entrance are physically remote. So, typically the ac neutral and the transformer casing are connected to earth right at the transformer location via a so-called **power company ground** (see Figure 5.9b). Then the neutral is earthed again at the service entrance panel via the facility earth electrode, sometimes termed **code ground** by reference to the NEC Article 250, which in the U.S. stipulates this connection. Notice that both rods are interconnected by a solid wire since, ultimately, fault currents will return at neutral-ground connection.

The terms **service entrance** and **service equipment** apply to the area where electric service enters the building and the switching or protection equipment within that area. The safety practices required at and downstream from the service entrance are to protect the occupants and equipment within the building.

So, as far as the reference point for the building safety bus, the service entrance earth electrode is the single node for returning branch circuits, safety or green wires. This final connection is never to be opened; however a solid copper strap can be provided for access to make earth resistance measurements.

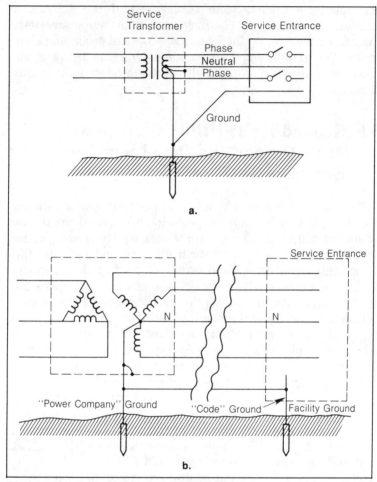

Figure 5.9—Grounding Schemes at Service Entrance for (a) Small and (b) Larger Installations

5.7 Grounding at Local User's Distribution

Power grounding internal to the building must obey the safety rules already discussed in Sections 4.3 and 4.4, the main theme being to ensure the continuity and fault current capability of the grounding wire. This wire must be an insulated wire (green in the U.S., green/yellow elsewhere) of at least the same size as the main conductors, but no less than 1 mm diameter (AWG 18). It shall never go through interrupting devices or fuses. Each receptacle capable of receiving Class I (or Class II grounded) equipment must have a ground pin permanently wired to this building safety conductor. The ground pin and its mating terminal on the equipment flexible power cord must establish the contact first when the equipment is plugged in. The green wire in the receptacle must connect with a ring-type termination. Spade lugs and fast-disconnect types are not permitted.

5.7.1 Interior Wiring and Grounding with Standard Receptacles

The safety ground conductor is run with power conductors. Running them exactly in the same pathways (conduits, cables or raceways) decreases the possible loop areas and the ensuing 50/60 Hz or higher-frequency induced voltages. In many cases these conductors are enclosed in a metal conduit or metal tray. U.S. code permits the conduit or metal raceway to be considered as the grounding conductor provided that continuous electrical bonding is ensured between all the segments of conduits, junction boxes, fittings, etc. Nevertheless, this termination of a metal raceway, when it is used as the circuit grounding conductor, is often neglected. Commonly, the service entrance contains no metal floor plate. The metal conduits are run or stubbed up through a concrete floor as to terminate within the open floor area inside the boundaries set by the equipment. The following defects appear quite often:

1. The metal raceways or cable trays are not thought of as electrical conductors (the equipment grounding conductor), and no connection is made to the stub end extending into the equipment enclosure.
2. The grounding lead from the raceway is thought to be needed only as a static drain and is connected to the ground bus with only a thin conductor which is not rated for mains fault current. Metal raceways that serve as the circuit grounding conductor and terminate at the side sheets or cover plate of the equipment enclosure should

be attached tightly with double lock nuts and perhaps supplemented with a bonding jumper if the duty is severe. Large conduits, as a parts of a high-capacity system, require substantial bonding clamps and cable interconnection to the equipment frame rather than terminating them with lock nuts and bushings in a sheet metal panel which is fastened to the frame with only a few sheet metal screws or small bolts. Inadequate termination can lead to a burnout at the connection to the sheet metal panel or the sheet metal screws (or both), serious damage to the equipment and danger to personnel when fault currents flow.

For these reasons, some countries do not allow metallic conduit to be a substitute for a real ground wire, although these conduits still have to be bonded together and connected to safety ground. Figure 5.10 shows a properly wired internal distribution circuit. If receptacles are metallic, they should be grounded as per Fig. 5.10a Notice that in Fig. 5.10b, although the wiring is correct, a possible loop current circulates in shields between equipment A and B if the two branches are far apart, due to field induced noise in loop DAB. This problem is minimized with the arrangement of Fig. 5.10c). This topic will be covered in detail in Chapter 6.

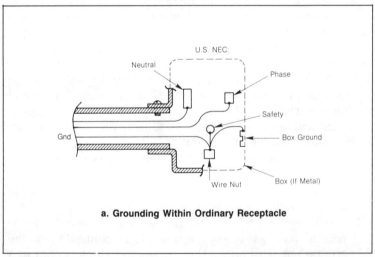

a. Grounding Within Ordinary Receptacle

Figure 5.10—Properly Wired AC Distribution (from Ref. 6) (continued next page)

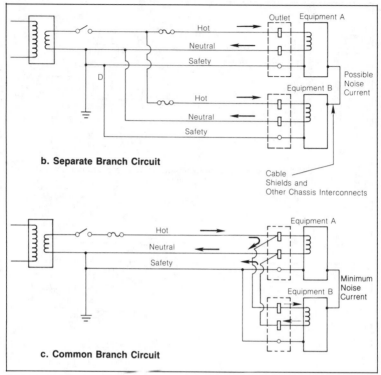

Figure 5.10—(continued)

5.7.2 Noise Problems with Improper Wiring

In contrast to the previous installation of Fig. 5.10, Fig. 5.11 shows the effects of improper wiring. The condition of Fig. 5.11a is that of reversal of the **hot** (black) and **neutral** (white) conductors. Although a violation of the NEC, it does not automatically produce stray or return currents in the safety wire (or equipment cabinet/conduit system). The conditions of Fig. 5.11 parts b and c represent the most likely problems and are the most troublesome from the standpoint of stray noise.

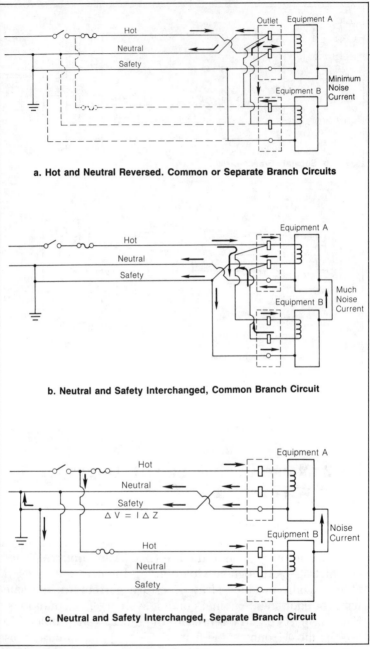

a. Hot and Neutral Reversed. Common or Separate Branch Circuits

b. Neutral and Safety Interchanged, Common Branch Circuit

c. Neutral and Safety Interchanged, Separate Branch Circuit

Figure 5.11—Noise Problems Resulting from Improper Wiring (from Ref. 6)

Interchange of the neutral and ground conductors frequently exists because no short circuit is produced and the condition may go undetected unless of course a differential circuit breaker or ground-fault detector is used. The full load current of terminating equipment, however, returns through the safety wire/conduit/cabinet ground system. The resultant common-mode voltages and currents pose a severe threat to interconnecting circuits between equipment elements A and B. The condition shown in Fig. 5.11a is the most troublesome from the standpoint of power-frequency common-mode noise because of the higher voltage drop developed by the return current traveling through the longer path).

Conditions shown in Fig. 5.11 parts b and c are the sources of many facility ground noise problems. Improperly grounded neutrals can occur in a piece of terminating equipment or can be the result of improper wiring at an outlet, junction box or switch panel. (The most common cause is improper wiring.)

If the neutral is grounded at any point except at the service disconnect, part, if not most, of the load current returns from the load back through conduit, raceways, equipment cables (including coax and cable shields) and structural support members. Voltage drops associated with this return load current appear as common-mode noise sources between separately located equipment, as illustrated. If this equipment must be interconnected with signal paths, appropriate common-mode rejection measures must be employed.

5.7.3 Special Isolated Ground Circuits and Receptacles

In buildings with sensitive electronic equipment which shares the power network with all kinds of loads like air conditioners, heaters, copiers, elevators, electric tools, etc., power line pollution is a well-known problem. This has become more acute with the proliferation of distributed data processing, EDP networks, etc. where power line interference causes data corruption and all of its consequences. Increasingly, it has been found that even the sacrosanct ground wire where filters, Faraday shields and cabinets have been anchored is not solving the problem; instead, it is part of the problem. Connecting all these guards to an already noisy reference is worse than ineffective, so the concept of a "clean," "dedicated" ground was born. The concept was not bad, but it evolved into a myth wherein a computer is said to need an absolutely separate grounding/earthing system, **up to and including** a separate earth electrode.

There are cases of computer rooms installed at the tenth or twentieth floor of high-rise buildings where fortunes have been spent to drive a special rod deep down to the water table 30 m underground and to earth the computer system to it through 100 m or so of heavy-gauge wire or bus bar. Even though this earthing connection certainly has an extremely low dc resistance, it becomes useless above a few kHz where the inductance of the long path predominates (see Chapter 2).

What the computer system needs is an equipotential "mat" between all its frames and terminals **and** a grounding arrangement such that the conducted noise from other systems does not flow in the computer ground. Nothing dictates that this mat has to be exactly zero-impedance, connected to some legendary earth reference. Not only has this myth led to some costly installations, but it has caused safety problems. Figure 5.12a shows such an example where a ground rod has been driven separate from the service entrance rod. Because of the physical separation of the two ground rods (due to an obstinate misconception of the "clean" ground), in case of a phase-to-ground fault, the short-circuit current has to flow across two earthing resistances. Assuming 5 Ω for each rod (which is rather good for a single electrode), the fault current is limited to 12 A, and people can be electrocuted, but the fuse or circuit breaker does not trip.

Figure 5.12b shows how the concept of a "dedicated" ground should be understood. The computing center is connected to a dedicated green wire that nobody else is permitted to use. This dedicated ground is earthed at the same point as the neutral grounding point. As a complement to this measure, the computer is also fed from a branch circuit separate from the noisy loads. This avoids to some extent the phase-to-ground transients due to other loads seeking a path through the computer ground. An additional benefit is that differential-mode (phase-neutral, phase-phase) disturbances caused by the other loads do not affect the computer as much. This is because their voltage drop along the noisy user's wiring occurs downstream.

This arrangement is a significant improvement in many cases, and it does not create the safety hazard of Fig. 5.12a. However, Fig. 5.12b still has few weaknesses which may cause problems in specific installations:

1. If field practices are to use metallic conduits, as in the U.S.A., these conduits have to be bonded continuously and connected to the building ground. So unless they are run very carefully and earmarked or painted as "computer only" (which is very complex and hard to guarantee over an installation's lifetime) they will unavoidably interconnect with the "ordinary" conduit system. These uncontrolled connections nullify the "dedicated ground" purpose.

2. To prevent the above problems, EMI specialists sometimes recommend termination of the metallic conduit to the computer frame via some kind of insulating sleeve. Although this certainly opens the loop and avoids random grounds in parallel with the dedicated ground, it may constitute a safety code violation and must not be generalized.

3. Keeping the dedicated computer branch, and especially the ground circuit, from being used by anyone else is easier said than done. Little by little, over the years, all sorts of ancillary equipments will be found tapped onto this dedicated ground, again polluting it. A solution to this is shown in Fig. 5.13 with special ground receptacles.[3] These receptacles are identified by a different color. The ground terminal is not connected to the receptacle but only to the dedicated green wire of the computer branch. For safety purposes, the receptacle frame (if metallic) is grounded via the metallic conduit or via a distinct wiring, down to the service entrance ground where both wires connect.

Returning to Fig. 5.12c, we see a further improvement where a separate transformer is supplying the computer center. A neutral grounding node is re-created at the secondary of this transformer, as explained in Section 5.8. This way, the computer is more immune to voltage fluctuations caused by the other loads. In addition, if the transformer is a Faraday-shield type, the ground-loops which may exist between the computer and the equipments under its control (machine tools, air conditioning, access control, telex, etc.) are broken.

Figure 5.12d shows an even better installation where the Faraday shielded transformer has been installed near the computer. The computer safety ground is derived from the transformer neutral grounding point. For safety reasons, this grounding point is also brought to the service entrance ground earthing point via a solid wire. But this connection has no EMC purpose at all and, to the contrary, may create residual noise. Therefore, EMI is addressed via a ground grid which is provided underneath the computer system. Here, all the frames are attached by short straps (see Sections 2.6 and 9.3). This grid acts as the real RF ground for the computer system. To prevent residual noise appearing on the green wire from polluting this grid, an RF choke or ferrite can be used in series in the green wire. **By no means can this grid be considered as a substitute for the safety ground.**

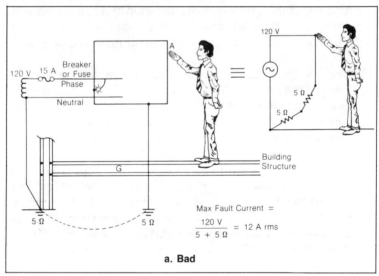

a. Bad

Figure 5.12—Various Power Distribution Grounding Options to Isolate Computers from the Rest of the Building Power and Ground Noise. (continued next page)

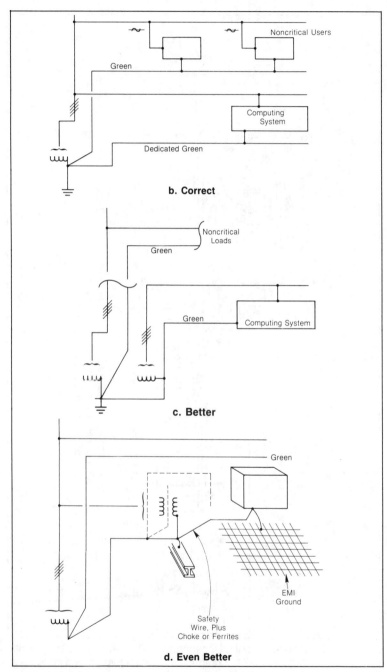

b. Correct

c. Better

d. Even Better

Figure 5.12—(continued). In (c) and (d) a dedicated transformer is used.

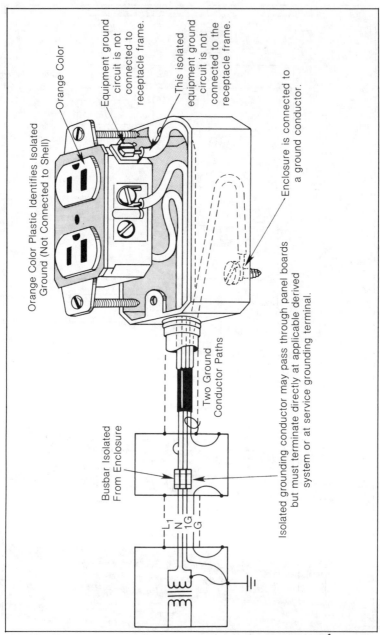

Figure 5.13—Isolated Ground Receptacles. When Installed per National Electric Code Article 250-74, Exception 4, at least two ground conductor paths are required; one for the receptacle ground pin and the other for the receptacle enclosure.

5.8 Grounding of Faraday Shielded Isolation Transformers

Isolation transformers (ITs) with electrostatic (Faraday) shields are often used in power distribution to break ground loops and deliver "clean" power to some specific branch of the ac networks (computer rooms, instrumentation, measurement labs, etc.). Figure 5.14 is a reminder of the principle of operation of Faraday shielded transformers. Without the shield, the primary-to-secondary parasitic capacitance is bridging the insulation at high frequencies. Figure 5.15 illustrates a typical Faraday shielded commercial isolation transformer.

For instance, a 1 kW ordinary transformer may have parasitic capacitance of several nanofarads. For a 1 μs transient, this represents only a few hundred ohms of primary-to-secondary isolation; that is, a common-mode spike will pass through virtually unaffected.

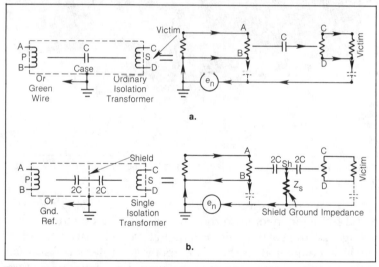

Figure 5.14—(a) Coupling of Common-mode Noise from Primary to Secondary in Ordinary Isolation Transformers and (b) Improvement by Faraday Shield

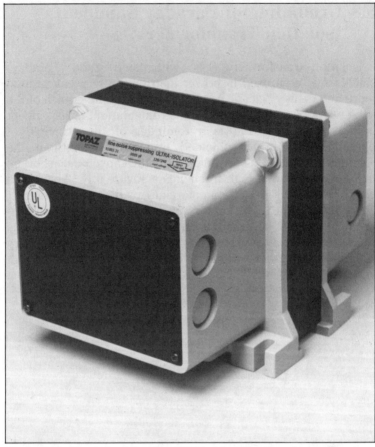

Figure 5.15—Example of Faraday Shielded Isolation Transformer (Courtesy of Topaz Corp.)

With an electrostatic shield separating the windings, the metal foil is connected to the reference of the common-mode voltage, i.e. the earth plane or building ground. However, if the shield is connected to the common-mode "reference" too far from the transformer, the impedance of the shield connection may render the shield itself noisy (impedance Z_s in Fig. 5.14) by the following process:

1. Primary noise V_{CM} induces a shield current Is. This is a normal mechanism.
2. Due to the too high Z_s, the shield rises above local ground to a potential $V_s = Z_s \times I_s$.

5.40

3. This V_s voltage is transferred to the secondary, defeating the purpose of the isolation transformer.

To avoid this and to satisfy both safety and EMC requirements, the following is illustrated in Fig. 5.12, parts c and d:

1. The IT should be close to its load(s) rather than located near the service entrance. If the IT is too far from its users, a new ground loop is created between the IT secondary and the loads. That is, a V_{CM} originates (due to ground potential differences or electromagnetic field pickup) in the right-hand side loop of Fig. 5.14b.

2. Because of the above, in large facilities it is better to use several distributed ITs rather than a single centralized one (see Fig. 5.12d).

3. Just as for any power conditioning, a new ac source grounding point must be re-created at the IT secondary (neutral). This is in accordance with U.S. NEC, Article 250 (separately derived sources). This grounding is connected to the local building structure, room metal grid, etc. and becomes the safety and fault return path for all the loads serviced by the secondary of this IT. Obviously, this is also the point where the shield is connected. This point, in turn, is connected to the service entrance earthing by the conduits and the normal building safety bus, since from that point of view, the IT is seen as a "user."

5.9 Grounding of Other Types of Power Plants

The grounding practices in ships, vehicles and aircraft power plants differ quite significantly from those of power utility companies. There are some positive aspects in these specific grounding situations, such as:

1. The whole power system is self-contained in a rather limited area.

2. Due to the quasi-absence of overhead power lines, there is less exposure of the power network to conducted lightning from the mains.

3. Grounding can be made to metallic structures, with much fewer unponderables than with earthing.

4. The available power in case of fault (or the short circuit amperage) is more limited.
5. There is less risk of nonspecialists tampering with the power wiring, faulty equipments being plugged in, etc.
6. There is a more regular maintenance.

On the other hand, there are some detrimental aspects:

1. Because of economic considerations or weight penalties, the power return is very often done via the structure (hull, fuselage, body, etc.). This causes an enormous problem due to common-impedance EMI coupling (see Chapter 6).
2. Systems generally operate at higher temperatures while conductor sizes are reduced to the minimum for the same economic and weight considerations. Therefore voltage drops are generally higher.
3. The vehicle, aircraft, etc. power system will be periodically plugged into other ground-based power systems during maintenance or off-duty times, where the grounding techniques and practices can vary widely. This is sometimes beyond the designer's control.
4. The increasing use of nonconductive composite materials complicates the issue.

5.9.1 Vehicles

Civilian and army vehicles generally belong to the Case #1 of Fig. 5.1, where all the load currents return via the metal body. The fault protection scheme is a miniature version of that of a building, i.e., a sequential sizing of fuses and circuit breakers is used, such that the fault of a trivial, ancillary equipment does not causes a complete shutdown of possibly vital equipment. However, during the time it takes for the protection to clear the fault, an abnormal structural current can circulate, which causes an EMI problem to equipments which were not involved in that fault. Moreover, some uncontrolled joints (rivets, hinges, etc.) can cause the fault current to fluctuate, further retarding the action of the fuse or other circuit protection.

If one considers that in a typical vehicle, the installed electric power ranges from about 400 W for a light passenger vehicle to 3 to 5 kW for tracks and tanks, a rough estimate of the alternator and battery source resistances* gives short circuit amperages in the 300 to 3,000 A range, which will flow in common return. With tanks and armored vehicles, a special problem is posed by the rotating contacts of the turrets and other rotating platforms. These joints must be made with sliding contacts having the least possible resistance to carry the power return of motors and actuators from the platform, without creating EMI noise across the other analog and signal returns.

5.9.2 Aircraft

Most aircraft use 115/200 V, 400 Hz, three-phase wye, plus 28 Vdc for some emergency backup and standby power. For the ac wiring, the aircraft structure is used as the "fourth wire." Normally, the fourth conductor should carry no current if loads are balanced. In practice, a quasipermanent unbalance of phase currents exists during flight as various loads are energized. For instance, from Fig. 5.16, a load of 20 kVA is authorized up to 900 VA of steady unbalance. Also, load switching creates transient currents (inrush), causing larger temporary imbalances.

Consequently, one **must** effect a reliable connection between the airframe and:

1. The neutral terminal of the alternator
2. The "ground" terminal of three-phase equipment
3. The negative terminal of batteries and dc inverters

A frequent requirement for that grounding point of the alternator neutral or battery negative cable is that its dc resistance does not exceed 0.1 mΩ, to pass a steady full load current of 50 A, for instance, with less than a 5 mV drop.

---

*On a typical vehicle, the power plant is designed such that the voltage drop from no load to full load stays within 10 percent, regulation not taken into account. So from a simple Thevenin equivalent, one can derive that generator resistance is 0.11 times that of the resistance of the maximum load. For instance, a 28 V/100 A alternator will have a source resistance of 30 mΩ.

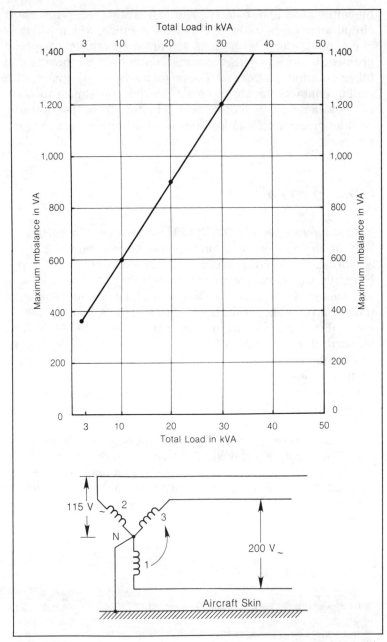

Figure 5.16—Maximum Steady Load Imbalance per Phase Allowed in Aircraft Power Systems

In a typical modern multiple-engine aircraft, it is quite common to have an installed electrical power of 10 to 100 kVA. Translated into structure current for a full phase return (temporary 100 percent imbalance) that represents 50 to 500 A of 400 Hz current. Assimilating the aircraft structure, between the neutral grounding point and the load grounding point, as an aluminum plane (which could be optimistic if the length-to-width ratio is >1), we find about 30 $\mu\Omega$/sq at 400 Hz for a 1 mm thick aluminum plane (see Section 2.4). This results in a common-mode voltage:

$$V_{CM} = 0.03 \text{ m}\Omega/\text{sq} \times 50 \text{ A (to 500 A)} = 1.5 \text{ mV/sq}$$
$$\text{(to 15 mV/sq) of rms voltage}$$

This ground noise may still be excessive for some low-level analog transducers and servo feedback which may need to have an isolated power return.

Power supplies in many aircraft U.S. and worldwide conform to MIL-STD-704.[4] Recently there has been a revival in interest for dc power systems in aircraft, which makes the requirements on the airframe conductivity more stringent.

With nonmetallic (or partly nonmetallic) aircraft, the composite material (carbon, boron, etc.) cannot be used as a power return, although by metalization it can be used as a decent EMI shield, antenna counterpoise and lightning current path. Therefore a dedicated wire has to be used for power return.

5.9.3 Ship Power System Grounding

Weight requirements are not so stringent in ships as in aircraft, so the hull is not used as a fourth conductor for the 400 Hz three-phase power; a dedicated neutral wire is used instead. The neutral is grounded to the ship's structure at the power source as for buildings. In some cases, this connection can be lifted as for some military vessels where a "combat" switch allows the neutral to float. This allows the boat to take a severe hit which possibly causes a phase-to-ground short and yet does not cause a power failure. The discussion of the relative merits of floated versus grounded neutral is somewhat reminiscent of the one covered earlier in this chapter.

The avoidance of the hull as a return conductor effectively

reduces EMI coupling. Single-wire power lines are not recommended, and twisted multiwire cables are used instead. Power cables are to be run as close as possible to the metallic hull or deck. Power cables need not be shielded except in following cases, where shielding is advisable:[5]

1. On the open deck
2. Near the radio room
3. In ships using thyristor controlled power plants

On ships (e.g., mine sweepers) which are constructed with nonconductive materials, an artificial safety ground bus is created (described in MIL-STD-1310) in addition to the neutral wire. This ground "tree" originates from "earthing" plates installed exterior to the hull. These plates are made of 3 cm thick copper and must provide a total area of 1.5 m^2, equally distributed on each side of the queel such as they are constantly immersed in water. The two plates are interconnected, and from them, using through bolts, two heavy-gauge stranded copper wires (AWG #0, or 8 mm dia) extend in an arborescent, three-dimensional pattern whose branches reach all spaces containing electrical or electronic equipment. The engine and all large metallic masses must be connected to this bus. For lightning protection purposes all metallic rigging, superstructure, mast, etc. must connect to a ground bus branch.

5.10 References

1. IEEE Green Book, *Grounding of Industrial and Commercial Power Systems*.
2. ANSI/National Fire Protection Association, *National Electrical Code (NEC)*.
3. *Guideline on Electrical Power for DP Installations*, (National Bureau of Standards, 1983, published as FIPS Publication No. 94).
4. MIL-STD-704A through D, "Aircraft Electric Power Characteristics."
5. *Electrical Installations in Ships*, (IEC, Publication 92).
6. Denny, H.W., "Grounding of Buildings and Facilities for Safety Protection," *EMC Technology* magazine, Jan. 1983.

Chapter 6

Ground-Related Interference

Interference is any extraneous electrical or electromagnetic disturbance that tends to disturb the reception of desired signals or produces undesirable responses in a circuit or system. Interference can be produced by both natural and man-made sources either external or internal to the circuit. The correct operation of complex electronic equipment and facilities is inherently dependent upon the frequencies and amplitudes of both the signals utilized in the system and the potential interference emissions that are present. If the frequency of an undesired signal is within the operating frequency range of a circuit, the circuit may respond to the undesired signal (it may even happen out of band). The severity of the interference is a function of the amplitude and frequency of the undesired signal relative to that of the desired signal at the point of detection.

The coupling paths by which a source creates (or a victim receives) EMI are of five kinds, as developed in *EMI Control Methodology & Procedures*, Vol. 8 in the Interference Control Technologies handbook series. They are:
1. Common-impedance coupling
2. Common-mode induction or radiation
3. Differential-mode induction or radiation
4. Wire-to-wire coupling (crosstalk)
5. Power source coupling

In this book devoted to grounding, the interference couplings of interest are the first and the second ones since they involve the common ground return, be it a chassis, safety wire, earth, ship's deck, etc. This chapter will show which problems result from these couplings and how they can be controlled by proper grounding techniques.

6.1 Basic Mechanisms of Ground-Related Interference

The basic mechanisms of ground-related interference are shown in Fig. 6.1. Figure 6.1a shows the signal return path of the circuit of concern sharing the ground or reference conductor with other circuits or systems. This mechanism is called "common-impedance coupling." Although it will appear due to any impedance that culprits and victims are sharing (e.g., the power supply internal impedance and the impedance of the power hot wires), this chapter specifically address the common-ground impedance coupling.

Figure 6.1b describes the other mechanism, which is called **common-mode induction** or **radiation**. This is the phenomenon by which a radiating source induces a common-mode (CM) voltage in the loop formed by the circuit (or circuits) and a common ground, otherwise termed **ground loop**. If the field is predominantly electric, this CM voltage will appear transversely line-to-ground. If the field is predominantly magnetic, this CM voltage will appear in series and its value will be:

$$V_{CM} = -(dB/dt) \times area$$

Reciprocally, if the circuit shown is regarded as a potential source of EMI, its relation to ground will dictate the way it will radiate.

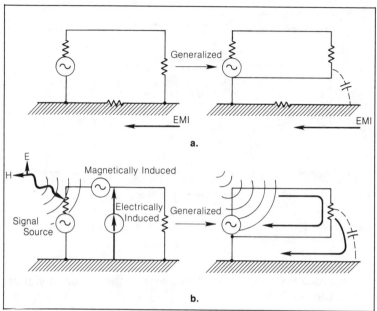

Figure 6.1—Basic Mechanisms of Ground-Related Interference, Originating (a) from Conduction and (b) Radiation.

6.2 Common-Impedance Coupling

Coupling can be defined as the means by which a voltage or current in one circuit induces a voltage or current in another circuit. Since practical reference planes or conductors do not exhibit zero impedance, any currents flowing in such paths will produce potential differences between various points on the reference ground. Interfacing circuits referenced to these various points can experience conductively coupled interference in the manner illustrated in Fig. 6.2. The voltage V_c developed across Z, the equivalent impedance of the return ground, from the potential culprit EMI source, is:

$$V_c = \frac{ZV_1}{R_{g1} + R_{L1} + Z} = \frac{ZV_1}{R_{g1} + R_{L1}} \text{ for } Z << R_{g1} + R_{L1} \quad (6.1)$$

6.3

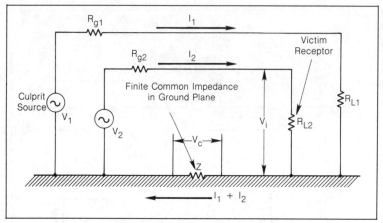

Figure 6.2—Common-Mode Impedance Coupling between Circuits

The resulting voltage, V_i developed across the potential victim load in Circuit 2 is:

$$V_i = \frac{R_{L2} V_c}{R_{g2} + R_{L2}} \text{ for } Z << R_{g2} + R_{L2} \qquad (6.2)$$

Substituting Eq. (6.1) into Eq. (6.2) yields:

$$V_i = \frac{ZR_{L2} V_1}{(R_{g1} + R_{L1})(R_{g2} + R_{L2})} \qquad (6.3)$$

The coupling between the two circuits due to common-mode impedance coupling, then, may be expressed in dB as a math model:

$$K_{dB} = 20 \log [ZR_{L2}/(R_{g1} + R_{L1})(R_{g2} + R_{L2})] \qquad (6.4)$$

where,

 Z = common impedance

Notice that the current flowing into the common impedance Z may be either a normal, steady current which is related to intentional operation of all other circuits, or a casual, intermittent current which occurs due to abnormal events (lightning, power fault, electromagnetic pulse EMP, etc.). This section will cover both topics.

6.2.1 Common-Impedance Coupling from Normal Current Flow

In many circumstances, several circuits of a system can use the same conductor as an intentional return path.

6.2.1.1 Power Supply Return

Although this is not a recommended practice, considerations of cost, weight, etc. dictate that in vehicles, aerospace and light aircraft, helicopters and other vehicles the mainframe will be used as an active power supply return.

Illustrative Example 6.1

Let us consider for instance an aircraft in which 30 A of 400 Hz current normally returns via the aluminum skin. The total impedance of the aluminum path plus the joint resistance between the different sections represent 0.5 mΩ at 400 Hz. So,

$$V_{CM} = 0.5 \text{ m}\Omega \times 30 \text{ A} = 15 \text{ mV}$$

If an analog signal also uses the fuselage as a common return, and it has a sensitivity threshold of 1 mV, the analog link will almost never work within its expected parameters. A too-high return impedance can even interfere with the power regulation itself and cause the voltage at the far-end loads to drop below the regulation tolerance. Generally, the impedance of the hot wire supplying the current is greater than the return plane impedance, but "two wrongs do not make a right."

In a combat vehicle with a 28 V battery, if the positive battery bus represents 10 mΩ of resistance and the vehicle body (including joint resistances) represents 3 mΩ, a fraction of $3/(10 + 3)$ of total voltage dump will be due to the common impedance. If 1,500 A is drawn from the power plant to supply the hydraulic pump during a heavy current demand such as aiming a gun, a total voltage drop of $1,500 \times (10 + 3) \times 10^{-3} = 19.5$ V will occur, 4.5 V of which is created across the vehicle body.

6.2.1.2 Signals Sharing the Same Return Path

Conductive coupling of interference through the signal reference plane of interfaced equipment can occur in a manner similar to that described above for power circuitry. In Fig. 6.3, if Circuit 1 represents two pieces of paired equipment and Circuit 2 represents a different pair of interfaced equipment, then a current flowing in either circuit may produce interference in the other circuit.

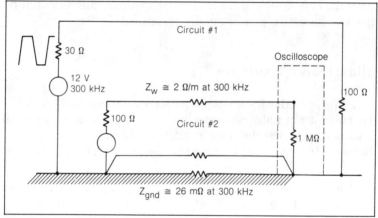

Figure 6.3—Signaling Pulses and Monitoring Oscilloscope Sharing a Cable Tray Ground (Example 6.2)

Illustrative Example 6.2

Two conductors are run down the cable tray described in Chapter 2, Section 2.4 and use the tray as a ground return (a bad practice). The first circuit is carrying 300 kHz signaling pulses with 12 V amplitude. Source and load impedances for Circuit 1 are 30 Ω and 100 Ω respectively. The second circuit (victim) is an oscilloscope monitor with a sensitivity of 1 mV, sensing a transducer output. The source and load impedances of this Circuit 2 are 100 Ω and 1 MΩ respectively. Determine if an EMI problem exists.

Looking back to Table 2.6, at 300 kHz, $Z = 6.94$ mΩ/sq for steel. So,

$$Z_{CM} = 6.94 \times 2 \text{ m}/0.50 \text{ m} = 27.76 \text{ m}\Omega$$

The interference voltage, calculated with Eq. (6.3), is:

$$V_i = \frac{27.76 \times 10^6 \times 12 \text{ V}}{130 \times 10^6} = 2.56 \text{ mV}$$

Because 2.56 mV > 1 mV, EMI will exist. Notice that CM impedance coupling may exist even when the chassis or other conductive structure is **not used** as an intentional return.

Figure 6.3 shows a case where a dedicated signal return has been provided for the analog sensing in the system of the previous example. In good faith, the designer will believe that his return wire will "shunt" the ground noise existing between the two ends of the cable tray. However, there is no way a wire (or even an ordinary coaxial cable shield) can represent less, at 300 kHz, than the 27 mΩ of the tray. Therefore the assumed "dedicated" return wire is just another impedance across the voltage source represented by the 2.56 mV across the steel tray. Not much improvement will be seen until one of these conditions exists:

1. A dedicated wire is used for the 300 kHz signal, and at least one end is floated with respect to the tray.
2. At least one end of the analog sensor line is floated.
3. A good-quality coaxial cable with low transfer impedance is used for the analog sensing.

Any of these methods is viable at low frequencies (let's say below about 3 MHz for a 10 m interconnect cable). The first and the second are termed **single-point grounds** (**SPGs**) or **star grounds** as explained in later chapters of this book.

6.2.1.3 Filter Capacitor Current Return

In addition to the safety issue posed by EMI filter capacitors between power supply wires and ground, a problem may result from the permanent leakage current they let circulate in the structures at the power mains frequency. This current does not exist, of course, with dc supplies.

Illustrative Example 6.3

A 400 Hz supply system on board an aircraft is feeding various electronic boxes. Twenty are equipped with EMI filters and installed at the tail end of the fuselage, remote from the power plant. Each EMI filter uses a 0.5 μF capacitor to ground. Do the filter capacitors create an objectionable ground noise?

$$I = \frac{115 \text{ V}}{\Sigma X_c} = 115 / \frac{1}{0.5 \times 10^{-6} \times 20 \times 2\pi \times 400}$$

$$= 2.88 \text{ A}$$

Assuming, as in Example 6.1, a return path impedance (including joint resistances) of 0.5 mΩ, this corresponds to a common-mode voltage of 1.44 mV at 400 Hz, notwithstanding the effect of all the harmonics in the current spectrum, which will be additional to the voltages already discussed. For this reason, designers of military systems should be extremely careful in using capacitive filters. They should be sure to exhaust all avenues of circuit improvement via inductive filters and lossy ferrites before installing filtering capacitors line to ground.

6.2.1.4 Control Techniques

Control techniques to reduce common-ground impedance coupling can be summarized by this pragmatic statement: if one wants to reduce the Z × I product in the common path, he has to reduce either Z, I or both. Since the solutions also apply for the "casual" current flow, they will be regrouped and discussed at the end of this chapter.

6.2.2 Common-Impedance Coupling due to Casual Current Flow

The term "casual" applies here to currents which are not normally flowing in the ground path but may exist due to outside events (e.g., lightning, EMP, ESD, CW transmitters), abnormal system conditions (power faults, etc.) or permanent, unintended ground routes (stray currents, ground loops, circuit unbalance, etc.). Unlike "normal" currents, these currents generally exhibit frequencies, rise times or amplitudes for which the ground path may have not been optimized or even designed.

6.2.2.1 Noise Drainage

Historically, the existence of a ground seems to have invited designers to sink all the undesirable currents into one path. The myth of a friendly ground which can host all the EMI trash and yet remain in an equipotential state is instinctively anchored in engineer's mind, the author being no exception. To combat this regrettable tendency, each designer must remember that every time a noise decoupling device such as a filter, cable shield, transformer Faraday shield, etc. is connected to ground, the ensuing current will flow into this ground. He must take care that the ground impedance can handle this current without creating a new problem.

Illustrative Example 6.4

In a telecommunication center, a Faraday shield is installed to decouple ambient EMI picked up by outdoor power lines. The primary winding-to-shield capacitance is 300 pF. Due to nearby CW transmitters, a CM voltage of 1 V (AM modulated) at 1.5 MHz exists on the incoming power line. Assuming the Faraday shield is connected to the signal ground bus, what EMI current will result?

The shield current sinking to ground via the signal ground wire will be:

$$I = \frac{V}{X_c} = 1\ V \times 300 \times 10^{-12} \times 2\pi \times 1.5 \times 10^6 = 3\ mA$$

An ordinary wire (see Section 2.2) has an impedance of about 10 Ω/m at 1.5 MHz. This corresponds to a noise voltage of 30 mV per meter length, appearing in series in the signal ground reference where the Faraday shield has been connected.

6.2.2.2 Lightning and EMP

Although lightning and EMP are of different origin, they share in common the generation of high dI/dt induced by radiation, and high ground currents. The designer generally does not expect his system to work error-free during these temporary conditions, but once the few microseconds of the transient have passed, the system should return to normal operation with no hardware failure. The common impedance problems caused by lightning obey the general model of Fig. 6.2, but lightning current can flow in the following paths:

1. Structures, beams, pipes, etc., with dynamic impedances (normalized to 1 μs rise time) ranging from 30 mΩ/m to 1 Ω/m length (see Section 2.5). That is, a 10 kA/μs lightning current flowing over such a steel structure will cause about 300 V to 10 kV transient voltages between two points 1 m apart along this structure. The designer has to be sure that such points do not relate to sensitive electronics or, alternatively, install transient protectors at the circuit input.

2. Lightning rod down conductors, surge arrestor grounding conductors, shield grounding conductors. By their very nature, these conductors are not active devices, so they normally do not include power or signal return paths. Therefore they should not normally cause common-impedance coupling, with the exception of cable shield grounding conductors which are tied to signal grounds or daisy chained (a poor practice).

3. Ground grids. As seen in Section 2.6, quasi-infinite metal grids have impedances ranging from less than 1 μΩ at dc and VLF to about 1 Ω at 300 kHz (the reciprocal bandwidth of 1 μs). Lightning currents flowing into ground grids can therefore develop common-impedance voltages in the kilovolt range between two points of the grid. However, in contrast with wires and beams, this voltage will be almost independent of the distance between the two points: for a 1 μs rise time, two points distant by 30 m on a grid will still represent about 1 Ω, while a 30 m thin structure would represent about 30 Ω.

4. Earth. The flow of lightning current spreading into earth resistance is one of the very critical issues with lightning strokes. Figure 6.4 represents the voltage appearing between two earthing points separated by X meters during a 100,000 A lightning stroke whose point of impact is at a distance d.

Dist D	Earth Potential Difference in Volts						
in m	Axial Distance X in Meters						
	10	20	30	50	70	100	200
10	796 k	1.06 M	1.19 M	1.33 M	1.39 M	1.45 M	1.52 M
15	424 k	606 k	707 k	816 k	874 k	923 k	987 k
20	265 k	398 k	477 k	568 k	619 k	663 k	723 k
30	133 k	212 k	265 k	332 k	371 k	408 k	461 k
40	79.6 k	133 k	171 k	221 k	253 k	284 k	332 k
50	53.1 k	91.9 k	119 k	159 k	186 k	212 k	255 k
70	28.4 k	50.5 k	68.2 k	94.7 k	114 k	134 k	168 k
100	10.5 k	26.5 k	36.7 k	53.1 k	65.5 k	79.6 k	106 k
150	6.6 k	12.5 k	17.7 k	26.5 k	33.8 k	42.4 k	60.6 k
200	3.8 k	7.2 k	10.4 k	15.9 k	20.6 k	26.5 k	39.8 k
300	1.7 k	3.3 k	4.8 k	7.6 k	10.0 k	13.3 k	21.2 k
400	970	1.9 k	2.8 k	4.4 k	5.9 k	8.0 k	13.3 k
500	624	1.2 k	1.8 k	2.9 k	3.9 k	5.3 k	9.1 k
700	320	632	934	1.5 k	2.1 k	2.8 k	5.1 k
1 k	158	312	464	758	1.0 k	1.4 k	2.7 k
2 k	40	79	118	194	269	379	723
3 k	18	35	53	87	121	171	332
5 k	6	13	19	32	44	62	122
10 k	2	3	5	8	11	16	31

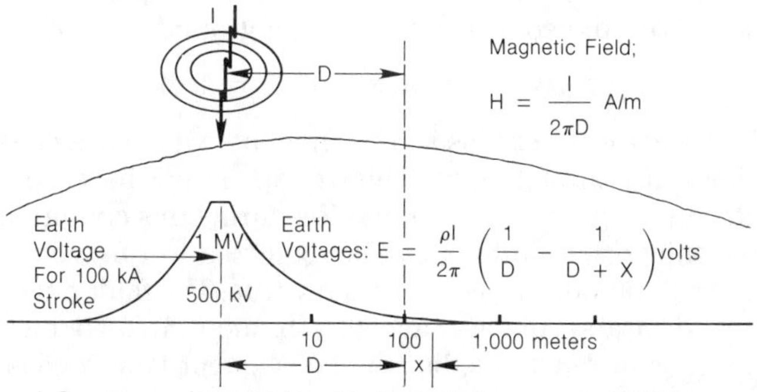

Magnetic Field;

$$H = \frac{I}{2\pi D} \text{ A/m}$$

Earth Voltage For 100 kA Stroke

1 MV

500 kV

Earth Voltages: $E = \frac{\rho I}{2\pi} \left(\frac{1}{D} - \frac{1}{D + X} \right) \text{volts}$

10   100   1,000 meters

I Stroke = 100 kA, Earth Resistivity ρ = 1,000 Ωm

Figure 6.4—Earth Potential Differences between Two Points Separated by X Meters, at a Distance D from Stroke Impact. For currents other than 100 kA and resistivity other than 1,000 Ωm, the correction is proportional to I and ρ.

6.2.2.3 Power Faults

Either for safety (safety green or green-yellow wire) or for power return, the power source has one terminal connected to earth or metal ground. As a result, any incidental contact of a live conductor with ground will cause a short circuit current to flow in the common ground until a fuse, a circuit breaker or other emergency disconnect opens the circuit. Therefore during a period of time ranging from milliseconds to several minutes, a ground current will flow which greatly exceeds the steady ground current.

Illustrative Example 6.5

In a 115 V distribution, assume that the total impedance of the power source, the phase wire of this branch circuit and the short itself represents 0.3 Ω. The impedance of the safety wire represents 50 mΩ at 60 Hz. During a short to ground, the temporary current will be:

$$115/(0.3 + 0.05) = 328 \text{ A rms}$$

Until the fuse blows, the chassis of the equipments most remote from the source will exhibit a ground shift of:

$$\Delta V = 328 \text{ A} \times 0.05 \ \Omega = 16.4 \text{ V}$$

with respect to the chassis of equipments which are closest to the neutral earthing point. This voltage is not hazardous, but electronic circuitry may malfunction during this condition. One might object that nothing can be expected to run trouble-free during a fault, but this is not actually true. The fault might have occurred in a secondary, ancillary branch circuit which supports no vital functions, but the consequent failure caused by the ground shift may create a severe issue such as an industrial process being erroneously initiated or shut down.

6.3 Techniques for Reduction of Common-Impedance Coupling

Realizing that common-impedance coupling will always exist, the techniques for keeping it at a tolerable level are the following:

1. Lower the impedance of the common return path to such a value that the product of $Z_{gnd} \times \Sigma I_{gnd}$ is no longer a threat for victim circuits referenced to this ground.
2. Limit the other currents $I \neq I_X$ circulating in the return path used for circuit X. This, too, will decrease the product of Z_{gnd} by ΣI_{gnd}.
3. Design a system which can tolerate the existing (or expected) level of ground noise. Many techniques have been invented to permit a signal to be processed even with the noisiest ground foreseeable in a given application (Ref. 1).

The choice of (1), (2) or (3) is based on feasibility, cost, frequency ranges and safety aspects. From the grounding of an IC chip to the grounding of a facility, it also depends on the physical size of the circuits. Since this book is devoted to grounding techniques, and given that case (3) assumes that the designer has no way of achieving a good enough ground system, the following section will more specifically address solutions (1) and (2). Solutions using approach (3) will be summarized only briefly since ample details about them can be found in Ref. 1.

6.3.1 Decreasing the Common-Ground Impedance

Obviously, given a mix of currents flowing into common-ground impedance Z_{CM}, one way to decrease the ground noise is to decrease Z_{CM}. As shown in Fig. 6.5, this can be accomplished by several methods:

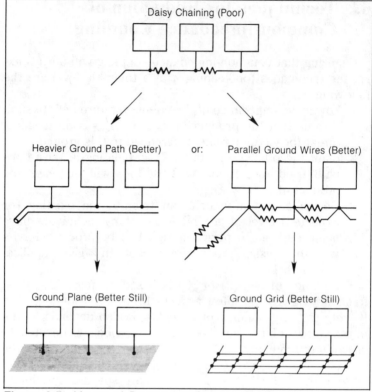

Figure 6.5—Means of Decreasing Common-Impedance Coupling by Decreasing Ground Path Impedance. From the bad practice of daisy-chain (top) the improvement evolves toward a plane (left) or a grid (right)

1. Reduce the conductor length between the multiple grounding points.
2. Increase the conductor cross section between the same points.
3. Put several ground conductors in parallel.
4. Choose conductor shapes which minimize self-inductances.
5. Use a ground plane or ground grid as a common return.

The last solution is by far the best for high frequencies since (as was shown in Chapter 2), a metal plane has a HF impedance several orders of magnitude lower than any discrete wire or strap. This solution is in fact the basis of the multipoint grounding system, which will be seen in more detail in Chapter 8.

6.3.2 Decreasing Ground Currents (Opening Ground Loops)

The other way to decrease $Z_{CM} \times I$ is, of course, to decrease I. However, this is easier said than done. Most of the currents flowing in the grounds, which have been defined previously as "normal" or "casual," are either functional or out of the designer's control. So this solution is more accurately described as "decreasing ground currents flowing into critical paths."

By proper segregation of ground routes, careful location of ground nodes and elimination of unnecessary ground loops, one can avoid the flow of objectionable currents between two grounding points having a given ground resistance or impedance. This is the basis of the star ground and ground segregation networks. Here, separate ground paths are provided for circuits which have different functions and sensitivities, and ground loops are avoided. The limitation of this solution is that above a certain frequency, ground currents will depart from their carefully planned routes and will flow in many parallel paths due to stray capacitances.

A typical ground segregation in a complex system will consider separate grounds for:

1. Low-level analog returns
2. High-level signal returns (relay drives, etc.)
3. Protective shield grounds (multipair cable shields,transformer Faraday Shields, etc.) exclusive of coaxial shields
4. RF coaxial shield returns
5. High-speed logic returns
6. Power returns
7. Safety
8. Lightning

It is very likely that some of these conductors will have one point in common. But to avoid circulating currents between the different layers of the grounding hierarchy, the rule is that **they must not have more than one common point**. As shown in Fig. 6.6, the common connection point is needed only if analog and digital circuits are functionally related and have no galvanic isolation. If the power source has a single output common to analog and digital (a bad practice), this connection must not exist. In this case, it would create a ground loop that allows logic current returns to flow into the analog ground.

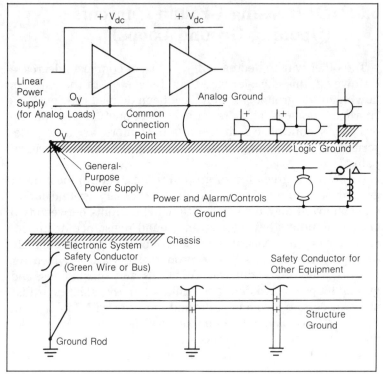

Figure 6.6—The Concept of Ground Segregation

Note that the preceding list shows eight different grounds! This does not mean that every system must have eight different ground networks. But it means that if several of them are merged into a single conductor or plane, this has to result from an engineering decision based on calculations and not from an arbitrary "gut feeling." The calculation steps should be as follows:

1. List all the ground paths (wires, planes, straps, earth, etc.).
2. Evaluate the amplitude and frequency range of all currents (normal and casual) flowing through these common paths. This must include spurious and interference frequencies as well as intended signals.
3. Calculate (using, for instance, the data of Chapter 2 plus bond impedances) the impedance range of each path within the frequency ranges found in step (2).
4. Calculate the ground potential drift $Z \times I$ for each path.

5. Compare the calculated data to the noise immunity (threshold level) of the most susceptible circuit which has more than one point tied to this specific path.

Figures 6.7 through 6.10 depict incorrect and proper amplifer circuit grounding schemes.

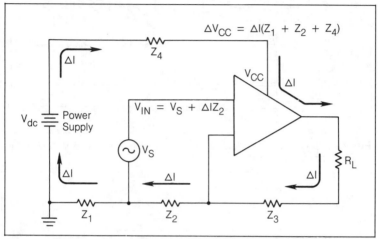

Figure 6.7—Generalized Amplifier Circuit, Incorrect Grounding

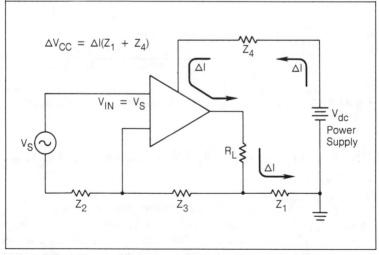

Figure 6.8—Generalized Amplifier Circuit, Proper Grounding

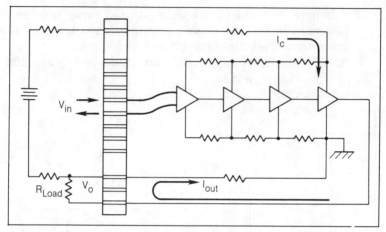

Figure 6.9—Recommended Grounding Scheme for PC Board Mounted Chain Amplifiers (from Ref. 2)

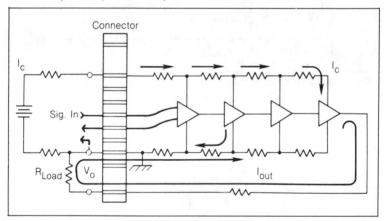

Figure 6.10—Interstage Coupling Caused by Improper Grounding (from Ref. 2)

Illustrative Example 6.6: Z_{CM} Reduction vs. I_{CM} Reduction

Let's assume a single input analog amplifier, with 1 mV sensitivity, monitoring the output from a position transducer as shown in Fig. 6.11. Initially, the signal return is sharing a common path, over some length of PCB, with the power return of a stepper motor. The motor is driven by pulses having 2 A peak current and a relatively low frequency of 1 kHz. At this frequency, the segment AB represents 10 mΩ of impedance. Therefore, at each current pulse, an error voltage of:

$$V_{AB} = 2 \text{ A} \times 10 \text{ m}\Omega = 20 \text{ mV}$$

is appearing in series in the sensor line, 20 times larger than the amplifier threshold.

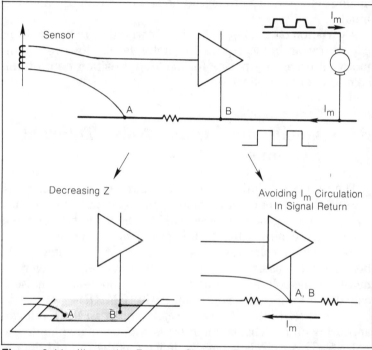

Figure 6.11—Illustrative Example Showing Z_{CM} versus I_{CM} reduction.

Solution 1: Decreasing Z_{CM}

If the wire or trace AB is replaced by a plane, a PCB copper layer of 0.03 mm thickness represents 0.5 mΩ/sq at 1 kHz. The voltage drop in the common path is now:

$$0.5 \text{ m} \times 2 \text{ A} = 1 \text{ mV}$$

This is just equal to the amplifier threshold. (There is no safety margin at all, and in fact the input dynamic range or S/N ratio is degraded. But at least the system is viable.)

Solution 2: Decreasing I_{CM} by Ground Segregation

Instead of lowering Z_{CM}, assume we provide a dedicated signal return all the way down to amplifier common. Provided **the sensor itself is not grounded** (that would create a ground loop), the motor current is no longer flowing in the analog return, and virtually no noise is seen on the amplifier input.

A variation on the I_{CM} reduction fix would be to decouple via capacitors or inductors at the motor level. However, if the motor is driven by pulses for accurate position control, this solution is not applicable.

6.3.3 Designing Ground Noise Tolerant Systems

The ultimate solution is to design circuits which will work even in the presence of common-mode voltage between their two (or more) ground references. That is, if the two previous solutions are not viable or not sufficient, we must devise a system which tolerates a certain amount of voltage shift between its chassis grounds or earthing points. The figure of merit for the tolerance of a circuit to common-mode noise is called **common-mode rejection ratio (CMRR)**.

The CMRR is the ability to reject (not react to) voltages appearing on both signal input leads with same amplitude and polarity. This ratio is generally defined as the ratio of the CM voltage causing a given output response V_O to the normal input voltage (differential) which would cause the same output response. CMRR is usually very high for good-quality differential amplifiers, on the order of 80 to 120 dB.

However, this figure simply indicates the common-mode tolerance of one device only, under bench test conditions at 60 Hz, and is of little value when the device is mounted in a real-world configuration where source impedance, wiring inductances and stray capacitances come in to play. So a better measure of ground-noise tolerance of a complete link is called (from Ref. 1) **ground-loop coupling (GLC)**. Also called **mode**

conversion, this factor is a dimensionless number which relates the common voltage V_{CM} appearing in series between the two grounding or earthing points of a link to the true differential voltage V_O resulting at the input terminals of the victim device, as shown in Fig. 6.12. Therefore:

$$GLC = \frac{V_O}{V_{CM}}$$

or,

$$GLC_{dB} = 20 \log \frac{V_O}{V_{CM}}$$

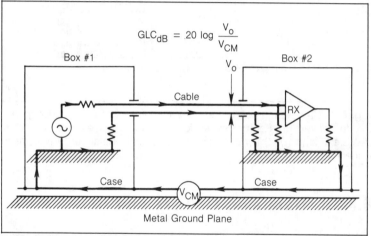

Figure 6.12—Definition of Ground-Loop Coupling (or Mode Conversion)

So, for instance, a signal link having 60 dB of GLC factor in a given frequency domain will receive only 1 mV of differential noise when 1 V is applied common-mode. An extensive explanation through mathematical modeling and equivalent circuits is given in Ref. 1, along with the operation and limitation of various ground-noise rejection solutions. We will briefly enumerate these solutions, along with their essential features. An example of the values of the GLC factor is shown in Fig. 6.13 for a 10 m interconnection with the ground loop closed (zero-volt to ground) or open (floated zero-volt).

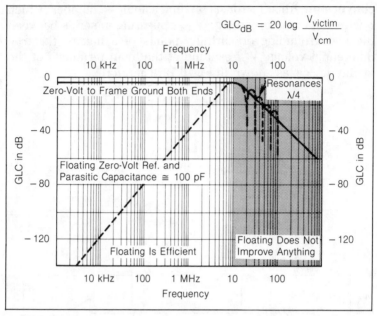

Figure 6.13—Example of Numerical Value of the Ground Loop Coupling (Mode Conversion) Factor, Shown for Two Boxes with a 10 m Wire Pair (AWG #22) and 100 Ω Termination at Each End, Unbalanced Drivers and Receivers

6.3.3.1 Balanced Drivers and Receivers

With balanced drivers and receivers (see Fig. 6.14), both legs of the intended circuit (including source resistance, wire impedance and receiver impedance) are made equal, or as equal as possible. Therefore, the common-mode voltage forces two equal currents to flow in the two branches. At the receiver end, the potential of Point A versus ground is equal to $Z_{A\text{-}G} \times I_{CM1}$ while the potential of Point B is equal to $Z_{B\text{-}G} \times I_{CM2}$. Since both terms, ideally, are equal, there is no differential voltage $V_{A\text{-}B}$. Generally, a high degree of balance becomes difficult with increasing frequencies since the balancing of both legs includes symmetry of the following:

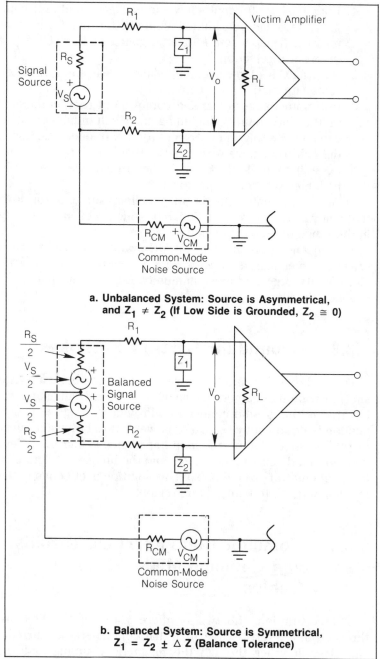

a. Unbalanced System: Source is Asymmetrical, and $Z_1 \neq Z_2$ (If Low Side is Grounded, $Z_2 \cong 0$)

b. Balanced System: Source is Symmetrical, $Z_1 = Z_2 \pm \triangle Z$ (Balance Tolerance)

Figure 6.14—Balanced versus Unbalanced Configuration with Respect to Common-Mode Loop Voltage

1. Both halves of signal source impedance (real and complex). This can be trimmed within better than 0.1 percent up to at least a few kilohertz, giving at least 60 dB of theoretical rejection.
2. Both halves of receiver impedance (real and complex): same situation.
3. Both impedances (real and complex) of each conductor of the wire pair(s), including their self-inductance and capacitance to ground. Except for low frequencies, this is difficult to achieve within better than 3 to 5 percent, that is, -30 to -34 dB. So at higher frequencies the cable becomes the limiting factor.

In summary, balancing is an excellent solution for low-frequency analog, voice, etc. It can provide excellent immunity in the range of -60 dB or better.

At frequencies in the 1 to 30 MHz range, digital balanced driver/receiver pairs still, with some precautions, can provide 20 to 30 dB of ground-noise immunity. Beyond this, balancing is generally not used.

6.3.3.2 Ground (or Earth) RF Chokes

These chokes (generally a few tens of turns around a ferrite slug) provide inductances in the 30 to 1,000 μH range and are inserted in the ground connection. Provided this ground connection **is not** an active signal or power return but just a safety or reference conductor, the loop impedance is increased, less common-mode current circulates and the link can "tolerate" a larger amount of ground noise. This solution is effective in the few kilohertz to few megahertz region.

6.3.3.3 Common-Mode Ferrites, Toroids and Common-Mode Absorbing Cables

In this solution, the two or more wires of the link are threaded into a ferrite tube such that common-mode currents cancel each other through the magnetic coupling and the resistive losses of the ferrite material. The best ferrites create an insertion impedance of 300 to 500 Ω in the VHF (30 to 300 MHz) range. Therefore, the ground-noise immunity of a system having, for example, 30 Ω source resistance and 100 Ω load resistance, is improved by:

$$\frac{300 + 100 + 30}{100 + 30} = 3.3 \text{ times or } 10.4 \text{ dB}$$

This solution is excellent for low-impedance VHF circuits but has virtually no effect on low-frequency or high-impedance ones. As an extension of this concept, ferrite loaded wires have been developed. An interesting point is that the useful differential signal is not affected at all.

6.3.3.4 Balancing Transformers

Inserting isolation transformers into the signal link will break the ground loop and prevent the ground common-mode voltage from injecting a current into the signal paths. Such transformers can also create a balanced link between an otherwise unbalanced driver and receiver pair. Except for the bandwidth of the transformer (which cannot, of course, process dc or too low-frequency signals), this solutions allows any system to work with practically any amount of ground noise, including the transients in the kilovolt range that occur in the process of sinking lightning currents. The high-frequency limitation resides in the parasitic input-to-output capacitance of the transformer.

6.3.3.5 Circuit Bypassing

Properly classified as a filtering technique, the use of common-mode capacitors will divert the CM current from the sensitive circuit. In this way, CM currents will still circulate in the link, but they will be diverted from flowing into the signal source and load impedance provided that the capacitors are quasi-ideal; that is, they have no parasitic inductance (feed-through or planar capacitors). This solution is excellent over a wide frequency range, as long as:

1. The capacitors are adequately located, preferably at the connector interface.
2. Their bonding to the connector shell or box housing has minimum resistance.
3. The value of C is large enough to be a low-impedance path for EMI currents from the ground, but not to the point that the line termination would be too heavily shunted by the two capacitors in series; that is, C/2.

6.3.3.6 Optical Isolation

Isolation via optical isolators or fiber optics is an especially effective means of achieving ground-noise immunity. It is perfectly suited for digital links or even analog signal links as long as low levels and high accuracy are not required. For low-level analog (less than 10 mV) and accurate tracking, optical isolators and fibers can be used but at the expense of more complex circuitry.

Provided that all steps are taken to keep the ground noise from affecting either the light source or the light detector (in which case EMI would be transferred in form of light) there are practically no frequency limitations. The basic limitations are only that:

1. The designer must check the surge withstand capability (case-to-ground) of the optical transducer at both ends. This surge capability should be checked not only in dc terms, but also in dynamic terms of V/s.
2. Above 10 to 30 MHz, the intrinsic parasitic capacitance of optical isolators starts to shunt the device in the common mode.

All the above translates into practical ground-noise rejection of 120 dB or more at dc, down to 20 to 30 dB at 30 MHz.

6.4 Common-Mode Radiation into or from Ground Loops

The second EMI mechanism involving ground is a radiation mechanism wherein, as shown in Fig. 6.15, the ground loop acts as a receiving or transmitting antenna. Here the quality of the ground (resistance or impedance) does not play an important role because the EMI voltage (for susceptibility) or the emitted field (for emission) is mainly a function of the grounding scheme; that is:

1. Interconnect cable length and height above grounding plane or conductor
2. Intentional or fortuitous ground loop created by 0 V-to-chassis connections, safety ground wires and straps, stray capacitances, etc. (Exact math models and coupling factors for these mechanisms are amply given in Ref. 1)

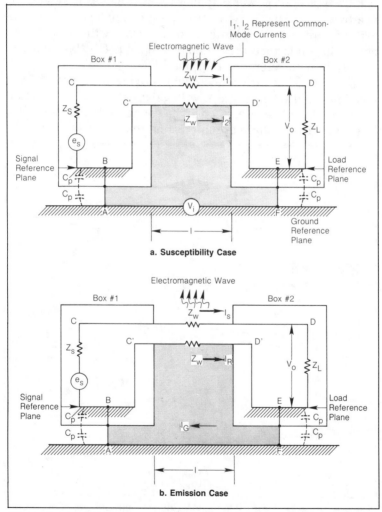

Figure 6.15—CM Radiation into and from Ground Loops

6.4.1 Electric and Magnetic Near-Field Couplings (Susceptibility)

Near-field coupling into ground loops refers to the case where the radiating source is close to the victim cabling in terms of wavelength, or more precisely when they are at a distance less than $\lambda/2\pi$. For E-fields, this occurs in the presence of nearby AM or low-frequency CW transmitters, high-voltage lines or power supplies. For H-fields, it relates to nearby high-current, low-voltage power supplies, ad-to-dc inverters, motors, etc. This is also the case with the extreme near-field condition represented by CM cable-to-cable coupling (crosstalk with reference to ground).

Figure 6.16 shows conceptually how E-field and H-field couplings end up in a noise voltage appearing across victim terminals. If we are interested in the voltage at the load end Z_{V2} of victim's cable, there are interesting remarks to be made:

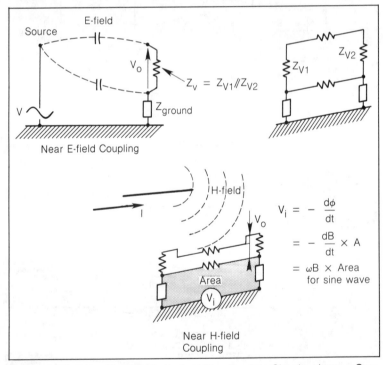

Figure 6.16—Near-Field (or Induction) Coupling into Circuits above a Conductive Ground

1. For E-field coupling, Z_{V2} is shunted by Z_{V1}, so in a configuration where at least one end of the line is a low impedance, the coupled voltage is minimal. Conversely, high-impedance terminations will enhance E-field interference.

2. For H-field coupling, the induced voltage appears in series in the ground loop, so the largest impedance takes up the largest fraction of the induced voltage V_i.

3. For both situations, the smaller the grounding impedance between the electrical circuit reference and the ground plane, the higher the victim voltage V_o (another aspect of the conflict where safety requirements create an increase in circuit noise).

6.4.2 Coupling from Plane-Wave (Far-Field) Ambients

When the radiating source is farther away from the victim installation (at a distance greater than $\lambda/2\pi$), the E- and H-field terms are in phase and related by the 377 Ω free-space impedance. There is no more "predominant" E- or H-field coupling, and coupled voltage can be calculated from either electric or magnetic models. However, as for near fields, impedance configuration still plays a role, and this role generally favors H-field coupling due to its series induction nature (see Fig. 6.17).

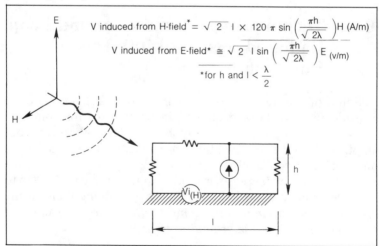

Figure 6.17—Electromagnetic (Plane-Wave) Field Coupling

6.4.3 Emission From Ground Loops

In addition to being a receptor, a ground loop can radiate an electromagnetic field. The aerial, made by the entire cable and ground plane, is excited by the cable-to-ground voltages (E-field generation) the loop common-mode current (H-field generation) or both. Here again, this radiation has nothing to do with the quality of the ground plane but with the existence of intentional or fortuitous ground loops and the presence of unbalanced (noncompensated) voltages and currents in these loops (see Fig. 6.18).

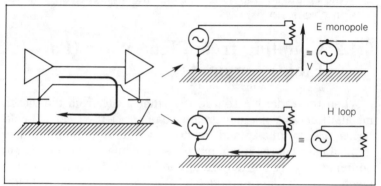

Figure 6.18—Reciprocity Concept of Emission from a Ground Loop

6.4.4 Techniques to Reduce Ground Loop Radiated Susceptibility and Emission

Some of the methods of reducing ground-related coupling are identical to those described in Section 6.3 for common-impedance coupling and apply here. Some others are not applicable, and some solutions are peculiar to the radiation mechanism. Specifically:

1. One way to decrease ground loop radiated problems is to decrease ground loop currents by confining them to the less critical areas or forcing them to circulate into the smallest loops via ground segregation.

2. The approaches of designing ground noise-tolerant systems and using systems which are balanced with regard to ground (see Section 6.3.3) are perfectly applicable methods of controlling both radiated susceptibility and emissions.
3. Reducing the size (length and area) of the ground loop is one solution which does not affect common-impedance coupling. It will, however, reduce radiation problems.
4. To the contrary, decreasing the ground plane or wire impedance would have no effect on the radiation problem.

6.5 Application of Ground-Noise Suppression Concepts

Applications of the various solutions described in Sections 6.3.1, 6.3.2 and 6.3.3 to reduce ground noise interference are summarized in Fig. 6.19, which shows the hierarchy of common-ground EMI reduction from the PCB level down to the facility level. At the top, reducing common impedance is achieved at PCB level by using copper planes, a 0 V grid net or at least very large 0 V traces. In fact, this concept is even applied upstream, at the chip level. However, wide copper zones may still be too noisy for low-level analog applications if they share the same card as high-speed logic. The right-hand side of the column shows the application of a "decreasing current concept" where the analog and digital 0 V references are distinct on the card. Also, chip decoupling capacitors confine high-frequency currents close to the chip, preventing them from circulating in the whole card 0 V circuit.

Next we see the application continuing at motherboard and backplane levels. Here the concept of lowering Z is easier to apply: because there is no crisscrossing of traces, large copper areas or entire ground planes are readily achievable.

The next step down is the grounding scheme of internal subassemblies in an equipment. To avoid ground loops, it is not recommended to connect each 0 V to the chassis. Also (exceptions accounted), turning a complex chassis into a low-impedance ground at radio frequencies is generally expensive, requiring careful HF bonding and assembly techniques. In most commercial and industrial equipment, this cost would be prohibitive, especially considering that they contain many plastic elements. So the solution lies more in current segregation where the 0 V references are collected by wire or bus to the 0 V terminal of the power supply regulator and single-point grounded to the chassis (safety ground).

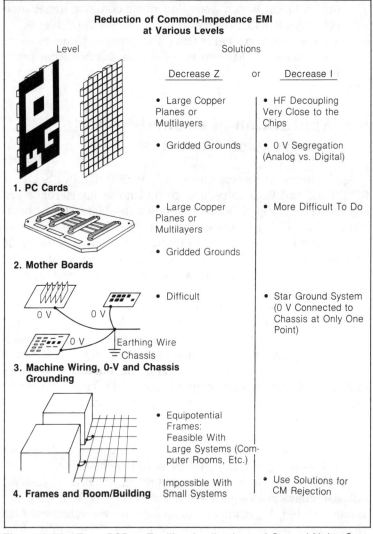

Reduction of Common-Impedance EMI at Various Levels

Level	Decrease Z	or	Decrease I
1. PC Cards	• Large Copper Planes or Multilayers • Gridded Grounds		• HF Decoupling Very Close to the Chips • 0 V Segregation (Analog vs. Digital)
2. Mother Boards	• Large Copper Planes or Multilayers • Gridded Grounds		• More Difficult To Do
3. Machine Wiring, 0-V and Chassis Grounding	• Difficult		• Star Ground System (0 V Connected to Chassis at Only One Point)
4. Frames and Room/Building	• Equipotential Frames: Feasible With Large Systems (Computer Rooms, Etc.) Impossible With Small Systems		• Use Solutions for CM Rejection

(3. diagram labels: 0 V, 0 V, 0 V, Earthing Wire, Chassis)

Figure 6.19—From PCB to Facility, Applications of Ground Noise Suppression Concepts

Obviously, the +Vdc wires should run parallel with their respective 0 V returns. With this arrangement daisy chaining is avoided, and no supply return current of one subassembly is flowing into another's return path. If there are signal interconnections between these subassemblies, they **must** also carry their respective signal returns in the ribbon cables or coaxial shields to avoid forcing these signals to return via the power path. In any event, that parallel path will still exist and constitute a ground loop which can pick up or radiate ambient fields. The only solution is to make these loops physically as small as possible by proper cable layout and running them near the chassis. Ultimately, if a ground loop problem still exists, the subassembly interconnect should be immunized to CM interference by using one of the various solutions discussed in Section 6.3.3.

A notorious exception to the configuration of Step 3 (Fig. 6.15) is the case of RF equipment such as radio transceivers, radars, RF instrumentation, etc. Here performances and frequencies justify the concept of using a low-impedance chassis. Forthcoming chapters, especially Section 8.2, explain that multipoint grounding is quasi-mandatory for these devices.

Finally, the lower step of Fig. 6.19 shows what can be done to perpetuate the low Z × I concept at installation level. Lowering the ground impedance at high frequencies requires some extensive installation work (metal grids, etc.) which can only be afforded by computing centers, telecommunications switching centers, radio receiving stations, power switchyards, etc. For small systems and office products, the only solution which remains cost feasible is to make the product tolerant to ground noise, as explained in Section 6.3.3.

6.6 References

1. Mardiguian, M. and White, D.R.J., *ECI Control Methodology and Procedures* (Gainesville, Virginia: Interference Control Technologies, Inc., 1985).
2. Denny, H., "Grounding, Bonding and Shielding Practices for Electronic Equipment," Report No. FAA-RD75-315-II, Georgia Institute of Technology, Atlanta, Georgia, Dec. 1975.

6.7 Bibliography

1. Smith, A.A., *Coupling of External EM Fields to Transmission Lines* (Gainesville, Virginia: Interference Control Technologies, Inc., 1986).
2. White, D.R.J., *EMI Control in the Desing of PCBs and Backplanes* (Gainesville, Virginia: Interference Control Technologies, Inc., 1981).
3. German, R.F., "Use of Ground Grid to Reduce PCB Interference," 6th Annual EMC Symposium, Zurich, 1985.
4. National Bureau of Standards, "Guideline on Electrical Power for DP Installations," (FIPS Publications No. 94, 1983).

Chapter 7

Cable Shield Grounding

Where to ground a cable shield is one of the all-time dilemmas for the electrical or electronic equipment designer or field engineer. The thousands of reports, articles, specifications, math modeling and experiments published on the subject since the early days of telephony would probably amount to an impressive mountain of paper. And yet the classic scenario is that of a field technician with the braided shield end in one hand and a screwdriver in the other, asking desperately where he should ground this shield. Justifiably, he will have a gloomy expectation of getting as many different answers as the number of people he asks. Although Fig. 7.1 shows that he could not possibly get more than 32 answers, this is still too broad.

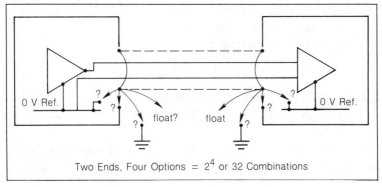

Figure 7.1—The Typical Dilemma of Shield Grounding

The major reason for this situation is a natural tendency of people to relate each new situation to their past experience and generalize "recipes" beyond their boundaries of application. There is no single recipe for shield grounding which is optimal from dc to daylight. In fact there is no recipe at all: a cable shield must be confronted to the frequency range and field parameters of interest, and only then can a sound engineering decision be made. Seasoned recipes which have proven to be good in specialized cases may cause more problems than they cure in general applications.

It would be presumptuous to pretend to cover in a single chapter a topic which has inspired so many writings, most of them by people more qualified than the author. But by compiling the essentials, this chapter will present some straightforward guidelines and impart a basic understanding of shield termination. This understanding is important because the word "grounding" bears many ambiguities and, in many cases, these relate to where and how the shield is connected. The ground (and which one?) just happens to be one possible connection point.

7.1 Generalities on Cable Shield Performances

Although the subject of shielding is covered in Vol. 3 of this EMC handbook series, it is important to briefly review the contributing factors to overall shielding performance:

1. The shield material itself
2. Its termination method
3. The installation geometry

7.1.1. Shield Material and Thickness vs. the Type of Noise

The cable shield can be made of a thin aluminum film flashed over a paper or mylar substrate, a copper braid, a wrapped thin metal foil, or a corrugated pipe and eventually a conduit. All these materials have basic shielding properties which are the combined effect of two mechanisms: **reflection** and **absorption.**

Reflection relates to radiated phenomena and is the result of the mismatch between the impinging wave impedance (the ratio Z_w = E/H of the incident field) and the shield barrier impedance. Therefore, for a given metal of given resistivity, the reflection will be considerably different against predominantly E-fields in comparison with predominantly H-fields. Even a mediocre conductor will provide a decent E-field reflection, but it takes extremely good conductivity to provide some H-field reflection (see Fig. 7.2).

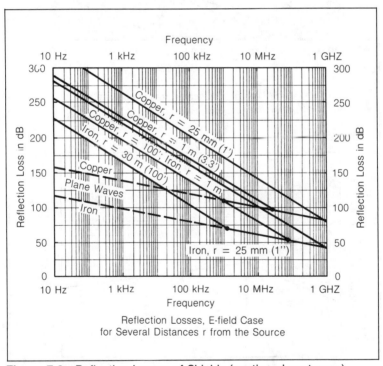

Reflection Losses, E-field Case
for Several Distances r from the Source

Figure 7.2—Reflection Losses of Shields (continued next page)

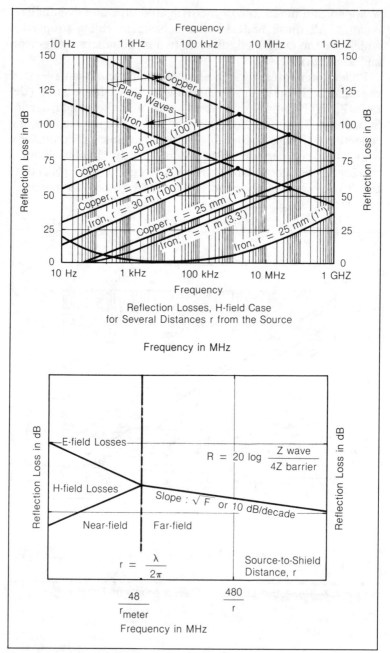

Reflection Losses, H-field Case
for Several Distances r from the Source

Figure 7.2—(continued)

   Absorption is a conducted phenomenon; that is, it will happen regardless of whether the shield current is due to a purely conducted EMI (like ground circulating currents) or is the result of an incident field. Absorption relates to the skin effect (see Chapter 2). Above a certain frequency, the current does not penetrate the whole shield thickness and circulates primarily on the skin of the shield facing the source; i.e. the outer skin if the EMI is exterior or the inner skin if the EMI is carried by the wires inside the shielded cable.

   From Fig. 7.3, it is clear that at low frequencies, typical cable shields with thicknesses of 0.1 to 0.3 mm or less cannot exhibit absorption effect since the skin effect does not yet occur (unless the shield material has a high permeability). So the only performance at low frequency of an ordinary shield would be by reflection, which requires good conductivity.

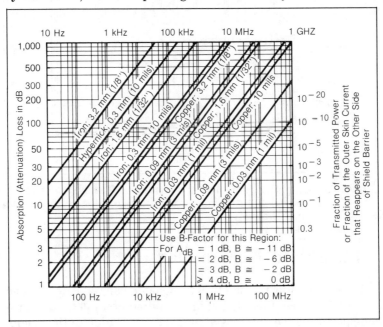

Figure 7.3—Shielding Absorption (Penetration) Loss for Several Materials and Thicknesses (Independent of Wave Impedance)

7.5

At frequencies high enough for the skin effect to occur (e.g., above 1 MHz for a 0.1 mm thick copper or aluminum shield) absorption takes over. If the shield is a solid tube, this absorption will rise exponentially and quickly reach values which are not even measurable. If the shield is a braid, all the minuscule rhombic apertures which result from the weave of copper wires will spoil the absorption effect by making the shield more and more "transparent" as frequency increases. Depending on the coverage of the braid (termed **optical coverage**) this effect can show up at frequencies as low as 1 to 10 MHz, and it will predominate (see Fig. 7.4).

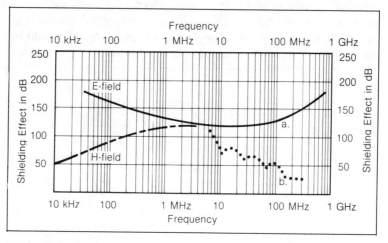

Figure 7.4—Combined Reflection and Absorption Shielding for a 25 μm Thick Copper Shield at 1 m Distance for (a) Solid Foil, and (b) Braided Shield with 3 mm Braid Pitch

7.1.2 Shield Termination

Where and how the shield is terminated can radically change its performance. Shielded cable manufacturers generally provide performance data based on ideal installation of the shield; i.e., corresponding to the intrinsic performance of the shield **wall.** Once a cable shield is mounted, its termination may be the weakest link in the chain, especially at higher frequencies.

As a general approximation, the quality of a shield can be associated with its sheath dc resistance, although this statement becomes invalid above the HF region. Since it is very difficult to terminate the shield by a connector clamp or pigtail whose impedance is much less than the shield impedance, termination hardware is always the limiting factor of the in-situ performance. That is to say, the bonding or grounding method of the shield always degrades its basic performance or, at best, gives almost equal overall performance. It cannot improve performance.

Let us consider for instance a very tight braid with a braid resistance of 3 mΩ/m. Assume a 0.75 m piece of this shielded cable interfacing two metallic racks. Unless special surface treatment, degreasing and tightening techniques are used, the typical bonding resistance of the braid to the serrated clamp will be 0.5 mΩ. An ordinary hand-tightened connector shell exhibits a contact resistance of about 3 mΩ. And finally, the contact resistance of the connector socket flange to the rack wall, assuming it is normally tool-tightened using four screws or a nut-and-washer fitting, is again 0.5 mΩ. Since there are two ends to this cable, the total termination resistance is:

$$R_{term} = 2 \ (0.5 + 3 + 0.5) = 8 \ m\Omega$$

Comparing this to the braid resistance,

$$R_{sh} = 0.75 \ m \times 3 \ m\Omega/m = 2.25 \ m\Omega$$

we see that the "grounding" contribution to the whole shield noise will be more than three times that of the braid alone. Trying to improve this situation, it is quite feasible to bring the total termination resistance down to 2 mΩ with the proper connector selection and tightening torque.

Not only can the shield termination method spoil the cable shield efficiency, but it can be the source of secondary mechanisms which can result in more EMI than if there were no shield at all. Figures 7.5, 7.6 and 7.7 show a few examples of these problems where a shield grounding wire or pigtail acts as a pickup element (susceptibility problem) or a radiating element (emission problem). The key to preventing or solving these problems is always the same: identify the current path(s). Recognizing where the shield current originates, where it goes and how it is returning to its source (including all the sneaky paths) is the most important step to the solution. **Often, people end up interrupting the shield when in fact it was the current flow into sensitive circuits which needed to be interrupted.**

7.7

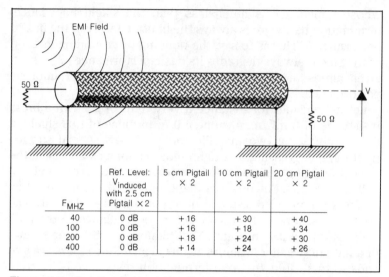

F_{MHZ}	Ref. Level: $V_{induced}$ with 2.5 cm Pigtail $\times 2$	5 cm Pigtail $\times 2$	10 cm Pigtail $\times 2$	20 cm Pigtail $\times 2$
40	0 dB	+ 16	+ 30	+ 40
100	0 dB	+ 16	+ 18	+ 34
200	0 dB	+ 18	+ 24	+ 30
400	0 dB	+ 14	+ 24	+ 26

Figure 7.5—Relative Degradation Due to Increase in Pigtail Length. The EMI increase is a combined effect of Zt increase plus the increasing area of the unmasked center conductor to ground.

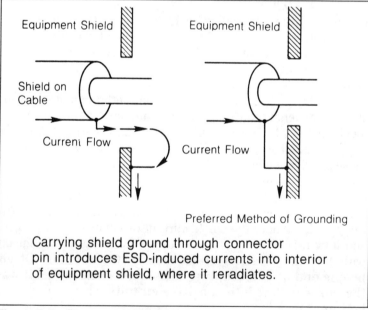

Figure 7.6—Conceptual View of EMI Pollution by Pigtails

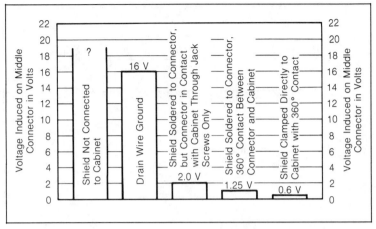

Figure 7.7—The Effect of Shield Termination on I/0 Flat Cables when a 10 kV ESD is Injected on the Metal Cabinet of the Host Equipment

7.1.3 Overall Geometry of the Installed Cable

A shielded cable can be regarded as a conjunction of two transmission lines, with the shield being the transfer medium between the two. This is shown in Fig. 7.8. The two parallel circuits are:

1. The intended circuit (Line 2), which has well-controlled parameters with regard to source and load impedances Z_g and Z_L, and characteristic impedance Z_{o2}. These parameters set the values of voltage and current at every point in this circuit, including reflection and standing wave effects.

2. The exterior circuit (Line 1), which has very poorly controlled parameters since each of its terminating impedances can vary from zero to infinity, depending on the grounding conditions, and its characteristic impedance Z_{o1}, depending on the ratio h/d of the height above ground plane versus cable diameter.

For values of Z_{o1} in the 30 to 100 Ω range, an approximate correlation between shielding effectiveness (SE) and transfer impedance of the shield Z_t is given by:[5]

$$SE_{dB} \approx 40 - 20 \log L - 20 \log Z \qquad (7.1)$$

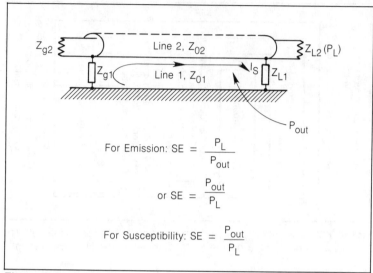

For Emission: $SE = \dfrac{P_L}{P_{out}}$

or $SE = \dfrac{P_{out}}{P_L}$

For Susceptibility: $SE = \dfrac{P_{out}}{P_L}$

Figure 7.8—A Shielded Cable as a Conjunction of Two Transmission Lines, with the Shield Being the Transfer Media Between the Two

The effectiveness of a shield is in fact the measure of the percentage of energy transferred from Line 2 into Line 1 in case of EMI emission, or transferred from Line 1 into Line 2 in case of susceptibility. The characteristic impedance of Line 1 has a large effect on this transfer of energy, especially at integer multiples of $\lambda/4$. Therefore, a given shield with given terminations will behave differently in the field depending its length and its height above ground.

7.1.4 What is Expected from the Shield?

A cable shield may be installed for emission suppression; i.e., to prevent the EMI in the cable to leak outside. On the other hand, a cable shield may be installed to cure susceptibility problems; i.e., to prevent EMI ambients from reaching the inner conductors. Finally, a cable shield may be installed for both purposes. The above paragraphs have shown that the same cable shield will behave differently in different installations with regard to emission and susceptibility, due to the very different E- and H-field conditions in each case.

7.1.5 Unbalanced vs. Balanced Shielded Cables

An unbalanced shielded cable (coax, triax, etc.) is a line where the return conductor (the shield), surrounds the forward conductor. In this case, the shield is an active conductor, carrying the intentional current returning from the load. A balanced shielded cable (shielded pair, twisted shielded pair, shielded ribbon or multipair cable) is a line where the current circulate back and forth in a pair while the shield plays essentially a **protective** role (Fig. 7.9), while it also provides some impedance balance of the pair wires to ground.

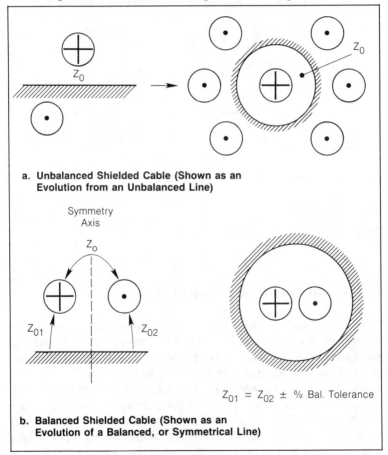

a. **Unbalanced Shielded Cable (Shown as an Evolution from an Unbalanced Line)**

b. **Balanced Shielded Cable (Shown as an Evolution of a Balanced, or Symmetrical Line)**

Figure 7.9—Balanced and Unbalanced Shielded Lines

The above distinctions may sound trivial, but it is fundamental to define a cable type in terms of what is expected from it. A common misunderstanding is illustrated Fig. 7.10 where someone is trying to reduce the radiated EMI by shielding a signal wire. However, the shield is connected to the chassis ground while the actual current is returning by some common 0 V wire. The installation of such a shield will be for naught since the radiating loop is practically unaffected. To see some results, the shield has to surround both wires; that is, the cable should be a shielded pair, or the shield itself has to be the return conductor, using a coaxial cable with the signal ground attached to both ends.

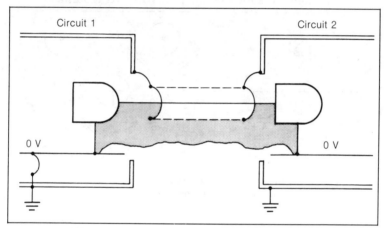

Figure 7.10—A Common Misconception of the Shield's Role

7.2 Grounding of Coaxial Shields

With a coaxial cable, the question of whether the shield should be grounded or left floated is irrelevant: **the shield, being the designated current return path, must be connected to the signal common on both ends.** The author remembers seeing equipments carrying video signals with a 20 MHz bandwidth where the designer, trying to stick to some traditional recipe carried over many decades ("thou shalt ground a shield at one end only to avoid ground loops") had left one end of the coaxial floated. The video signals were forced to return by the chassis, the only path left, causing all sorts of ground noise and radiated EMI, not to mention signal distortion due to mismatch.

However, having established that both ends of the coaxial shield must be connected at the signal references, we have yet to decide if the shield also has to be connected to the chassis, one end, both ends or not at all. As a foundation for this concept, as well as for the rest of this chapter, we need to explain briefly the concept of shield transfer impedance.

7.2.1 Shield Transfer Impedance

The transfer impedance concept, initially conceived by Schelkunof, allows us to relate the current flowing on the shield surface to the voltage it develops on the reverse side of this surface. Figures 7.11 and 7.12 show that the transfer impedance converts the cable surface current I_{sh} by diffusion into an inner longitudinal voltage V_i which appears in series in the inner (intentional) circuit. As a result, a voltage V_o will appear at each termination of the coax equal to:

$$V_o = \frac{I_{sh} \times Z_t}{2} \qquad (7.2)$$

if both ends are matched.

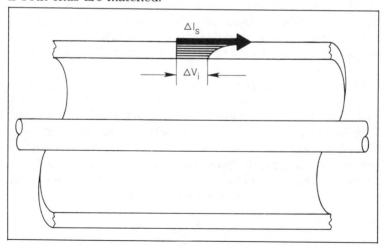

Figure 7.11—Coaxial Transfer Impedance

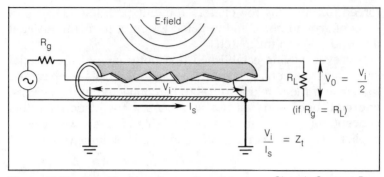

Figure 7.12—Transfer Impedance Coupling: I_s = Sheath Current Due to Ambient Field or to Ground Potential Difference

Figure 7.13 shows the Z_t values for few typical coaxial cables. Z_t is expressed in ohms and normalized to a 1 m length of shield. As seen from both Eq. (7.2) and Fig. 7.11, the lower the Z_t, the better the shield quality for EMI reduction.

Below about 100 kHz (this is called the **Ohm's law or diffusion region**), Z_t is practically equal to the shield dc resistance. Above about 3 MHz, Z_t is proportional to the leakage inductance between the shield and the inner conductor due to the multiplicity of minuscule rhombic loops of the braid. From then on, Z_t has mostly the dimension of an inductance, which could be expressed in nanohenries per meter. Above several megahertz, for loose braids, a capacitive coupling effect is added (transfer admittance) due also to these multiple holes.

Between the quasi-dc region and the inductive region, Z_t passes through a transition region. For double braid shields, this region shows a negative slope due to the skin depth effect actually occurring as per Fig. 7.11. For all practical purposes, this effect generally does not appear for single braid shields because it is immediately nullified by the weave of the braid. (Some optimized braids, due to a careful knitting pattern may show the beginning of a skin depth effect.)

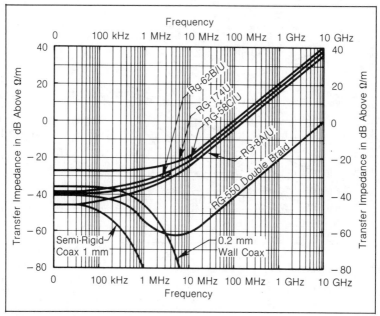

Figure 7.13—Transfer Impedance of a Few Typical Coaxial Cables

7.2.2 Where to Ground Coaxial Shields

Since both ends of the shield must at least be connected to the signal reference, the following rules and rationales can be established, supported by the transfer impedance concept.

7.2.2.1 Equipments with Floated Signal Reference

If the 0 V reference (signal ground) has been purposely floated from the chassis, the standard mount of the coaxial connector to the chassis automatically forces a 0 V-to-chassis connection, nullifying the purpose of the floating. Figure 7.14 shows the ground loop coupling (GLC) mechanism discussed in Section 6.3.3.

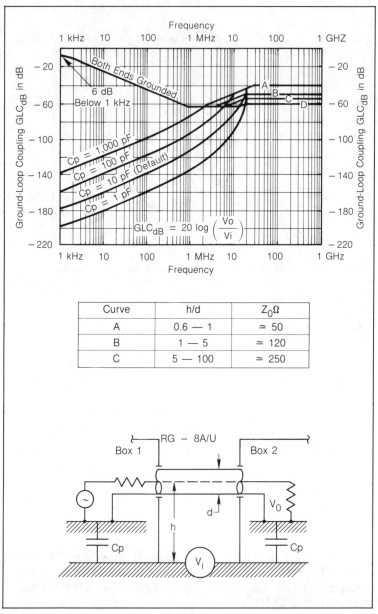

Figure 7.14—Ground-Loop Coupling (GLC) for a 10 m RG-8A/U Coaxial Cable, Showing the Effect of Insulating the Coaxial Shield from the Chassis

At frequencies below a few kilohertz, the automatic ground-ing to chassis caused by the connector results in a common-mode rejection of only 6 dB. This improves with frequency, due to the increasing loop impedance, while Z_t stays constant. If a special isolated coaxial connector is used instead (isolated BNC or other), or if the connector is PCB-mounted instead of chassis-mounted, this restores the ground loop opening, giving an enormous improvement at low frequencies (see Fig. 7.15, left-hand example).

This improvement diminishes as frequency increases, and it becomes null in the 1 to 10 MHz region. Interestingly (and this is not a coincidence), this is where the single-point or star ground systems do not work anymore and multipoint ground-ing should be substituted. This is explained in the next chapter, and particularly in Section 8.2.2. From the above we can derive:

Rule 1: With a floated signal reference (single-point ground systems), coaxial cables should be connected via insulated connectors if low-frequency ground loop prob-lems are anticipated. Above a few megahertz, this pre-caution becomes useless, as does the whole concept of floated reference, and ordinary coaxial connectors, bond-ed to the chassis, are preferred.

This rule leads to several corollaries:
1. At low frequencies, the designer must realize that in floating the signal reference for the sake of opening the ground loop he weakens the overall system shielding. However, if the problem is mainly a low-frequency struc-ture noise or earth gradient, the solution is valid.
2. If the system is subject to lightning strikes, the floated coaxial end is a real danger. A "transient" ground should be provided via a surge protector.
3. Because of all these complex tradeoffs, a coax is not the best media for low-frequency applications. Balanced, twisted, shielded pairs give more latitude for application of common-mode rejection techniques.
4. Triaxial or quadraxial cables reconcile the need for a floated signal ground and shield continuity to chassis (see Section 7.2.3).

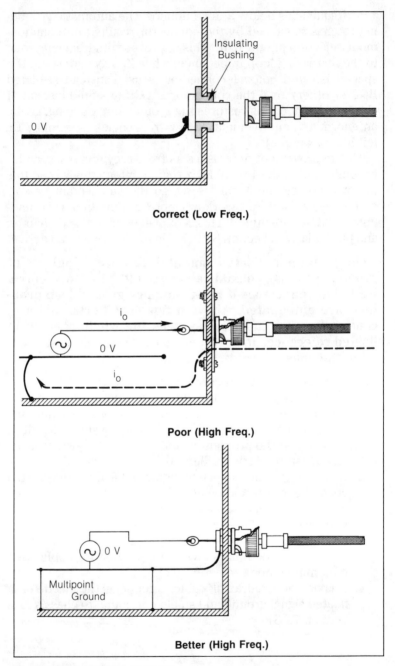

Figure 7.15—Coaxial Shield Connections

Illustrative Example 7.1

Shown in Fig. 7.16 is a VLF receiver installed in a submarine. The link between the receiving antenna and the receiver box is made by 10 m of RG 8A/U coaxial cable which is grounded both ends. There is 100 A of 400 Hz power mains current flowing in the ground plane (3 mm thick steel deck). The harmonics of the ac current fall of with frequency at 20 dB/decade. Determine if an EMI problem exists and fix the problem with a 26 dB safety margin (to meet a 90 percent probability goal that EMI will not exist. See *EMI Control Methodology & Procedures*, Ref. 10, Section 3.2).

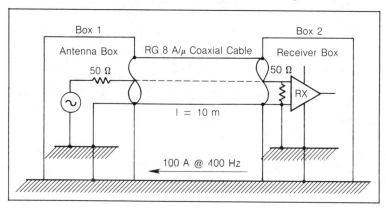

Figure 7.16—Example 7.1: VLF Receiver Coaxial Cable

The evaluation is made per the following steps, which are also summarized in the work sheet of Fig. 7.17, according to the calculation method of Ref. 10.

1. Interfering signal: harmonic of 400 Hz, current of 100 A
2. Receiver tuned to f_0 = 16.8 kHz, bandwidth = 10 Hz
3. Forty-second harmonic of 400 Hz = 16.8 kHz = f_0
4. Harmonic amplitude falls off at -20 dB/decade
5. Amplitude of fundamental = l_f = 100 A = 40 dBA
6. Amplitude of forty-second harmonic = 40 dBA $-$ 20 log 42 = 7.5 dBA = I_{42} dBA (I_{42} = 2.38 A = amplitude of forty-second harmonic)
7. Ground plane impedance (from Table 2.6, f = 16.8 kHz, 3 mm steel):

$Z_G \simeq 1.6 \text{ m}\Omega/\text{sq} = -55.9 \text{ dB}\Omega = Z_G \text{ dB}\Omega$

8. Voltage induced in ground plane by the 42nd harmonic:
$V_i\text{dBV} = I_{42} \text{ dBA} + Z_G\text{dB}\Omega = 7.5 - 55.9 = -48.4 \text{ dBV} = 71.6 \text{ dB}\mu\text{V}$ (Column 1)
N: sensitivity $= -160 \text{ dBm} +107 = -53 \text{ dB}\mu\text{V}$ (Column 2) Ambient/Noise: A/N $= 125$ (Column 3)

9. GLC (Fig. 7.14): GLC ≈ -28 dB (Column 4A)

10. Objective I/N $= -26$ dB (corresponds to 90 percent no-EMI safety margin)

11. Column 4 = Column 4A. Column 5 = 0 (Amplifier Rejection at $f_{EMI} = f_o$)

12. Column 7 = Columns 3 + 4 + 5 = 97 dB

Worksheet: EMI Prediction and Control of Example 7.1

	1	2	3	4A	4B	4C	4D	4E	4	5	6	7
Operating Conditions	AMB dBµV	N dBµV	A/N	GCM GLC	FCM GLC	DMC	C-C	PL-PS PS-Y	PICK 4A-4E	AMP REJ	Δ I/N	I/N
Objective												-26
Start: First Run	71.6	-53	125	GLC= -28					-28	0		+57
Float One End	71.6	-53	125	+6 -156					-156	0		-31

[I/N] dB: 7 = 3 + 4 + 5

Figure 7.17—Worksheet: EMI Prediction and Control of Example 7.1

To implement the first fix, float the coax the at boxes and float the signal reference at the receiver. From Fig. 7.14, and adding +6 dB degradation because one end rather than two is floated: GLC $= -156$ dB (for A/I $= 100$ cm, default value assumed) $+ 6$ dB. Column 7 is now equal to -31 db, so EMC exists (compatibility is achieved).

Several other solutions might be implemented:

1. Retune the receiver +200 Hz. This sets f_o between two adjacent harmonic frequencies. However, ship/submarine 400 Hz plants are **not** very stable: 200 Hz/16,800 Hz represents 1.2 percent stability, which is certainly not

guaranteed 90 percent of the time where the 400 Hz may vary by ±40 Hz. So the **EMI will drift too,** since it consists of harmonics of the 400 Hz, and the retuning of the receiver may not be a viable fix.

2. Use a balanced twisted pair which will perform about as well as coax.

3. In any case, the cable or coaxial shield, while floated, should be clamped to ground through a surge arrester to deal with the possibility of a lightning or EMP surge on the shield.

7.2.2.2 Equipment with a Grounded Signal Reference

If the 0 V reference (signal ground) is purposely connected to the chassis (multipoint ground) there is no need to try isolating the shield from the chassis. This case indeed reflects the various corollaries of 7.2.2.1. However, observations must be made:

1. Even though the signal ground is connected to the chassis ground, if this connection is physically remote from the coaxial connector, as direct a path as possible must be established between the signal reference and the connector back shell. This is to prevent the coaxial return current from flowing everywhere in the chassis (most of the current will seek the lowest impedance).

2. At least between 100 kHz and 10 MHz, coaxials with high-quality braid tend to "segregate" the EMI currents which will flow on the outer skin from the circuit current which will flow on the inner skin. The mounting recommended in No. 1, above, will favor this segregation (see Fig. 7.15, right-hand example).

This brings us to:

Rule 2: With a grounded signal reference (multipoint ground systems), coaxial cables should use standard connectors bonded to the chassis, with the signal 0 V plane or traces brought as directly as possible to the connector socket.

7.2.3 Triaxial and Multibraid Coaxial Cables

The term **triaxial** is sometimes confused with **double-braid,** but they are not exactly synonymous. One should distinguish between:

1. **Double-braided coaxial, with the two braids touching.** Since the two braids are not electrically insulated, the low-frequency benefit is merely that of a reduced dc resistance of the braid such as a typical 2 or 3 mΩ/m. However as frequency increases, the natural isolation by skin effect will appear between the two braids as described in 7.2.2.2.b, but more pronouncedly so. The rules for grounding are Rules 1 and 2 as previously described for ordinary coaxial cables.

2. **Triaxial, with the two braids isolated.** This is the real triaxial. This construction allows us to connect the outer braid to the chassis and the inner braid to the signal return (both ends) while still maintaining a floated electrical ground. To preserve this concept at low frequencies, a special connector (e.g., a special isolated N connector as depicted in Fig. 7.18) is required where the outer and inner sockets are insulated. At high frequencies, the double braid still provides the 30 dB improvement shown in Fig. 7.13 due to the decoupling between the two braids inductances (low inter-braid coupling).

3. **Quadraxial with three conductive layers.** Taking the concept one step further, the triax can be coated by a third conductive layer with all possible variations, such as one of the two outer layers being made of a ferrous wrap or high-permeability braid to enhance the magnetic shielding effectiveness. These cables have more efficiency, but the penalty is increased weight, stiffness and fitting complexity. The connection of the shields should obey the same rule as triaxial cable, i.e.:

Rule 3: True triaxial cables must have the inner braid tied to the signal ground at both ends, and the outer braid to the chassis at both ends. To realize the full benefit of the triaxial concept, special N connectors with two insulated sockets should be preferred.

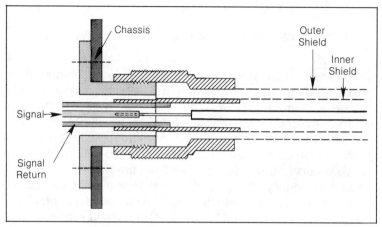

Figure 7.18—Triaxial Termination via an Insulated "N" Connector

7.2.4 Coaxial Shield Grounding and EMI Emissions

To minimize EMI emission, the grounding requirements for coaxial cables are similar to those described so far. For instance, at very low frequencies, if both ends of the shield are connected to the signal grounds, and if those signal grounds are connected to the structure, some of the return currents will flow in the chassis and structural grounds instead of the shield. This produces two effects:

1. The return currents will contribute to the general ground noise.
2. These currents will cause the whole shield-to-ground loop to radiate.

Let us consider, for instance, a 10 m cable, 1 m above ground. Assume that current returning by the unintended path is only 1 percent of the total circuit current. In other words, 99 percent of the current going to the coaxial load returns to the signal source by the shield (the intended path) and 1 percent by the chassis, frame, safety grounds, etc. (unintended path). If we compare the radiation from this loop to that of an unshielded, **balanced** link carrying the current I via a parallel wire path with 1 mm wire separation, we can establish a relative comparison based on the respective magnetic moments such that:

$$K = 0.01 \text{ I} \times 10 \text{ m}^2/\text{I} \times 10 \text{ m} \times 10^{-3} = 10$$

where,

K = radiation of the link with coax/radiation with a wire pair

Therefore, in relative terms, the low-frequency radiation of the coaxial link due to ground loop will be 10 times larger than the radiation from a typical untwisted pair with 1 mm wire separation. As a result, the benefit of coax will not be seen.

When the frequency exceeds a few kilohertz, an interesting phenomenon occurs, somewhat reciprocal to upper left part of the GLC curve shown in Fig. 7.14. This phenomenon has been well explained by Ott in Ref. 4. Due to a mutual inductance between the center conductor and the surrounding shield, the return current is "invited" to flow in the shield rather than in the increasing impedance of the ground loop. The value of the shield current I_s versus the total current I_c is expressed (from Ref. 4) as:

$$I_s = I_c \left(\frac{j\omega}{j\omega + R_s/L_s} \right) \tag{7.3}$$

where,

R_s = shield resistance
L_s = external shield-to-ground self-inductance

For typical single braid coax, R_s is about 5 to 10 mΩ/m, while L_s is in the 0.5 to 1 μH/m range, depending on the shield diameter and its height above ground. Therefore a typical value for R_s/L_s is 10^4. R_s/L_s is the reciprocal of a time constant and is termed ω_c, the shield cut-off pulsation in radians/s, or:

$$F_c = \frac{\omega_c}{2\pi} = \frac{R_s}{2\pi L_s} \tag{7.4}$$

= the shield cutoff frequency in hertz

For typical shields, ω_c being approximately 10^4 rad/sec, F_c is in the 1.5 kHz range.

Table 7.1 gives the approximate proportion of the total current which "elects" to return by the shield in a coaxial cable with both ends grounded to the metallic structure.

Table 7.1—Proportion of Total Current Returning by the Shield

F		I_s		$I_c - I_s = I$ ground	
1.5	kHz	0.7	I_c	0.3	I_c
7	kHz	0.98	I_c	0.02	I_c (-34 dB)
15	kHz	0.995	I_c	0.005	I_c (-46 dB)
150	kHz	0.9995	I_c	0.0005	I_c (-66 dB)

7.3 Shielded Multiconductor Cables (Balanced Lines)

As previously mentioned, in a shielded balanced line (parallel wire pair, twisted pair, ribbon cable, etc.) the shield acts purely as a barrier and does not carry the intentional current. Therefore, it appears that the designer has unlimited latitude to ground, float, etc. per the 32 combinations of Fig. 7.1.

Re-examining the fundamentals of interference control, in Fig. 7.19 we see that ideally, if a system must be isolated from coupling to or from its environment, it must be completely surrounded by a conductive barrier that prevents both space waves (radiation) and guided waves (conduction) from passing through it. This could be accomplished with a conductive envelope as shown in Fig. 7.19b. However, as shown in Fig. 7.19c, systems need to be related to a common ground by one or more functional or fortuitous ties (safety, power return, lightning and static sink, etc.).

If such a barrier is deemed necessary (meaning that this is not always the case), the cable shield is one element of that barrier which just happens to be tubular. This tube **must** surround the forward and return conductors. Because the shield is part of the barrier, it must be uninterrupted to avoid E- and H-field coupling with the wiring. Thus, whether or not the shield is **grounded,** it must at least be **closed** at both cabinet interfaces.

7.25

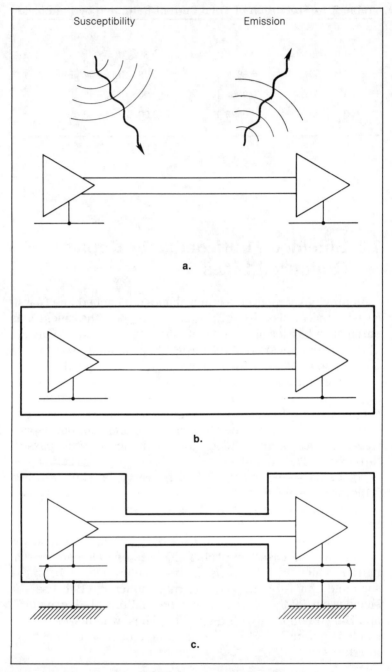

Figure 7.19—Fundamentals of Interference Control

The arguments about whether to ground a cable shield are an extension, and often an illegitimate one, of audio-frequency technology. What is important is to interrupt the current flowing in the shield because shield excitation means a certain amount of energy coupling to the inside. The idea of interrupting the shield current has sometimes degenerated into a concept where the shield itself becomes interrupted.

Connecting the shield to both boxes will preserve the overall system shielding concept (Fig. 7.20, top). But in case of noisy grounds (earth or chassis V_{CM}) or induced loop voltage (H-fields), a large shield current may circulate, aggravating the EMI into the inner circuit.

Connecting the shield only on the end where the 0 V is grounded will avoid the ground loop contribution by the shield but will create a noisy end if AB approaches $\lambda/4$ (Fig. 7.20, bottom). Therefore, interrupting the shield current without interrupting the shield implies that the loop is interrupted somewhere else in the path ABCDEF.

Interrupting the loop in this manner may pose installation or safety problems. The next sections will analyze these different facets and try to reconcile them in a orderly methodology.

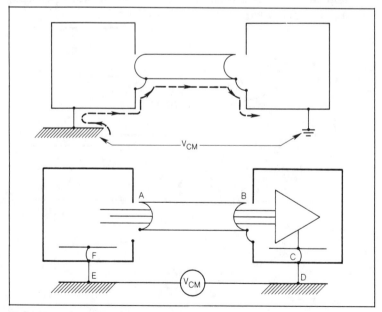

Figure 7.20—Interrupting the Shield Current without Interrupting the Shield

7.3.1 CM vs. DM Shield Performance

The purely differential action of a shield over a balanced line, infinitely far from any ground, is depicted in Fig. 7.21. This situation is often assumed in cable shield catalogs, where the shielding effectiveness of the "tube" (due to its metal type and thickness) is supposed to attenuate the wire pair illumination. The mechanism of this DM coupling can be broken into the following steps:

1. The time-varying field induces a shield current, a shield longitudinal voltage or both, since its barrier impedance is not zero. Note that the shield current (or displacement current) is due to the free-space capacitance of the shield element acting as a short dipole.
2. This current is more or less attenuated through the shield material, and the residual current and voltages appear inside.
3. The net magnetic or capacitive coupling to the wire pair inside would be zero if the balancing and twisting of the pair could be perfect. Since it cannot, some voltage appears across the pair, proportional to the pair's percentage of imbalance.

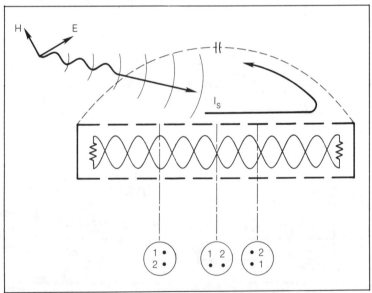

Figure 7.21—Purely Differential Coupling into a Balanced Shielded Pair

However, this configuration is purely academic since, except in a laboratory experiment, no one would use a shielded pair that way. A more realistic installation is that of Fig. 7.22 where an actual ground surface exists. The cable terminates into boxes which are strongly coupled and most often connected to this ground, forming a ground loop. As explained in section 6.4 and Figs. 6.11 and 6.12, for worst-case orientations of this ground loop versus field polarization, a low- impedance voltage source will appear in series in the loop due to magnetic induction, and a high-impedance current source will appear across the loop due to electric excitation. Depending on which one of these mechanisms is predominant, or if both of them are nuisances, the shield will behave differently.

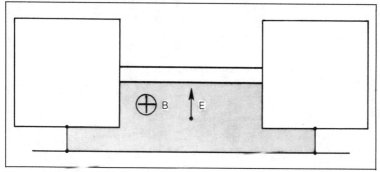

Figure 7.22—A More Realistic Configuration of Electric and Magnetic Coupling into a Shielded Cable between Two Equipments

7.3.2. Grounding of Cable Shields against Near Electric-Field Crosstalk: Faraday Cage Action

The case of a near electric-field coupling, as from low-frequency, high-impedance sources or capacitive crosstalk, is illustrated in Fig. 7.23.

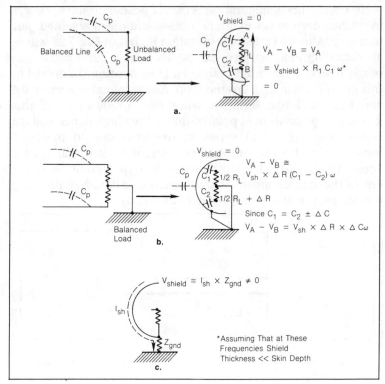

Figure 7.23—Shield Coupling in Case of Electric Field for (a) Unbalanced or (b) Balanced Load

Case 1: Unbalanced Load

In the case of an unbalanced load but still a balanced line (Fig. 7.23a), the electrical coupling can be depicted as a set of coupling capacitances C_p between the circuit of concern and the exterior. When a shield is added and grounded to the signal reference, the new coupling consists of a set of capacitances in series: the exterior-to-shield capacitance, approximately identical to the previous C_p, plus the shield-to-pair capacitances C_1 and C_2. C_1 and C_2 are several orders of magnitude larger than C_p; for instance, C_p can be a fraction of a picofarad per meter of cable while C_1 and C_2 are in the range of 30 to 100 pF/m. The voltage appearing across R_L is

$$V_A - V_B = V_A = V_{shield} \times R_L \, C_1 \omega \qquad (7.5)$$

However, if the shield is perfectly grounded, $V_{shield} = 0$ and $V_A = 0$.

Case 2: Balanced Load

In the case of a balanced load (Fig. 7.23b), ideally the two leakage currents would create equal and opposite voltages across R_L. Since in fact neither the load nor the pair-to-shield capacitance is perfectly balanced, the figure shows that a residual voltage due to the shield voltage coupling into ΔR_L through ΔC will exist. However, here again, since $V_{shield} = 0$, $V_A - V_B = 0$.

Now, as shown in Fig. 7.23c, if a fortuitous or deliberate impedance Z_{gnd} exists between the shield and the ground, the shield voltage is no longer null. The circuit becomes surrounded with a noisy shield which is strongly coupled by C_1 (or ΔC for balanced loads).

A more general model of this E-field screening is shown Fig. 7.24 where the impedance between the shield and the ground is in fact made of the shield termination (pigtail, solid wire, grounding pin, ctc.) plus the shield impedance Z_s. Since, except for dc fields, a current will flow on the shield, the product of this current by the total impedance $Z_s + Z_{gnd}$ will cause the shield to become increasingly noisy as we move away from its grounding point.

As long as the shield and its ground connection are still short with respect to the EMI wavelength, the amplitude of V_{sh} is generally small and tolerable. But if the worst case happens, i.e. the shield reaches $\lambda_{EMI}/4$ or an integer multiple, the shield impedance to ground looks infinite: the wiring in these regions is surrounded by a floated-like shield and the whole shield voltage is transferred into the inner circuit because C_1 and C_2 are quite large.

So, oversimplifying the model, we may say than when $l = \lambda/4$, a thin shield whose thickness is less than a skin depth has a quasi-null efficiency, or 0 dB. Going downward on a monotonic, $1/F$ slope, we may deduce that for $l = \lambda/40$, the same shield will start to offer an appreciable EMI decoupling of $1/10$, or -20 dB, and so on. Extending the discussion, it becomes obvious that grounding also at the other end, the middle or even at multiple points will parallel the grounding impedances and reduce the shield voltages.

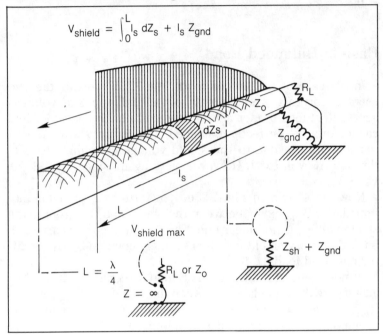

$$V_{shield} = \int_0^L I_s \, dZ_s + I_s Z_{gnd}$$

Figure 7.24—General Model of E-Field Screening

Indeed, if instead of focusing on the term **grounding,** we simply say that the other end of the shield is also connected to the box frame, the shield noise would decrease, and we would in addition achieve the overall shield integrity advocated in Figs. 7.19 and 7.20. Unfortunately, doing so may create another EMI problem, e.g. in a case for instance where the two boxes are grounded at a distance and a large ground potential difference exists. This mechanism will be explained in the next section, through the use of differential transfer impedance, a concept introduced by Mardiguian[6] and also DeGaucque.[7]

7.3.3 Quantifying the Ground Loop Contribution of the Shield Differential Transfer Impedance Z_{td}

In the absence of a shield, the existing ground loop cause some EMI induction and mode-conversion effects (GLC) which were briefly addressed in Section 6.4 of this book, and much more thoroughly in the *EMI Methodology and Procedures* handbook.[10] When a shield is added to the balanced cable, how does it interact with GLC? Does the shield render the two boxes equipotential, by shorting out the longitudinal CM voltage or does it, instead, aggravate the ground loop coupling? Looking at Fig. 7.25, we see that when a shield is added an additional path is offered for the common-mode current.

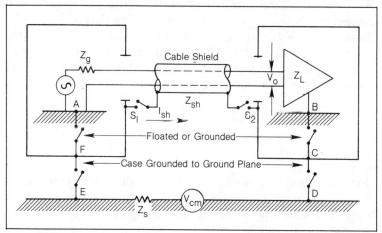

Figure 7.25—Cable Shield Interaction and Grounding Conditions

Since the ground plane source impedance Z_g is small compared to the shield external impedance Z_{sh}, it appears that the flow of I_{sh} does not influence the GLC factor which pre-existed before the introduction of the shield. I_{sh} is simply a new branch, draining a new current from the common-mode voltage V_{CM}, without reducing at all the currents already drained in the wire pair via the circuit loop ABCDEF. If either switch S_1 or S_2 is open, we are in the configuration of Section 7.3.3, i.e., a single-ended Faraday shield. V_i cannot virtually create any shield current I_{sh}, but the shield is only efficient against near E-fields, provided its length is much shorter than $\lambda_{EMI}/4$.

However, when S_1 and S_2 are both closed, the shield transfer impedance Z_t (see Section 7.2.1) causes an inner voltage V_i to appear inside the shield. This voltage V_i is equal to V_{CM} if all boxes are grounded and the shield is a thin layer, with no benefit of skin effect. It is less than V_{cm} if boxes are floated or if the boxes skin and shield skin are thick. If the cable was a coaxial, this noise V_i would appear directly in the signal return, a mechanism already addressed in Section 7.2.1 and Fig. 7.14. But since the circuit is balanced, an additional reduction is caused by the wire pair balance: only a fraction of V_i, proportional to the degree of pair symmetry, actually will show up as an undesired differential voltage V_o across the load. So, a more complex parameter is used, called Z_{td}, which is the differential transfer impedance such that:

$$Z_{td} = \frac{V_o}{I_{sh}} \qquad (7.6)$$

One sees that Z_{td} includes the cascading effects of Z_t, a characteristic of the shield material, and the pair percentage balance. Using typical values and measured results for both parameters, and since:

$$I_{sh} = \frac{Z_{sh}}{V_{CM}} \qquad (7.7)$$

we can derive a **shield coupling factor (SC)** such that:

$$SC = \frac{V_o}{V_{CM}} \qquad (7.8)$$

This will give a figure of merit of the shield contribution to the overall CM coupling. The smaller this coupling, the better.

Typical values of SC are shown in Fig. 7.26. For a better

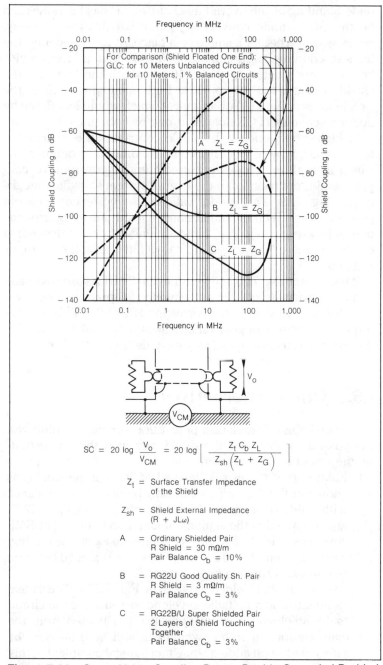

Figure 7.26—Ground-Loop Coupling Due to Double-Grounded Braided Shield

understanding of the overall mechanism, SC has been overlaid on the GLC (mode conversion) curve which exists anyway, regardless of whether a shield is in place. At any frequency, the highest coupling predominates. We see that at frequencies below a few megahertz (for a 10 m cable), the fact that the shield is connected to ground at both ends compromises the excellent isolation (100 dB or more) which would be offered by floating schemes (PCB floated at one or both ends).

At higher frequencies, the shield contribution is overridden by the GLC, which predominates. In addition, grounding the shield at both ends does not create any aggravation of coupling, and it contributes to the overall system shielding integrity per Fig. 7.19. This model validates, *a posteriori*, the old precept which recommended single-ended shielding grounds only at low frequency. The "low-frequency" frontier, depending on the source of the tradition, was defined as $\lambda/4$, or $\lambda/10$, or $\lambda/16$, etc.

If we look at Fig. 7.26 and assume that 2 MHz is approximately the crossover frequency below which SC predominates over GLC for a 10 m cable, this corresponds to $\lambda/15$. This number tracks the most stringent empirical findings but reveals that the most permissive ones ($\lambda/4$) were definitely too lax.

7.3.4 Other Alternatives

Provided some installation precautions or design additives, it is possible to decrease the shield current without interrupting the shield by several methods:

1. Float one of the boxes (instead of floating the shield) as shown in Fig. 7.27a. This can only be done in compliance with safety rules; that is, if no hazardous voltages (>42 V) are contained in the equipment and if no lightning or EMP concerns exist. If the latter concerns do exist, the method can still be employed if a surge arrestor is placed between the box and the conductive ground.

2. Use a double-shielded box as in Fig. 7.27b. The shield terminates on a metallic envelope surrounding the circuit to be shielded. This envelope itself is floated from the main equipment frame, which can still be grounded for safety. Although adding some mechanical complexity, this solution is used for high-accuracy, low-frequency instru-

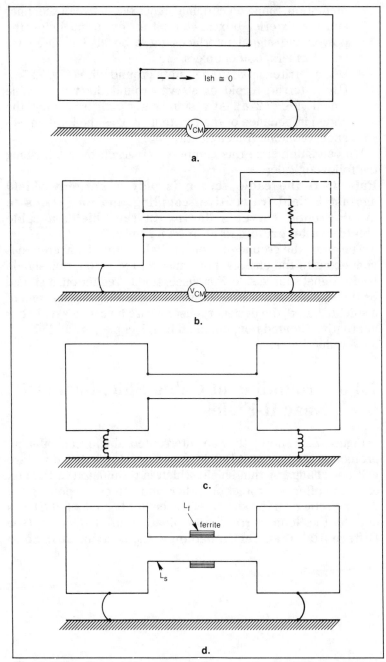

Figure 7.27—Several Alternatives to Decrease the Shield Current Without Interrupting the Shield

mentation. Since no coupling may exist between the inner and the exterior boxes, at least at low frequencies, the power and signal interfaces must be also isolated via transformers, optocouplers, etc.

3. Use a ferrite choke in the safety ground wire (Fig. 7.27c).
4. Use a ferrite toroid or sleeve around the whole cable shield (Fig. 7.27d). At a sufficiently high frequency, the added impedance of the ferrite increases the loop impedance, reducing the circulation of I_{sh}.

We can summarize this complex paragraph by establishing the following rule:

Rule 4: If the cable screen is only a Faraday shield against E-field (capacitive) coupling and one wants to avoid ground currents flowing in the shield, a cable shield can be grounded at one end only.

The end to be grounded is the one where the signal ground is connected to the chassis. For emission reduction, this should be the signal source side. For susceptibility reduction, it should be the signal receiver side. However, before leaving one end of a shield floated, the designer must be sure he can use no better alternative (floated box, double box, RF choke, ground impedance reduction, etc.).

7.3.5 Grounding of Cable Shield against Near H-Fields

Figure 7.28 shows that an interrupted shield can offer no protection at all against H-fields since the loop induced voltage will not change. A thin shield which is terminated at the box ends can offer no protection either, and can even spoil a good floating scheme if the signal reference has been floated. This is due to the loop current now floating in the shield (see **Differential Transfer Impedance Z_{td}**, Section 7.3.3). So to be efficient against magnetic coupling, a shield must be made of thick material, preferably ferrous or highly permeable, bonded by clamps or connectors to the equipment box at both ends.

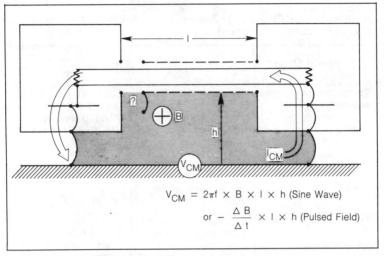

Figure 7.28—Cable Shield against Magnetic Induction

7.3.6 Recapitulation of Shield Termination Rules for Balanced Cables

Table 7.2 summarizes as simply as possible the cable shield grounding rules. Since it is supported by the math model and experiments of Section 7.3.3, the λ/16 border line has been retained as a rule of thumb.

**Table 7.2—Cable Shield Grounding Decision
(for Other Than Coaxial Lines)**

Options Available:
- Shield Grounding: Neither End, Receiver End, Transmitter End, Both Ends:
- Shield Termination: Use Pigtail (Inexpensive, Practical) or 360° Bulkhead (Expensive)
- Shield Material Choice: High Z_t (Inexpensive, Flexible, Light) or low Z_t (Can Be Costly, Rigid, Heavy)

Purpose of Shield	$L \leqslant \dfrac{\lambda_{EMI}}{16}$	$L > \dfrac{\lambda_{EMI}}{16}$
To reduce susceptibility? (EMI is outside the shield)	Electrically Short Shield. System should be a single point ground (STAR), with preferably 0 volt-to-chassis connection at Receiver side. Ground cable shield at this point. Ordinary braid and short pigtail are acceptable.	Electrically Long Shield. Ground both ends of shield to chassis. Use low Z_t shield and integral clamp. **No pigtails.**
To reduce emission? (EMI Source is Inside the Shield)	Electrically Short Shield. System should be a single point ground (STAR), with preferably 0 volt-to-chassis node at transmitting side. Ground cable shield at this point. Ordinary braid and short pigtail are acceptable.	Electrically Long Shield. Ground both ends of shield to chassis. Use low Z_t shield and Integral clamp. **No pigtails.**

7.3.7 Selective Grounding

Since cable shield grounding philosophy should fit the overall system grounding scheme (single point, multipoint, hybrid) used in the particular equipment of interest (see Chapter 8), situations may arise where the cable meets both the $< \lambda 16$ and $> \lambda/16$ conditions. An example is the case of a cable having to withstand a severe EMI ambient from VLF to UHF. A possible means on reconciling the two contradictory rules is to have the floated end of the shield grounded through a capacitor. In this way, it will be effectively grounded at high frequencies but shield current will flow at low frequencies (see Fig. 7.29). This solution is rather attractive and quite often employed.

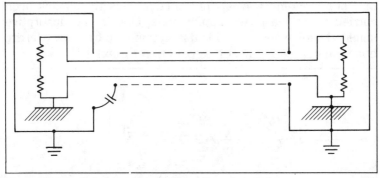

Figure 7.29—Selective Shield Grounding

However, a problem may arise due to the discrete capacitor lead length and the shield self-inductance. There will be a discrete frequency where a sharp resonance due to the series L, C arrangement will occur. If unfortunately (Murphy's law) the EMI threat or one of its harmonics happens to be at that very frequency, a peak of shield current will result, limited only by the shield resistance. One way to avoid this would be to create a selective shield grounding via an noninductive, lossy capacitive adaptor made of a tubular dielectric sleeve teamed with a lossy ferrite. This arrangement is illustrated in Fig. 7.30. Although this author's suggestion has yet to be manufactured, it could be an answer to cable shield termination dilemmas when ground loops are anticipated.

Looking back at Fig. 7.8 we see that, basically, Circuit 2 is the preferred one while in Circuit 1 unwanted energy is transferred, either from the outside (susceptibility) or from Circuit 2 (emission). Given the principle that energy can only be transferred to another place or transformed into another form of energy, if the unwanted electrical energy in Circuit 1 could be changed into heat, the radiation problem would be greatly reduced. Recognizing that the Circuit 1 will always behave as a mismatched line, voltage and current peaks will occur at multiples of $\lambda/4$ or $\lambda/2$, depending on whether the shield is grounded at one end or both ends. We see that none of the grounding schemes is really ideal for wasting energy in the form of heat, due to the mostly reactive nature of Circuit 1.

If, instead, Circuit 1 could be terminated into resistances equal to its characteristic impedance, the shield above ground would behave as a purely resistive circuit and no peaking of V or I nor standing waves would occur. This theory has been carried to at least two applications. One is the absorptive shielded cable where the shield is surrounded by a lossy ferrite compound, creating heat dissipation in Circuit 1.[12]

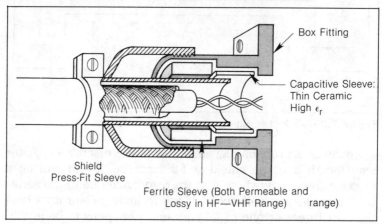

Figure 7.30—Author's Suggestion for a Nonresonant, Selective Shield Grounding Adaptor

The other is described in Ref. 8 and seen in Fig. 7.31. Here, the benefit of an "adapted" ground is seen with the 300 Ω grounded case. The benefit of low-frequency floating is preserved, and there is less peaking of the ground-loop resonance at 10 MHz. Knowing that the characteristic impedance of a cable shield above ground is in the hundreds of ohms range, the experiment shows that when the shield termination structure is "grounded" via 300 Ω resistors, a definite advantage exists which appears as a smoothing of the induced peaks.

7.3.8 Multiple Shield Cables

Adding a second insulated braid or foil over the first shield adds a second pole in the capacitive divider effect of the Faraday shield. It also reduces the effect of the noisy floated end in the case of single side grounding, since at each end the pairs are surrounded by at least one perfectly grounded shield (see Fig. 7.32).

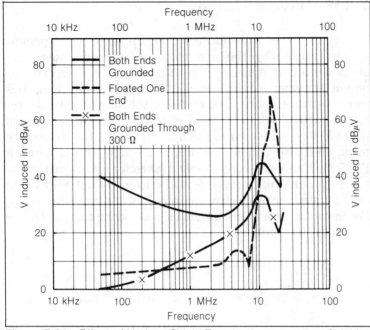

Figure 7.31—Effect of Various Shield Terminations on a 5 m Shielded Cable, with an H-Field Radiator 30 cm along the Wire

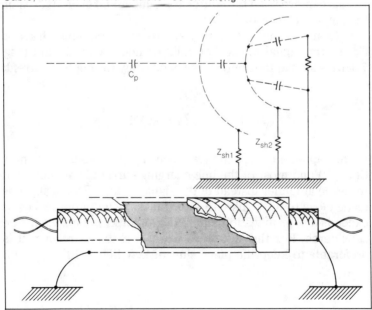

Figure 7.32—Double Shield over a Wire Pair

7.3.9 Driven Shields

With low-level transducers or an op amp, the capacitive loading caused by the wire-pair-to-shield capacitance may affect the output dynamic performance or may even drive the output amplifier into overload or destruction. To avoid this, some instrumentation or transducer schemes use the **driven shield** method where, instead of being tied to signal ground, the shield is connected to the upgoing signal. In this arrangement, no charge can flow during a transition. This is shown in Fig. 7.33. Without the driven shield (sketch a), the signal source has to provide not only the load current I_d but also I_c, the capacitive current to charge the wire-to-shield capacitance $C_{1\text{-}2}$. For instance, with a time-varying signal having a slope dV/dt = 1 V/μs, let us assume:

$$C_{1\text{-}2} = 100 \text{ pF/m}$$
$$\text{Length} = 10 \text{ m}$$
$$I_c = CdV/dt = 10^{-9} \text{ F} \times 1/10^{-6} = 1 \text{ mA}$$

This can overload the source transducer and eventually spoil the signal acquisition speed.

With an intermediate shield #3, driven by tapping a fraction "k" of the signal v, the potential of node A to ground (Fig. 7.33b) is kv and the source now needs only to supply a current:

$$I_c = C_{3\text{-}1} (v - kv)/dt$$

The apparent capacitance seen by the source is now $C(1 - k)$ and most of the line charging current is now drained from the amplifier instead of the signal source. Practically, k is made close to unity, like 0.8 or 0.9. If the length approaches or exceeds $\lambda/4$, propagation and reflection of kv versus v must be considered. For the system to work in a stable manner, it is preferable to keep the place shift of kv/v below 10°.

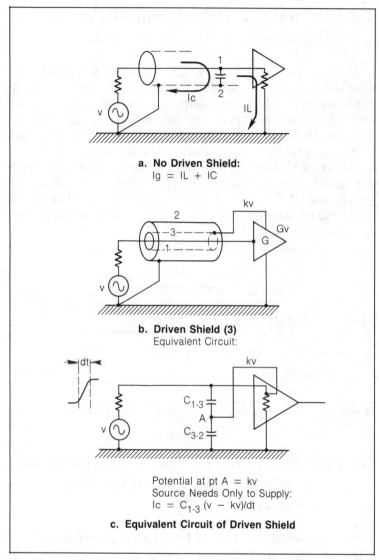

a. No Driven Shield:
$Ig = IL + IC$

b. Driven Shield (3)
Equivalent Circuit:

Potential at pt A $= kv$
Source Needs Only to Supply:
$Ic = C_{1\text{-}3} (v - kv)/dt$

c. Equivalent Circuit of Driven Shield

Figure 7.33—The Driven Shield

7.3.10 Dual Coaxial (Pseudo-Differential Line)

At the expense of some additional hardware, a balanced shielded pair can be replaced by a set of two coaxial cables. Each center conductor becomes one wire of the pair, while both shields are tied to the chassis ground. In this way, the shield of each coax is no longer a signal return. The advantage of this method is that the geometrical accuracy of a coaxial cable is much better than that of a shielded twisted pair which has an inherent eccentricity by construction. Therefore, the percentage of symmetry and characteristic impedance of a dual coaxial arrangement can be much better at higher frequencies (see Fig. 7.34).

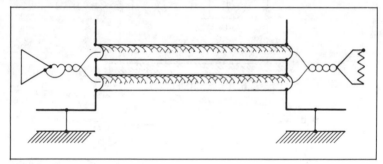

Figure 7.34—The Double-Coax, Pseudo-Balanced Line

7.3.11 Importance of Shield Termination Hardware and Impedance vs. Frequency

With the exclusion of coaxial shields (discussed in Section 7.2) where the shield must be fitted in the coaxial connector shell as part of the transmission line, the following methods exist for termination of balanced cable shields:
1. Terminating jumpers or drain wires and lugs (Fig. 7.35)
2. Terminating jumpers or drain wires and the use of some connector pins as shield/ground carriers (Fig. 7.36)

3. Shield formed in a pigtail and attached to a ground pin or tab (Fig. 7.37)
4. Halo ring or interlacing strap (Fig. 7.38)
5. 360° crimped clamp and flat strap (Fig. 7.39)
6. Integral clamps at connector strain reliever (Fig. 7.40)
7. Clamp at box penetration (Fig. 7.41)

Methods 1 through 3 imply the use of some length of discrete wire whose self-inductance seriously impairs the shield efficiency when frequency increases. This is explained in Sections 7.1.2 and 7.3.2. In addition, this piece of discrete wire can couple strongly with the wire pairs which, in just this area, are stripped from the shield protection. And, finally, when this piece of wire becomes a non-negligible fraction of EMI wavelength (like $\lambda/12$ or less as explained in Section 2.1) it acts as a radiating or pickup element.

Good practices, learned from experience and tradition, dictate that pigtails and jumpers are adequate for low frequencies but should not be used at high frequencies. However, the border line between "low" and "high" is often defined ambiguously if at all. For instance, the $\lambda/12$ criteria we indicated as causing a grounding jumper to be 10 times less efficient than a 1/4 wave monopole may be far too lenient for a shield termination as it would allow a shield to be terminated by a 2.50 m wire against a 10 MHz EMI! Therefore a better rationale is needed, which is:

Rule 5: Given a certain objective of shielding effectiveness (SE), a shielded cable is selected with a shield of equal or better performance. Then, knowing that the termination will always combine with the shield SE in a destructive manner, a termination method will be selected such that its contribution to the overall shield leakage is tolerable.

For instance, if a cable shield has an intrinsic performance of -40 dB (1 percent of coupling) at a given frequency, considering the principle of superposition, the jumper alone should not cause more than -60 dB (0.1 percent of coupling) to meet the initial objective. Actually, in this example, the overall result will be -39.1 dB (1.1 percent).

Cable Shield Grounding

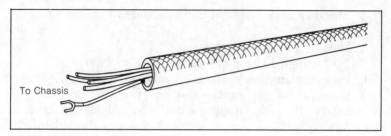

Figure 7.35—Jumper and Lug

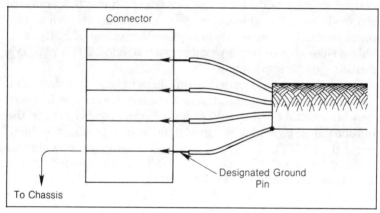

Figure 7.36—Jumper and Connector Pin

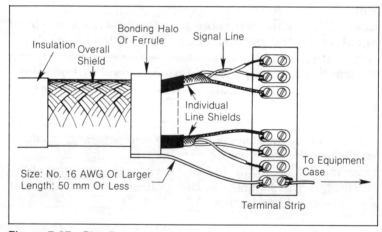

Figure 7.37—Pigtails

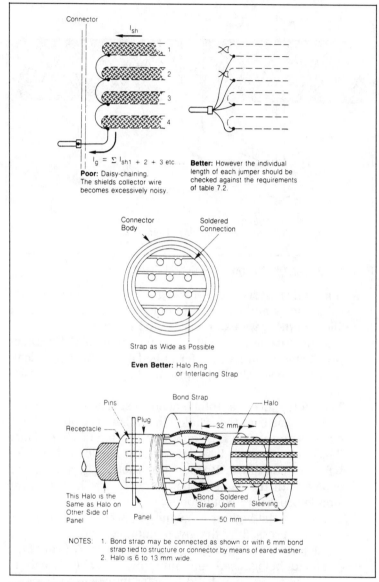

Figure 7.38—Halo Ring Concept

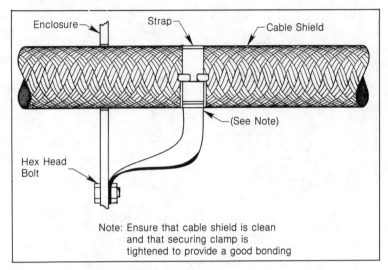

Figure 7.39—360° Crimped Clamp and Flat Strap

A thorough analysis of the shield grounding jumper coupling is feasible but would exceed the objective of this book. As a simplified method, we can consider the following:

1. The effectiveness of a shield from dc to upper VHF can be predicated from its transfer impedance Z_t which, at least for single-layer shields, approximately tracks its dc resistance.

2. Therefore, given a total shield resistance R_s, we can deduce that if in the whole Ohm's Law region of the Z_t curves (up to 100 kHz) the grounding jumper impedance Z_{gnd} does not exceed 0.1 times R_s, the shield performance will be maintained. Beyond this, both Z_{gnd} and Z_t will evolve with the same slope. Since $Z_{gnd} = R + jL\omega$, the simple procedure would be to:

   a. Identify the highest frequency F_x where EMI needs to be suppressed by the given amount.

   b. Identify the nominal transfer impedance Z_t Ω/m of the shield being used and multiply by cable length to obtain the whole shield transfer impedance ($Z_t \times l$).

7.50

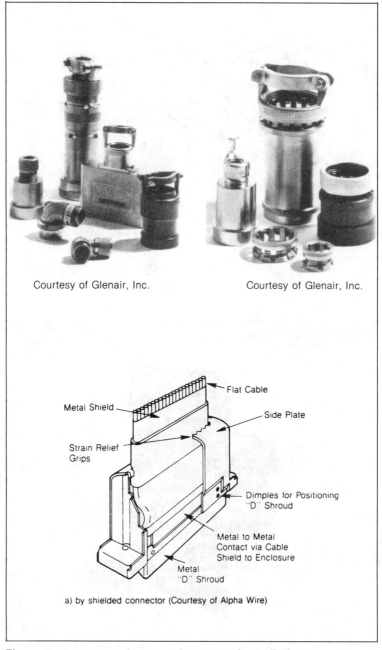

Courtesy of Glenair, Inc.   Courtesy of Glenair, Inc.

a) by shielded connector (Courtesy of Alpha Wire)

Figure 7.40—Integral Clamp at Connector Strain Reliever

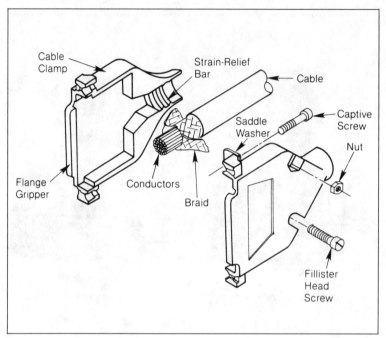

Figure 7.40—(continued)

Figure 7.41—Integral Clamp at Box Penetration (continued next page)

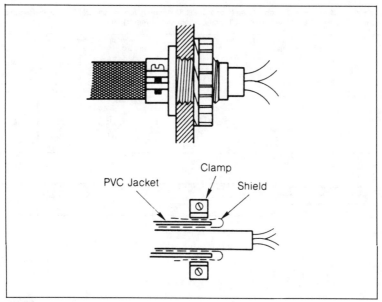

Figure 7.41—(continued)

    c. Find the jumper length whose impedance at frequency F_x does not exceed $0.1 \times Z_t \times 1$. This can be found from Table 2.2 or calculated from Eq. (2.12B).

To determine quickly the maximum permissible jumper length, Table 7.3 has been compiled. For instance, if one uses 10 m of a mediocre shielded cable (microphone cable type) with modest performance features against a 100 kHz EMI threat, up to 7.5 cm of jumper length can be tolerated without performance degradation.

But if an excellent shielding is needed and a cable with a shield resistance of only 5 mΩ/m is used, only a 0.75 cm pigtail is permitted at 100 kHz. Above this frequency no jumper termination at all can be used since the short length requirement would be impractical. Integral clamp or bonding will be used instead. Note that when cable length increases, jumper length requirements are relaxed since the shielding effectiveness of the cable decreases.

Table 7.3—Maximum Acceptable Length for a Shield Grounding Jumper vs. EMI Frequency Range and Type/Length of Shielded Cable (AWG 16, or 1.3 mm Dia. Jumper)

Cable Shield dc Resistance		Total Cable Length	SE Range Defined At < 100 kHz	Max. Length of Tolerable Pigtail at Highest EMI Frequency of:				
				1 kHz	10 kHz	100 kHz	1 MHz	10 MHz
Poor	50 mΩ/m	1 m	60 dB	15 cm	7.5 cm	0.75 cm		
		10 m	40 dB	1.50 m	75 cm	7.5 cm	0.75 cm	
		100 m	20 dB	no limit	7.50 m	75 cm	7.5 cm	0.75 cm
Good	16 mΩ/m	1 m	70 dB	5 cm	2.5 cm			
		10 m	50 dB	50 cm	25 cm	2.5 cm		
		100 m	30 dB	no limit	2.50 m	25 cm	2.5 cm	
Excellent	5 mΩ/m	1 m	80 dB	1.5 cm	0.75 cm			
		10 m	60 dB	15 cm	7.5 cm	0.75 cm		
		100 m	40 dB	1.50 m	75 cm	7.5 cm	0.75 cm	

L_{cm}

7.3.12 Low-Frequency Shield Grounding

In the **low-frequency** domain of a shield, as previously defined, shield termination methods by filar terminations as shown in Figs. 7.35 through 7.38 are acceptable. When the cable is a multipair cable with each pair having its own shield, all individual shields of low-frequency signal lines within a cable bundle must be insulated from each other to minimize cross-coupling.

Further, if the multipair cable has an overall shield over each individual shielded pair, this arrangement allows us to keep different ends of the individual shields floated. This follows the Faraday shield criteria of Section 7.3.2, as illuminated by Rule 4 and Table 7.2 and yet keeps an uninterrupted shield barrier on top of the whole system. In this case, individual shields must be isolated from the overall bundle shield, equipment chassis and enclosures, junction boxes, conduit, cable trays and all other elements of the facility ground system. When cables are long, extra attention must be directed toward maintaining the isolation of the individual shields at the ungrounded end and at all intermediate connectors throughout the cable run. The inner shields (mainly crosstalk shields) are grounded at either the receiver or driver end according to Table 7.2.

Shields of individual low-frequency signal lines at terminating equipment may be carried into the case or cabinet on separate pins, or they may be tied together to be carried in (or out) via a common connector pin, depending upon the characteristics of the equipment involved. If the common pin arrangement is used, it must not compromise the single-point grounding principle.

It is advisable to use one pin for low-level signal shields and a different pin for high-level signal lines. These individual shields should be terminated to the low-frequency signal ground network. Where shield pigtails must be used, the pigtail between the shield breakout and the connector pin should be as short as practical.

Each time a connector pin is used for a shield termination, care must be paid not to re-create a ground loop by improper pin assignment. Any shield-collecting pin is a potential noise carrier. For instance, it is definitely unwise to use a signal return (0 V or other) pin as a shield collector. This would inject shield noise in series into the signal return at a point which is likely to become a hot spot since a connector pin is an inductive and resistive part. At the end, the shielded pin will connect to the signal reference plane in the PCB or otherwise, and this connection is harmless (single point). However, sharing the same pin would create common impedance coupling.

Some of the individually shielded signal lines in multiconductor cables will be grounded at one end while other shields will be grounded at the other end. Careful attention must be given to the installation of such cables to prevent grounding of shields at both ends. Multiconductor cables which contain unshielded or individually shielded wires, or both, frequently have an overall shield provided for both physical protection and to provide supplemental electromagnetic shielding. Such overall shields should be connected to the equipment frame at each end of the cable run to provide a continuous RF shield with no breaks. On long cable runs where the cable is routed through one or more intermediate connectors, the overall shield should be grounded to the frame or case of junction boxes, patch panels and distribution boxes along the cable run (Fig. 7.42).

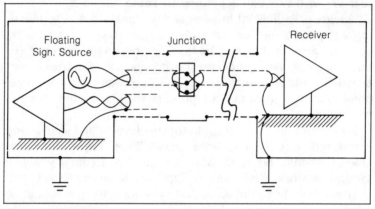

Figure 7.42—Connection of Overall Shield and Internal Shields with Low-Frequency (Audio or Analog) Links

For maximum shielding effectiveness, the overall shield should be effectively bonded with a low-impedance connection to the equipment case, enclosure wall or other penetrated (metal) shield as shown in Figs. 7.39 through 7.41. The best way to bond the overall shield to a connector is to run the shield wall inside of the connector shell and provide clean metal-to-metal circumferential contact between the shield and the shell. If the connector is not involved, the shortest practical lengths of connecting strap or jumper should be used. Where the overall shield terminates on a terminal strip, it may be grounded as shown in Fig. 7.37, but this is a low-frequency practice only.

7.3.13 High-Frequency Shield Grounding

High frequency situations, as defined on the right-hand side of Table 7.2, correspond to more than a few megahertz for typical installations. Here, no jumper or pigtail method can be acceptable, and direct bonding methods are required or the justification of the shield becomes questionable. Therefore methods shown in Figs. 7.39 through 7.41 are mandatory. The method of Fig. 7.38 is still acceptable if the halo ring has a direct, circular spring contact with the metallic connector shell.

The term **high-frequency domain,** referred to Table 7.2, applies not only to discrete frequencies but to the upper boundary of the frequency spectrum in cases of impulsive noise. Consider, for instance, the case of electrostatic discharge (ESD). The spectrum of a typical personal ESD, with a few nanoseconds rise time, extends up to several hundred MHz. This is a case where shield termination by jumpers is sure to fail.

7.3.14 Cable Shield Grounding with Lightning and EMP Threats

With lightning and EMP we must consider an additional parameter, which is the intense current which must be carried by the shield termination. Lightning creates shield currents from few hundred amperes in the case of nearby induction to several tens of kiloamperes for a direct hit on an overhead or slightly buried outdoor shielded cable. Rates of rise are in the 10 kA/μs range. The shield termination method must carry this current pulse without overheating, damage or excessive elevation of potential. A 1 m grounding jumper would represent 1 μH of inductance and, for 10 kA/μs would cause the "grounded" end of the shield to rise to:

$$\frac{10^4 \text{ A}}{10^{-6} \text{ s}} \times 10^{-6} \text{ H} = 10,000 \text{ V}$$

The case of EMP is similar except that rise times are in the 10 ns range. Therefore, in both cases calculations and tests must be carried out to verify that the shield termination at building, shelter or equipment entry is adequate.

7.4 References

1. Schelkunof, S.A., "Electro Magnetic Theory of Coaxial lines and Cylindrical Shields," (*Bell Systems Technical Journal*, Vol. 13, 1934).
2. Vance, E.F., *Coupling to Cable Shields*, (New York: John Wiley & Sons, 1978).
3. Ott, H.W., *Noise Reduction Techniques*, (New York: John Wiley & Sons, 1976).
4. Ott, H.W., "Ground: A Path for Current Flow," (*EMC Technology*, Jan., 1983)
5. Martin, A., "Introduction to Surface Transfer Impedance," (*EMC Technology*, July, 1982).
6. Mardiguian, M., "Transfer Impedance of Balanced Shielded Cables," (*EMC Technology*, July, 1982).
7. De Gaucque, P., "Tensions Induites sur un Cable Bifilaire Blindé," (*Colloque EMC*, Tregastel, France 1983).
8. Givord., A., "Cablage des Masses et des Ecrans dans les Centres Hertziens," (*Colloque EMC*, Tregastel, France 1983).
9. Smith, A.A., *Coupling of External EM Fields to Transmission Lines*, (Gainesville, Va.: Interference Control Technologies, 1986).
10. White, D.R.J., and Mardiguian, M., *EMI Control Methodology & Procedures*, (Gainesville, Va.: Interference Control Technologies, 1985).
11. Morrison, R., *Grounding and Shielding Techniques in Instrumentation*, (New York: John Wiley & Sons, 1977).
12. Meyer, F., "Absorptive Low-Pass Cables," (*IEEE EMC Transactions*, Feb., 1986).

Chapter 8

Equipment and System Grounding

An electronic equipment is fundamentally a collection of electronic circuits. These various circuits are basically interconnected source-load pairs. All of the active electrical and electronic circuits in a piece of equipment can be reduced to some combination (ranging from very simple to very complex) of sources and loads and their conductor paths.

The purpose of grounding within equipment is to realize the signal, power and electrical safety paths necessary for effective performance. Grounding from the EMI standpoint can be viewed as (1) realization of these functions without introducing excessive common-mode noise, and (2) establishment of a path to divert interference energy existing on external conductors, or present in the environment, away from susceptible circuits or components. **Equipment grounding** simply means the application of the principles and techniques at the equipment and circuit level that were set forth in the preceding chapters. Many grounding paths at the device and circuit level are extremely short, and grounding therefore often becomes synonymous with bonding, the subject of Chapter 3.

In some cases, various grounding philosophies or constraints within the same equipment or system are incompatible, and a tradeoff has to be made. This chapter explains the various techniques, their limitations and the rules for their selection.

8.1 Missions of Grounding at Equipment and System Levels

The grounding scheme inside a system must perform the following missions:

1. Analog, low-level and low-frequency circuits must have extremely noiseless dedicated returns. Due to the low frequencies involved, wires are generally used (more or less dictating a star ground system).

2. Analog high-frequency circuits (radio, video, etc.) must have low-impedance, noise-free return circuits, generally in form of planes or their extensions, i.e., coaxial cables.

3. Returns of logic circuits, especially high-speed logic, must have low enough impedances over the whole bandwidth (dictated by the fastest rises times) since power and signal returns share the same paths.

4. Returns of powerful loads (solenoids, motors, lamps, etc.) should be distinct from any of the above, even though they may end up in the same terminal of the power supply regulator.

5. Return paths to chassis of cable shields, transformer shields, filters, etc. must not interfere with functional returns.

6. When the electrical reference is distinct from the chassis ground, provision and accessibility must exist to connect and disconnect one from the other.

7. More generally, for signals which communicate within the equipment or between parts of a system, the grounding scheme must provide a common reference with minimum ground shift (unless, of course, these links are balanced, optically isolated, etc.). **Minimum ground shift means that the common-mode voltage must stay below the sensitivity threshold of the most susceptible device in the link.**

All the above constraints can be accommodated if their functional returns and protective grounds are integrated into a grounding system hierarchy as shown in Fig. 8.1. The application of this concept is the subject of the following sections.

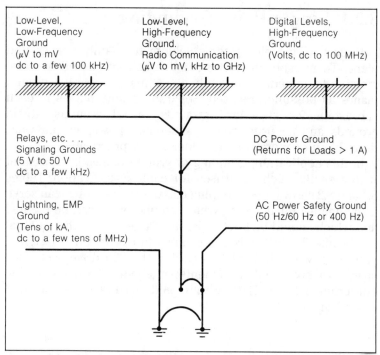

Figure 8.1—Grounding Hierarchy

8.2 Single vs. Multipoint Grounding

This section reviews the often controversial topic of whether equipments of subsystems should be grounded to a reference at one point or whether multipoint grounding should be used. The matter of hybrid grounds is also reviewed. It will be shown that all systems are continuations of each other at higher frequencies, but that certain correct practices should be followed. Conversely, the grounding scheme at lower frequencies is more clearly defined regarding correct and incorrect techniques.

8.2.1 Single-Point Grounding

Modern electronic systems seldom have only one ground plane. To mitigate interference such as that caused by common-mode impedance coupling, as many separate ground planes as possible are used. Separate ground planes in each subsystem for structural grounds, signal grounds, shield grounds and ac primary and secondary power grounds are desirable if economically and logistically practical.

In this application, grouping of ground planes is consistent with a similar technique used for cable classification. Tables 8.1 and 8.2 show cable grouping classifications which can serve as guidelines for deciding which ground paths can be merged and which should be kept separate. Table 8.1 is rather qualitative, while Table 8.2 is more quantitative. In the latter, the groupings were derived by dividing the 200 dB power level span into six equal increments of about 30 dB each. The borderline between EMI **culprits** and **victims** is set at around −20 dBm.

**Table 8.1—Qualitative Cable Grouping Classifications
(from AFSC Design Handbook)**

Class	Identification	Voltage Current or Power	Frequency
I	DC Power Circuit DC Control Circuit	> 2 A < 2 A	0 0
II	DC Reference Circuit AF Susceptible Circuits	< 1 V or < 0.2 A	0
III & IV	AC Power Circuits AC Reference Circuits AF Source Circuits	> 1 V or > 0.2 A > 0.2 A	< 400 Hz < 400 Hz < 15 kHz
V	RF Susceptible Circuits		
VI	EMI Source Circuits	> − 45 to − 75 dBm > − 75 dBm > − 75 to − 45 dBm > − 45 dBm	.15 to 5 MHz 5 to 25 MHz 025 to 1 GHz > 1 GHz
VII	Antenna Circuits		

Table 8.2—Quantitative Cable Grouping Classifications

Class	Power Range	Identification
A	> 40 dBm	High-Power dc/ac and RF Sources
B	+ 10 to + 40 dBm	Low-Power dc/ac and RF Sources
C	− 20 to + 10 dBm	Pulse and Digital Sources Video Output Circuits
D	− 50 to − 20 dBm	Audio and Sensor Susceptible Circuits Video Input Circuits
E	− 80 to − 50 dBm	RF and IF Input Circuits Safety Circuits
F	< − 80 dBm	Antenna and RF Circuits

These individual ground planes from each subsystem are finally connected by the shortest route back to the system ground point where they form an overall system potential reference. This method is known as a single-point ground and is illustrated in Fig. 8.2.

The single-point or star type of grounding scheme shown in the figure avoids problems of common-mode impedance coupling discussed in Chapter 6. The only common path is in the earth ground (for the earth-based structures), but this usually consists of a substantial conductor of very low impedance. Thus, as long as zero or low ground currents flow in any low-impedance common paths, all subsystems and equipments are maintained at essentially the same reference potential.

The problem with implementing the above single-point grounding scheme comes about (1) when interconnecting cables are used, especially ones having cable shields which have sources and receptors operating over lengths, l, above about λ/20, and (2) when parasitic capacitance exists between subsystem or equipment housings or between subsystems and the grounds of other subsystems. This situation is illustrated in Fig. 8.3. Here cable shields connect some of the subsystems together so a ground point exists. Unless certain precautions are taken, common-impedance ground currents could flow. At high frequencies, the parasitic capacitive reactance represents low-impedance paths, and the bond inductance of a subsystem-to-ground point results in higher impedances. Thus, again common-mode currents may flow or unequal potentials may develop among subsystems.

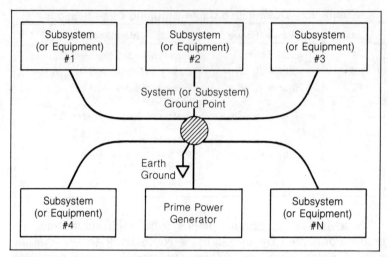

Figure 8.2—Single-Point or Star Grounding Arrangement

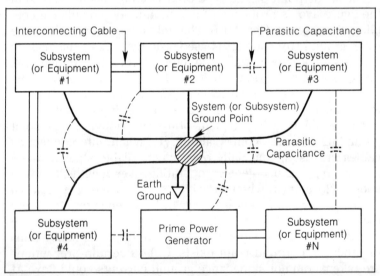

Figure 8.3—Degeneration of Single-Point Ground of Fig. 8.2 by Interconnecting Cables and Parasitic Capacitance

8.2.2 Multipoint Grounding

Supporters of the multipoint grounding concept argue that, pragmatically, the situation shown in Fig. 8.3 exists in any case, rather than that of the ideal single-point ground shown in Fig. 8.2. To eliminate the uncontrolled situation as shown in Fig. 8.3, they suggest heavily bonding everything to a solid ground conducting plane to form a homogeneous, low-impedance path, thereby minimizing common-mode voltages and other EMI problems. An example of such a situation is shown in Fig. 8.4, where each subsystem or equipment is bonded as directly as possible to a common low-impedance **equipotential** ground plane. The ground plane then is earthed for safety purposes.

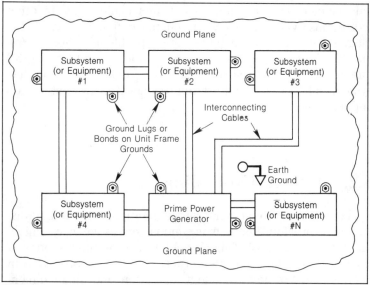

Figure 8.4—Multipoint Grounding System

The facts are that a single-point grounding scheme operates better at low frequencies and a multipoint ground behaves best at high frequencies. If the overall system, for example, is a network of audio equipment with many low-level sensors and control circuits behaving as broadband transient noise sources, then the high-frequency performance is irrelevant* since no receptor responds above audio frequencies. Conversely, if the overall system were a receiver complex of 30 MHz to 1,000 MHz tuners, amplifiers, and displays, then low-level, low-frequency performance is irrelevant. Here multipoint grounding applies, and interconnecting, unbalanced coaxial lines are used.

The above dichotomy of audio versus VHF/UHF systems makes clear the selection of the correct approach. The problem then narrows down to one in defining where low- and high-frequency crossover exists for any given subsystem or equipment. The answer here partly involves the highest significant operating frequency of low-level circuits relative to the physical distance between the most distant equipments. In other words, this twilight crossover frequency region involves (1) the magnetic versus electric field coupling problems of Section 6.4, and (2) the ground-plane impedance couplings of Section 6.2 due to separation. Hybrid single and multipoint grounding systems are often the best approaches for twilight region applications.

8.2.3 Hybrid Grounding

The matter of single-point versus multipoint grounding discussed in previous sections is summarized as a general guideline model in Fig. 8.5. This model is based on the relations of Eq. (2.19) and the separation criteria of $l = \lambda/20$ presented in Section 2.4. For low-frequency operation and small dimensions, use single-point grounding. For transitional situations, one or the other may perform better as shown in the figure. Hybrid grounds perform best where portions of the low-frequency systems use single-point grounding while high-frequency portions use multipoint grounding, with all connected in a ground-tree fashion.

---

*Assuming no HF spurious or parasitic responses, which is not always the case.

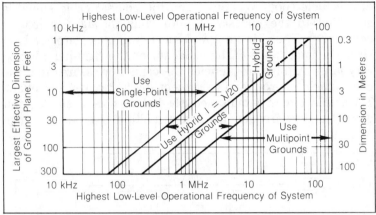

Figure 8.5—Crossover Regions of Single-Point vs. Multipoint Grounding

Mathematical modeling and predicting the general EMI which results from grounding is extremely difficult to accomplish for anything but relatively simple system configurations and single-point grounding schemes. The number of significant parasitic reactances in complex systems or at HF levels and above render modeling of a grounding situation very complex. Accordingly, the following prediction guidelines are used:

1. For low-frequency ($l \leq \lambda/20$), single-point grounds, employ the ground-impedance and common-mode impedance techniques discussed in Sections 6.2 and 6.3.
2. Use cable coupling models for all equipment cables.
3. Use case penetration and leakage models between all applicable shielding boxes, equipments and subsystems.

The term **hybrid grounds** is sometimes used in two somewhat different senses: (1) when a grounding scheme either appears as a single-point ground at low frequencies and a multipoint ground at high frequencies, or appears different at both frequencies, and (2) when a system grounding configuration employs both single-point and multipoint grounds. Each of these is discussed below.

Figure 8.6 shows a low-level video circuit in which both the sensor and driven circuit chassis must be grounded to the skin of a vehicle (not by choice) and the coaxial cable shield is grounded to the chassis at both ends through its mating connectors. There is no low-frequency ground current loop since the impedance of the capacitor on the right-hand box is very large. At high frequencies the capacitor assures that the cable shield is grounded to protect the Faraday-shield effect. Thus, this circuit simultaneously behaves as a single-point ground at low frequencies and a multipoint ground at high frequencies.

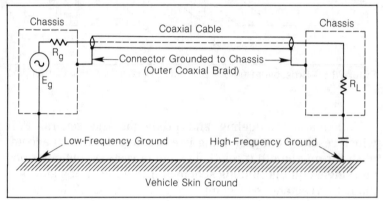

Figure 8.6—Low-Frequency Ground Current Loop Avoidance with a High-Frequency Ground

A different kind of an example is shown in Fig. 8.7 in which all the computer and peripheral frames must be grounded to the power system green wire for safety purposes (shock-hazard protection) pursuant to the National Electrical Code. Since it is recognized that the green wire generally contains significant electrical noise trash, this code conflicts with the desire to float the computer system ground from the noisy green wire ground. Thus, one or more isolation coils of about 100 μH value are used to provide a low-impedance (less than 0.1 Ω) safety ground at ac power line frequencies and RF isolation (on the order of kilohms) in the 50 kHz to a few megahertz spectrum. This corresponds to the typical bandwidth of slowest serial or parallel interfaces. This inductor helps keep induced transient and EMI noise in the green wire off the computer logic busses.

8.10

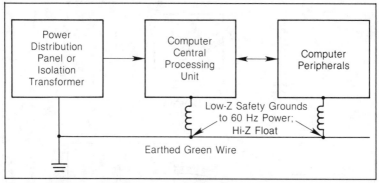

Figure 8.7—Safety Ground with High-Frequency Isolation

8.3 Grounding Requirements According to Size and Function

The term **system** encompasses whatever the user wishes. For example, a system may represent a small, self-contained electronic circuit totally within the confines of an equipment rack, or it may refer to many consoles distributed over a wide geographical area. (The grounding requirements and procedures will be markedly different for the two different types of systems).

One way of distinguishing between different types of systems to select the proper grounding scheme is to examine the manner by which power is obtained and how the equipment elements are interconnected with each other and with other systems. Based on these two considerations, H. Denny, the author of several works mentioned in this book, divides system grounding into several classifications:

1. Isolated
2. Clustered
3. Distributed
4. Multiple-distributed
5. Central with extensions

All five are illustrated in Fig. 8.8, parts a through e. The properties of these types and the associated grounding requirements are presented in the following sections.

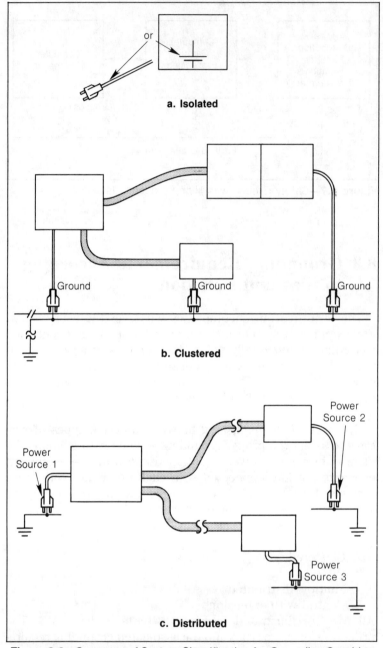

a. Isolated

b. Clustered

c. Distributed

Figure 8.8—Summary of System Classification for Grounding Considerations (continued next page)

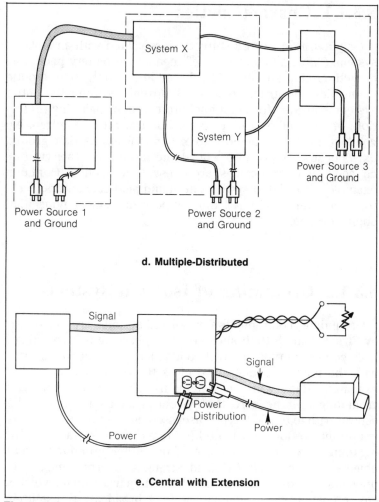

d. **Multiple-Distributed**

e. **Central with Extension**

Figure 8.8—(continued)

8.3.1 Isolated System

An isolated* system is one in which all functions are accomplished with one equipment enclosure. In a sense, it is a stand-alone or self-sufficient system.

---

*An isolated system should not be confused with a floating system which has no external ground. Some isolated systems may be floating, but others must be grounded.

8.3.1.1 Characteristics

Only a **single power source** is associated with an isolated system. ("Single power source" means one battery pack, one branch circuit supply, etc). In addition, only one ground connection (to structure, to earth, to hull, etc.) for the entire system is needed for personnel protection or lightning protection, or no facility ground connection at all is required. No conductors except the power cord and the appropriate ground exist because no power or signal interfaces with other grounded equipment or devices are present or needed. Common examples of isolated systems are hand-held calculators, desktop computers (off line), home-type radios, most household appliances, etc.

8.3.1.2 Grounding of Isolated Systems

Grounding requirements for isolated systems are illustrated by Figs. 8.9 and 8.10. If single or multiphase ac is involved, an isolated system typically will include a safety ground wire run with the power conductors (unless the equipment is double insulated). Battery-driven systems usually do not require any grounding (but be sure the system is isolated and not the central-with-extension type discussed in Section 8.3.5). It is important to locate isolated systems some distance from lightning down conductors, or from other grounded metal objects in very high RF field strength environments. This prevents flashover and arcing. In certain very high-level RF environments, such as adjacent to a broadcast transmitter, supplemental case grounds may be necessary to prevent hazardous RF voltages from appearing on equipment cases. The internal signal grounding requirements of the isolated system are those determined by the designer to be necessary for proper operation (see Sections 8.1 and 8.2)

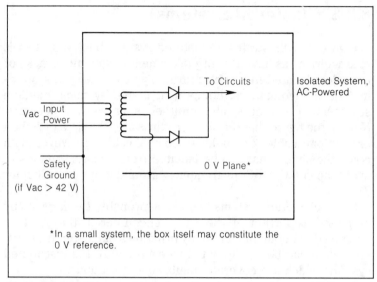

To Circuits

Isolated System, AC-Powered

Vac Input Power

Safety Ground
(if Vac > 42 V)

0 V Plane*

*In a small system, the box itself may constitute the 0 V reference.

Figure 8.9—Minimum Grounding Requirements for an AC-Powered Isolated System

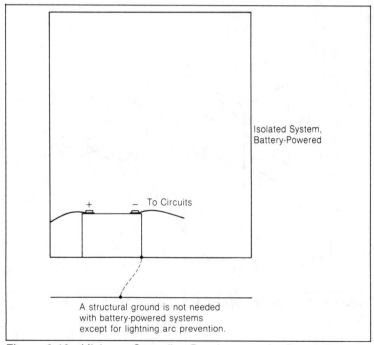

Isolated System, Battery-Powered

+ − To Circuits

A structural ground is not needed with battery-powered systems except for lightning arc prevention.

Figure 8.10—Minimum Grounding Requirements for Battery-Powered Isolated System

8.3.2 Clustered Systems

Figure 8.11 illustrates a clustered system. Such a system is characterized as having multiple elements (equipment racks or consoles) located in a central area. Typical clustered systems include minicomputers, component stereo systems, medium scale data processors, and multi-element word processors. Note in the figure that the signal returns are 0 V wires of ribbon or multipair cables or shields of coaxial cables. However, with coax, the shields have to be isolated from chassis grounds to avoid the creation of low-frequency ground loops (see Chapter 7).

Since clustered systems represent probably the largest (by number) proportion of the cases encountered, they will be examined in detail. In fact, many principles of clustered system grounding can be extrapolated to each cell of the distributed systems which are covered in subsequent sections.

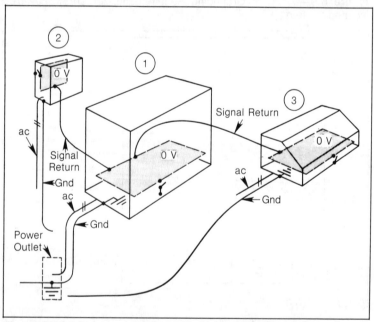

Figure 8.11—Clustered System with Single-Point Signal Ground

8.3.2.1 Characteristics

A distinguishing feature of a clustered system is that it utilizes one common power source, e.g., a battery or a single ac power connection. There are likely to be multiple interconnecting cables (signal, control and power) between the members of the system but not with any other system. A clustered system only needs one facility (structure) ground tie to realize personnel safety and lightning protection requirements.

8.3.2.2 Grounding a Clustered System

Grounding for a clustered system requires that one connection be made to structural ground. If the power supplied is single-phase ac, the third wire ground provides this connection.

If the power supply is three-phase ac, an appropriately sized (according to Paragraph 250-95 of the National Electrical Code) supplemental ground conductor is used. Battery-powered systems should have one ground connection to the structure. The RF ground referencing scheme used between the elements of the system should reflect the particular signal characteristics (frequency, amplitude, etc.) of the various pieces of equipment. This scheme may be single-point* or multipoint. If multipoint, the RF ground may be realized with cable shields or with auxiliary conductors, or it may utilize a wire grid or metal sheet under or above the array of equipment.

In a benign (quiet) EM environment, signal grounding with cable shields or auxiliary conductors between the interconnected pieces is acceptable. This method of grounding a clustered system is depicted in Fig. 8.12a. However, in high-level, multisignal environments, this type of grounding scheme should be avoided because of the antenna pickup effects of the multiple conductors.

---

*A more detailed discussion of single-point grounding is provided in Section 8.2.

Signals coupling to the ground conductors produce common-mode voltages between various source-load pairs and raise the threat of interference. A better method of grounding is shown in Fig. 8.12b. Here broad metal paths are provided between the various pieces of equipment. Overhead or underfloor duct work, cable trays and wire channels usually can provide the necessary signal grounding and fault protection network for a clustered system.

The best approach, and the one recommended for use in high-level RF environments, is that shown in Fig. 8.12c. A close-mesh wire grid or a solid metal sheet is provided for mounting the various pieces of equipment of the system. (In extremely severe environments as in the vicinity of a transmitter, the solid sheet is preferred over the grid.) Each cabinet is carefully bonded to this grid or sheet. All interconnecting signal leads, power buses, etc. should be routed inside enclosures and beneath the ground plane, preferably in conduit or in raceways. Note that the evolution from the poorest to the best approach is aimed at rendering the system and its cables successively less effective as pick-up antennas for radiated RF energy, particularly in the broadcast, HF, VHF and UHF bands.

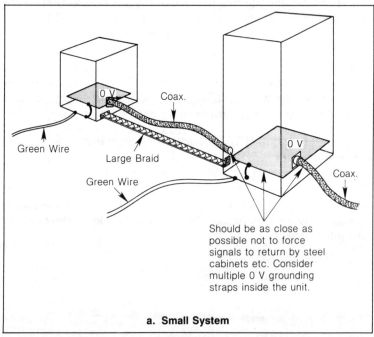

a. Small System

Figure 8.12—Clustered Systems with Multipoint Signal Grounds (continued next page)

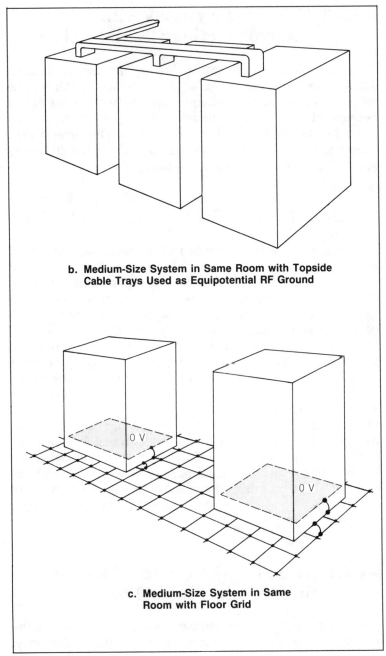

b. **Medium-Size System in Same Room with Topside Cable Trays Used as Equipotential RF Ground**

c. **Medium-Size System in Same Room with Floor Grid**

Figure 8.12—(continued)

8.3.2.3 Clustered Systems with Interconnecting Coaxial Cables

If, based on the wavelength dichotomy discussed in Section 8.2, a single-point grounding scheme has been retained, one must be sure that the system does not use coaxial cables because of the "forced" grounding of signal return that the coaxial connector (BNC, etc.) creates at each box penetration. Otherwise, isolated connectors must be used or the grounding scheme needs to be changed to a multipoint one.

8.3.2.4 Why Not Float Completely?

A question sometimes arises with a single-point grounded system as to whether the signal reference should be connected to chassis at all. Since the virtues of floated circuits have been amply demonstrated against low-frequency ground loops, and since signal voltages are generally harmless, why not add some benefit by completely floating? Although this would improve somewhat the ground loop isolation (exactly by 6 dB if parasitic capacitances at each equipment were equal) it creates the following safety issue: if an incidental primary-to-secondary insulation breakdown occurs in the power supply transformer, the whole low-voltage secondary circuits can rise to 115 V (or 230 V) above the earth or structure potential. This voltage will go unnoticed until an unsuspecting field engineer performs some power-on maintenance operation. When he touches the presumably harmless low-voltage circuits, he will receive a shock. For this reason, and to provide for drainage of possible static electricity, it is safer to ground the signal reference at one point.

8.3.2.5 Selecting the Center Node for Single-Point Grounding

Although this is often determined by a trial-and-error "method," a more deterministic approach exists: the center node must be the equipment which has the largest parasitic capacitance between the signal reference (PCB zero-volt, etc.) and the structure. The parasitic capacitance of each equipment can be measured with a simple hand-held capacitance meter after isolating the signal ground. By default, one can assume that the larger capacitance will exist, for obvious reasons, in the physically largest unit.

In any case, due to possible variances in installation configurations, it is a good practice always to provide an accessible strap option within each equipment. This will allow some flexibility to float or ground.

8.3.2.6 Clustered Systems Powered from Different AC Outlets within the Same Area

Although a clustered system by definition is powered by a unique source, this source can still be delivered by distant outlets in the same room, floor level or building area. Figure 8.13 shows the kind of local ground loop this arrangement may create. The loop exists between the signal/data cable and the safety wire. Besides some obvious field induction problems, the most frequent result of this configuration is that ground currents from other loads will cause a common-mode voltage between the ground pins of the two ac receptacles.

Figure 8.14 shows an example where the transient oscillatory ground current around 100 kHz from a compressor's power on-off switching causes several volts potential between the two outlet's ground pins, which are only 3 m distant. Unless ground loop isolation techniques have been designed into the system (see Sections 5.7 and 6.3), a coarse, temporary solution is to reroute the power cord of the terminal and to plug it into the same outlet as the main unit (Fig. 8.15).

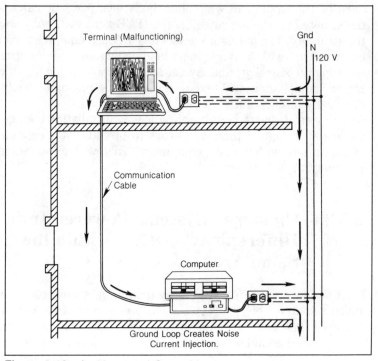

Figure 8.13—An Unwanted Ground Loop

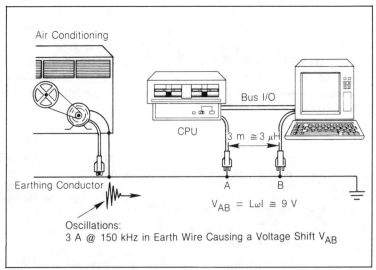

Figure 8.14—Numerical Example of Ground Noise with Clustered System Using Different Outlets

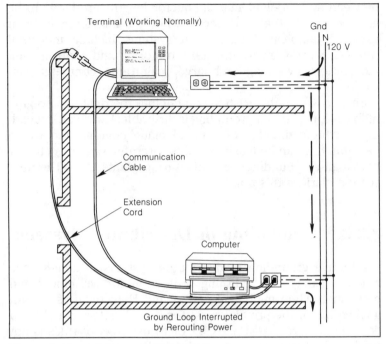

Figure 8.15—A Temporary Solution

8.3.3 Distributed Systems

A distributed system is one in which major elements are physically separated in a manner that requires equipment to be fed variously from different power outlets, branch circuits, different phases of the line or perhaps even different transformer banks (Fig. 8.8c).

8.3.3.1 Characteristics

In a distributed system, separate safety and lightning protection grounds to facility (vehicle) structures (frames) are required. Another common characteristic of a distributed system is that multiple conductor (signal and control) paths exist between system elements. Conductor lengths are likely to be greater than $\lambda/20$ at frequencies where an interference threat exists. Examples of distributed systems include industrial process control, environmental monitoring and control, communication switching and large mainframe computer networks.

Since a distributed system will fall into the right-hand region of Fig. 8.5, multipoint grounding is desirable. However, depending on the availability of a metal plane covering the whole location, this can be feasible (ships, aircrafts, satellites etc.) or not (high-rise buildings, manufacturing plants etc.). The next section clarifies this point.

8.3.3.2 Grounding of Distributed Systems

Effective grounding of distributed systems to achieve the required safety and lightning protection for equipment and personnel, while minimizing noise and EMI, requires careful application of the principles set forth in Chapters 5 and 6. To describe a stereotyped network or to list a set of rules is not prudent. However, some general guidelines may be suggested.

If the system is ac powered, consider each major element (consisting of one or more types of equipment in a particular location) as either an isolated or clustered system, as appropriate. Ground each major element as discussed in Sections 8.3.1.2 and 8.3.2.2. **Each and every signal port** on these isolated or clustered subsystems that must interface with other portions of the total system, i.e., other isolated and clustered subsystems, **should be viewed as having to interface with a noisy world.** As such, the techniques discussed in Chapter 6 for controlling unwanted coupling of radiated and conducted interference into the signal paths must be fully employed. Obviously, discretion will be necessary. There will be situations in which no additional protective measures are required, depending upon the properties of the signal being transmitted from terminal to terminal, the characteristics of the signal path and the nature of the electromagnetic environment.

Common battery-distributed systems present a particular challenge. Such systems are commonly found on aircraft (and vehicles) where the fuselage is used for dc power return. The use of the equipment rack, structure, hull or fuselage for the power return path means that the structure becomes the circuit reference. Therefore, voltage differentials between various points in the structure appear in series with any single-ended, unbalanced signal paths. Again, adequate rejection against such conducted interference must be obtained through application of the various techniques discussed in Chapter 6.

8.3.4 Multiple Distributed Systems

As the name implies, the characteristics of multiple distributed systems are similar to that of a distributed system except that there are usually several systems contained and operating in the same general area. Typically, the multiple systems share the primary power sources at each respective location (Fig. 8.8d). A distinguishing feature of multiple distributed systems is that they typically run a high risk of interfering with each other and are susceptible to interference from facility noise and the external environment. Thus, in addition to having grounding requirements like those discussed for distributed systems, additional shielding and filtering requirements are necessary to minimize intersystem interference.

8.3.5 Central System with Extensions

This type of system was illustrated previously in Fig. 8.8e. It is distinguished from an isolated or clustered system in that integral elements of the system extend out from the central portion at long physical and electrical distances.

8.3.5.1 Characteristics

This system is distinguished from a distributed system in that the extended elements obtain their power from the central element. Connections to a power source are not made anywhere except at the main element. An example of this type of system is an industrial process controller with sensors and actuators located remotely from the data logger or controller.

8.3.5.2 Grounding of a Central System with Extensions

The central or primary element of this type of system should be grounded as though it were a clustered or isolated system. Depending upon the operating frequency ranges and signal levels of the extension elements as well as the characteristics of the EM environment, a single-point tree or star grounding scheme may be used, or a multipoint scheme may be appropriate. It is likely that most central-with-extensions configurations will involve relatively low frequencies (audio or below) with operating bandwidths encompassing the power frequencies. If this is the situation, a single-point tree is recommended.

The ground node would be at the central element with one connection (the safety ground) made to the structure (or earthing). Extended elements should be floated or balanced. Twisted pair or balanced signal transmission line conductors should be used between the central element and the extended elements. If radiated coupling proves to be a problem, the extended elements should be configured, if at all possible, so that the shields from the central element (e.g., on coaxials) can be continued to enclose the extended elements.

8.4 Instrumentation Grounding

Many data instrumentation systems are concerned with measurement or detection of physical phenomena that require observation periods ranging from a few milliseconds to several minutes or hours. Because of the relatively slow nature of the event, the fundamental frequency of the transducer output may range from 0 (dc) to a few hundred hertz. Outputs of the transducer are commonly analog. Power distribution systems, electromechanical switches and atmospheric noise produce extraneous voltages whose energy content is strongly concentrated within this low-frequency region. Because of this overlap, special techniques are generally required to keep voltages and currents produced by the extraneous sources from obscuring the transducer outputs.

Because primarily low-frequency conditions exist, a basic single-point ground should be implemented. The signal return line should be grounded at one end only or not at all; i.e., it should be balanced. Similarly, **individual** cable shields around signal lines should be grounded at one end only. This is because the generally high impedances of the circuits invite E-field coupling.

Keeping in mind that the frequencies of concern are generally low and that the threat is mostly electrical coupling (capacitive) to very high-gain amplifiers with high input resistances, the following rules apply:

1. An electrostatic guard should be connected to the zero-volt signal reference of the circuitry contained in the shield.
2. By priority, the shield of an input cable must be tied to the signal zero-volt reference. Whether this reference is earthed or not is to be checked against ground loop problems, but the first condition should prevail.
3. The cable shield must be tied to the signal zero at the signal earthing point.

All the above is to ensure that, at least at low frequencies, the currents picked by capacitive coupling will flow in the shields and not in the active leads.

To be effective, the shield, if thin (less than one skin depth thick) must stay at the zero signal reference along its entire length. This is only true as long as $l \leq \lambda/16$ as already explained in section 7.3.2 (see Figs. 7.15 and 7.16).

8.4.1 Grounded Transducers

The bonded (grounded) thermocouple illustrated in Fig. 8.16 is used with a single-ended data amplifier whose output drives recording devices such as oscillographs, strip-chart recorders, and magnetic tape recorders. Certain important aspects which should be considered are as follows:

1. The shield which surrounds the transducer signal leads should be grounded at the same point as the transducer.

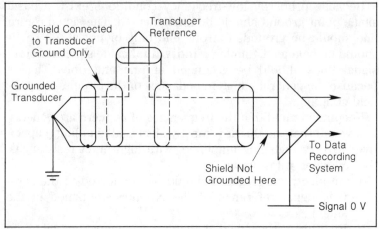

Shield Connected
to Transducer
Ground Only

Transducer
Reference

Grounded
Transducer

Shield Not
Grounded Here

To Data
Recording
System

Signal 0 V

Figure 8.16—Grounding Practices for Single-Ended Amplifiers (Nonisolated Type)

2. When the bonded thermocouple is connected to an isolated differential amplifier as shown in Fig. 8.17, the shield of the input cable should be connected to the amplifier internal guard shield to continue the signal shield to the interior of the amplifier. Notice that a grounding bus is shown connected between the data system signal reference and earth ground (structure) of the test area. This ground bus is necessary in any instrumentation system which uses isolated differential amplifiers. This is done to provide the necessary safety earthing and to minimize the common-mode potentials that otherwise exist between the amplifier's input and output if the data recording system is grounded to a separate earth or facility ground. However, this in turn may create a safety or damage issue, if the earth differences between G_1 and G_2 are too large, because this difference would appear between points A and G_2 in the same unit. A better alternative is to use an amplifier which can withstand large input-output voltages. Notice that the amplifier case and output shield are connected to the data system (or load end) ground.

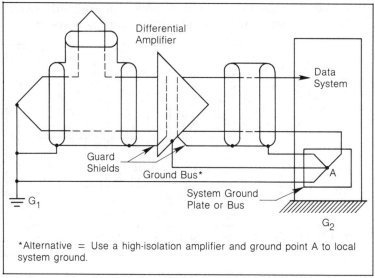

*Alternative = Use a high-isolation amplifier and ground point A to local system ground.

Figure 8.17—Grounding Practices for Differential Amplifiers

3. Grounded bridge transducers should be excited with a balanced dc source. By balancing the dc excitation supply relative to ground as shown in Fig. 8.18, the entire bridge will be balanced with respect to ground. Any unbalanced impedance presented to the amplifier input will be due to the leg resistances in the bridge. Although a ground loop still exists, its effect is greatly reduced by a balanced excitation supply.

4. Do not use single-ended (nondifferential) amplifiers with grounded bridge transducers.

5. Provide a single common-signal ground reference point for all grounded transducers at the test area or on the test item.

6. Connect the instrumentation cable shield of each data channel as close to the transducer ground connection as possible.

7. Use twisted shielded transducer extension wires.

8. Use a floating load on the output of a single-ended data amplifier when the amplifier input is a grounded transducer.

9. Always use insulated shielded cables. Uninsulated shields should never be used in data instrumentation systems.

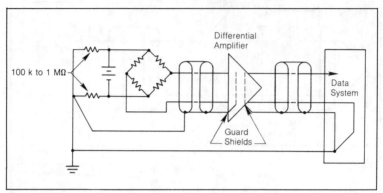

Figure 8.18—Method of Grounding Bridge Transducers

8.4.2 Ungrounded Transducers

Grounding techniques recommended for ungrounded transducers are illustrated in Fig. 8.19. The metallic enclosure of the transducer is connected to the cable shield, which is tied to the zero reference of the single-ended amplifier as shown in Fig. 8.19a, the shield of the input cable should not be connected to the amplifier. The case of the amplifier should be earthed at the load side.

When using an isolated amplifier, the recommended method of grounding the system is as shown in Fig. 8.19b. (Certain types of non-isolated differential amplifiers require that a transducer ground path be provided for proper amplifier operation. The instructions supplied by the amplifier manufacturer should be consulted.)

Other recommendations are:

1. Provide a single common-ground reference point for all cable shields.
2. Ground all input cable shields at the transducer.
3. Connect the isolated amplifier guard shield to input cable shield.
4. Do not allow more than one ground connection in each input cable shield.

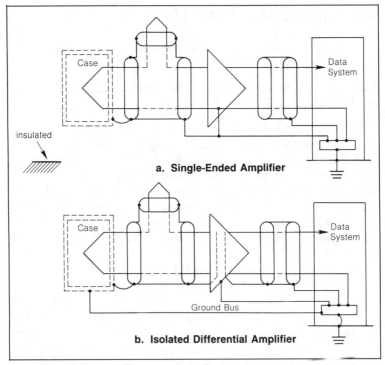

Figure 8.19—Recommended Grounding Practices for Floating Transducers

8.4.3 Transducer Amplifiers

Several recommendations are offered for transducer amplifiers:

1. Single-ended amplifiers can be used in digital data acquisition systems if channel-to-channel isolation is provided, e.g., through the use of floating loads.
2. Single-ended amplifiers should not be used with grounded bridges (to avoid short circuiting one leg of the bridge).
3. Connect the amplifier output guard shield to the data system ground bus.
4. If a permanent and unavoidable instrumentation ground exists at the test item as well as at the data system, use isolated differential amplifiers to break the ground loop.

8.5 Application Examples

To illustrate some of the concepts discussed previously, a few applications will be shown.

Illustrative Example 8.1: Application of Hybrid Ground in a Cabinet Rack

To illustrate a hybrid ground system, Fig. 8.20 shows a 19-inch cabinet rack containing five separate sliding drawers. Each drawer contains a portion of the system. From top to bottom, these are RF and IF preamplifier circuitry receiving microwave signals; IF and video signal amplifiers; display drivers, displays, and control circuits; low-level audio circuits and recorders for documenting sensitive multichannel, hard-line telemetry sensor outputs; and secondary and regulated power supplies.

Several factors produce the hybrid aspect:

1. The RF and IF video drawers are similar. Here, unit-level boxes or stages (interconnecting coaxial cables are grounded at both ends) are multipoint grounded inside the drawer. The drawer is then grounded to the dagger-pin, chassis-ground bus as suggested in Fig. 8.20. The power ground to these drawers, on the other hand, uses a single-point ground from its bus in a manner identical to the audio drawer.

2. Each of the chassis or signal ground and power ground busses constitutes a multipoint grounding scheme to the drawer level. The individual ground busses are single-point grounded at the bottom distribution block. This avoids circulating common-mode current between chassis or signal ground and power grounds since power-ground current can vary due to transient surges in certain modes of equipment operation.

3. Interconnecting cables between different drawer levels are run separately, and their shields, when used, are treated in the same grounding manner as at the drawer level.

4. The audio and display drawers shown in Fig. 8.20 use single-point grounding throughout for both their unit-level boxes (interconnecting twisted cable is grounded at one end to its unit) and power leads. Cable and unit shield

strike-plate holes are all grounded together at the common dagger-pin bus. Similarly, the outgoing power leads and twisted returns are separately bonded on their dagger-pin busses.

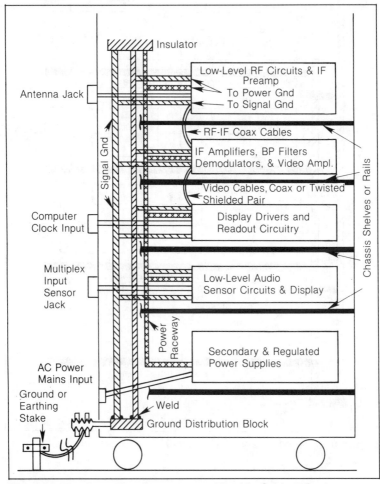

Figure 8.20—Grounding Arrangement Used in Cabinet Racks

Using the block diagram of Fig. 8.21 to account for the frequency range and to correlate the above scheme with Fig. 8.5, the following is observed:

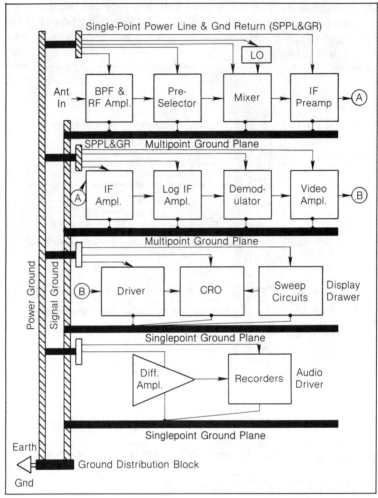

Figure 8.21—Block Diagram Detail of Hybrid Grounding of Fig. 8.20

1. The audio and display drawers have ground runs of about 0.6 m (2 ft) and an upper operational frequency of about 1 MHz (driver and sweep circuits). Thus, single-point grounding to the strike pins is indicated.
2. The RF and IF drawers process UHF and 30 MHz signals over a distance of few feet so that multipoint grounding is indicated.

8.34

3. The regulated power supplies furnish equipment units having transient surge demands. The greatest length is about 2 m (6 ft), and significant transient frequency components may extend up in the HF region. Here, hybrid grounding is indicated: single-point within a drawer, and multipoint from the power bus to all drawers.

When miniature and printed circuits and ICs are used, network proximity is considerably closer. Thus, multipoint grounding is more economical and practical for cards, wafers and chips. Interconnection of these components through hybrid substrates, multichip modules, mother boards, etc. should use a grounding scheme following the illustrations of previous paragraphs and the general criteria of Fig. 8.5. In all likelihood, this will still represent a multipoint or hybrid grounding approach in which any single-point grounding (for hybrid grounds) would be employed to avoid low-frequency ground current loops and common-mode impedance coupling.

Illustrative Example 8.2: Application of Single-Point Ground at Facility Level

The configuration illustrated by Fig. 8.22 represents one approach to a facility-wide, single-point ground. It uses individual ground busses which extend from a single point on the facility ground to each separate electronic system. In each system, the various electronic subsystems are individually connected at only one point to the ground bus. Another single-point ground bus network, illustrated in Fig. 8.23, assumes the form of a tree. Within each system, each subsystem is single-point grounded. Each of the system ground points is then connected to the tree ground bus with a single insulated conductor.

EMP protection methodology calls for a zoned single-point ground configured as illustrated in Fig. 8.24. In this zonal concept of grounding, one and only one ground connection interconnects the zonal boundaries. No ground connection passes through a zonal boundary; it must terminate at the boundary. Internal grounds to a zone begin at the boundary.

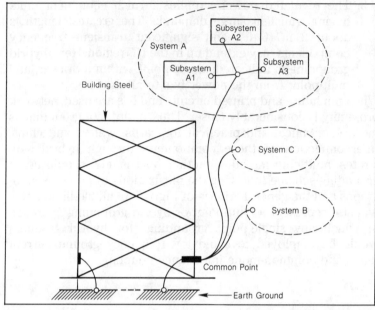

Figure 8.22—Single-Point Ground Bus System Using Separate Risers

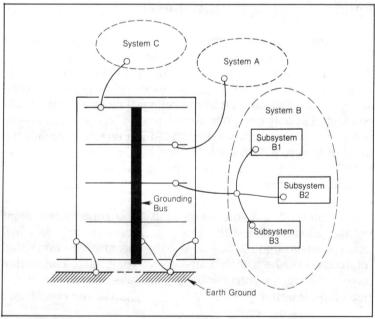

Figure 8.23—Single-Point Ground Bus System Using a Common Bus

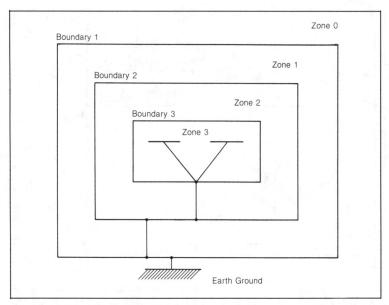

Figure 8.24—Zonal Grounding

Zone 0 usually means the region outside of the facility (out-of-doors). Zone 1 is the mildly attenuated region just inside facility walls. Zone 2 is the further attenuated region inside a room or an enclosure. Zones 3 and higher exist inside equipment enclosures or in compartments within equipment. A zonal boundary is any well-defined and controlled interface or wall that offers some degree of electromagnetic shielding to an electromagnetic wave in Zone 0. Care must be taken that the separate ground points remain isolated except through one path.

Illustrative Example 8.3: Application of Multipoint Ground at Facility Level

Figure 8.25 shows an example of multipoint grounding at facility level. To be effective, the building structure must play the role of a low-impedance grid. Often, this is not readily achievable.

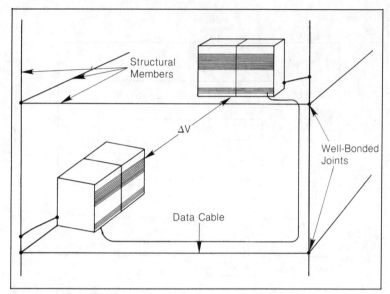

Figure 8.25—Multiple Equipment Grounding, when Building Can Act as a Low-Z Grid

A condition which must be met for multipoint grounding to be effective is that the voltage differentials on the ground plane must be reducible by the added ground paths. For example, the voltage differentials existing within a steel frame building from stray power currents are not likely to be significantly affected by supplying additional grounding conductors between the equipment elements distributed throughout the building. To exert a noticeable influence, the combined impedance of the added ground conductors should be at least an order of magnitude lower than what already exists between all points of the existing ground system. The criterion is actually based on that required to ensure that any interference is below victim sensitivity.

The realization of such a low impedance may not be feasible or economical. As an example, assume that two data processing units although subsets of a larger system, are located on different floors of a building as shown in Fig. 8.25. Further assume that the steel frame building is effectively bonded at the joints so that a low-resistance path exists throughout. If independently supplied with power, each equipment cabinet will have a safety ground that will likely put each cabinet in contact with the structure near its respective location. Any ΔV from stray power currents, radiant RF sources, etc. which exists between these two structural locations is not likely to be affected by any reasonably-sized auxiliary ground bus between the two equipments. The reason is that structural members, although of mediocre conductive materials, typically offer enough cross-sectional area to yield a lower impedance than any practical grounding bus. So the solution is to install floor-level ground grids as described in Section 2.6. These will tend to behave as planes.

8.6 References

1. Denny, H., *Grounding, Bonding and Shielding Practices, Vol. I, II and III*, (Report FAA-RD-75-215).
2. *MIL-Handbook 419, Grounding Practices*.
3. Morrison, R., *Grounding and Shielding Techniques in Instrumentation*, (New York: John Wiley & Sons, 1977).
4. Morrison, R., *Instrumentation Fundamentals*, (New York: John Wiley & Sons, 1984).
5. Fowler, E.P., "Instrument Systems with High Interference Immunity," (Montreux: 1975 EMC Symposium).
6. Ott, H., "Ground: A Path for Current to Flow," (*EMC Technology*, January, 1983).
7. Mardiguian, M., and White, D.R.J., *EMI Control Methodology and Procedures*, (Gainesville, Va.: Interference Control Technologies, Inc., 1985).
8. "Guideline on Electrical Power for DP Installations," (FIPS Publication 94, National Bureau of Standards, 1983).

Chapter 9

Architectural Grounding

The need for structural grounding was discussed at length in Chapters 4, 5 and 6. Three purposes for grounding were reviewed:

1. To prevent a shock hazard to personnel if an electrical equipment frame or housing develops a dangerous voltage to frame due to accidental breakdown (short circuit) of wiring or components
2. To protect a building and its contents from lightning damage by providing a very low-impedance path from the top of building to earth
3. To provide a reference voltage (usually called a **zero-potential plane**) for all electrical and electronic systems and equipments to avoid both a shift in operating voltage levels and to prevent circulating ground-current loops which result in common-impedance coupling

Apart from the soil impedance problem discussed in earlier sections, a non-zero earth potential results from earth ground pollution due to both ac and dc currents. It should be avoided as a reference for EMC purposes. Two examples are:

1. Gas distribution lines are kept at -0.8 V with respect to a reference electrode buried in earth. While modern gas lines are insulated in earth and at the meter services, nicks in insulation, called holidays, cause current leakage into earth.

2. Regarding ac power distribution, a significant portion of the 50/60 Hz unbalanced current is returned through earth. Ground currents of the order of 1,000 A have been measured at substations.* While a typical building ground is not located at a substation, considerably lesser but significant unbalanced currents can flow through the local earth to cross-modulate 60 Hz and associated RF contamination upon the EMI grounding complex.

Many, if not most, man-made electromagnetic noise sources emanate from electrical, electromechanical and electronic devices located in buildings of all types. Consequently, a building represents a plethora of broadband electrical noise culprits which can result in EMI to many receptors also located within the same building. This building noise-maker complex also constitutes a threat to receptors in other nearby buildings or areas. While a building offers some natural RF shielding, if properly designed it could both protect the inside receptors against outside-world electromagnetic ambients as well as mitigate pollution to this ambient from within.

A building represents a maze of electrical wiring routed throughout and between all floors. This wiring acts as a huge pickup antenna to both internally developed electrical noise and emissions from without. This antenna complex will conduct EMI to victim receptors as well as reradiate along the length of the wiring. Further, it is not uncommon for taller buildings to locate an "antenna farm" on the roof. Here, antennas may be transmitting (e.g.: land mobile, broadcast and microwave relay) as well as receiving both intended signals and unintentional noise from nearby sources.

---

*Near the boundaries of some substations two ground rods driven into the earth 0.6 m (2 ft) apart produce a voltage sufficient to light several 100 W bulbs connected to the ground rods.

This chapter on architectural grounding covers buildings of all types, such as:

1. Apartment houses	2. Hospitals	3. Oil refineries
4. Airline terminals	5. Houses	6. Power plants
7. Department stores	8. Light industry	9. Restaurants
10. Garages	11. Steel factories	12. Manufacturing plants
13. Heavy industry	14. Medical centers	15. Theaters
16. High rises	17. Offices	18. Warehouses

It is not uncommon for small buildings (e.g., less than 1,000 m^2 of floor space) to have more than 1,000 discrete electromagnetic emitters and receptors. Large buildings (over 10,000 m^2 of floor space) may have in excess of 10,000 discrete emitters and receptors. For example, every fluorescent lamp is an emitter, and every telephone and intercom station is an electromagnetic receptor. Table 9.1 illustrates only a few of the many emitters and receptors existing in buildings. Immersed in the electromagnetic ambient, it is clear that a modern building constitutes both an EMI pollution threat and victim. The above serves to illustrate that lightning and power safety earth grounds may not provide a quiet EMI-control reference. Special effort is necessary to assure that there exists no significant common-impedance earth grounding path, i.e., that a true single-point ground exists. Chapter 8 indicated that single-point grounding, if accomplished at dc and ac, only applies up to a frequency for which $l \leq \lambda/20$.

Thus, ordinary 50/60 Hz building grounds with buses or beam lengths (beam length $\equiv$ run length) in the 50 to 100 m range may be effective up to 200 kHz, more or less. For higher frequencies, ordinary building structural grounds become ineffective and local ground grids or planes may be necessary.

This chapter adresses the architectural aspects of grounding, with particular attention to lightning and EMI.

Table 9.1—A Few Representative Emitters and Receptors Found in Buildings

Emitters and Receptors	Air Terminals	Dept. Stores	Garages	Heavy Industry	High Rises	Hospitals	Houses	Light Industry	Manufacturing Plants	Med. Centers	Offices	Steel Factory	Petroleum Refineries	Restaurants & Cafeterias	Power Plants
Typical Emitters															
Adding Machines	X	X	X			X		X	X	X	X	X	X	X	X
Appliances	X				X	X	X	X		X	X			X	
Arc Welders			X	X				X	X						
Autos	X		X												
Computers	X			X		X		X	X	X	X	X	X		X
Diathermy						X				X					
Elevators		X			X	X				X	X	X			
Escalators	X	X				X									
Fluorescent Lights	X	X	X	X	X	X	X	X	X	X	X	X	X	X	X
Machine Tools			X	X				X	X			X			
Office Machines	X			X		X									
Overhead Cranes	X		X	X					X			X	X		X
Power Tools	X			X		X	X								
Reproduct.		X				X		X	X	X	X	X			
Ultrasonic Cleaners			X	X		X		X	X	X					
Typical Receptors															
Automatic Controls	X			X		X		X	X			X	X		X
Bio-medic. Instrum.						X				X					
Computers	X		X	X		X		X	X			X	X		X
Intercoms	X	X	X	X	X	X	X	X	X	X	X	X	X	X	X
Radios	X	X			X	X	X			X	X				
Recorders/Displays	X			X		X				X		X	X		X
Security Systems		X		X	X			X	X			X	X		X
Telephones	X	X	X	X	X	X	X	X	X	X	X	X	X	X	X
Television	X	X		X		X	X			X			X		X
Test Instrum.	X		X	X				X	X			X	X		X

9.4

9.1 Lightning Protection of Buildings

Although the basic principles of lightning rods were well established by Benjamin Franklin in 1753, lightning protection of buildings is still perceived by many people as black magic: lightning experts are ranked somewhat between fortune-tellers and gurus. This is unfortunate because, since the beginning of the twentieth century, many analytical and experimental works have followed the path lighted by Franklin's intuitive genius. In particular, the 1960s works of Berger and Golde, and Uman (U.S.A.), and the 1970s works of the "Saint-Privat d'Allier" Group (France) have resulted in good quantitative predictions of lightning events and, hence, a rationale for optimal protection.

> The lightning current is like any electric current, following the laws of electrophysics, provided the circuit is correctly modeled. All practical means of protection can be summarized by this: **offer to the current [the] easiest possible path.** Lightning is a formidable entity whom it is very risky to oppose. It disposes of megavolts to shatter the thickest insulators, but can flow unnoticed in rather small wires. If, during its descent, the flash wants to explore several possible paths, it is wiser to help it to do so, rather than trying to block it with futile barriers.

This rather romantic statement, taken from a speech by P.G. Laurent, former supervisor at Electricité de France (the French National Power Company) expresses perfectly the basic elements of lightning protection.

9.1.1 Lightning Aerials

The lightning rod (or other aerial) being the first link of a building's protection system, the following questions need to be considered:
1. When is a lightning rod/aerial necessary?
2. What is the radius (or dome) of protection that it should cover?

9.1.1.1 Assessing the Need for Lightning Aerials

The need for lightning protection is based on the risk of lightning strokes on a particular building and the criticality of its consequences in terms of people's safety, material damage, explosion, etc. To quote Golde, "Assuming that the average amount of damage is known which is caused by lightning to a given type of building in a given region, as well as the average cost of an adequate protection, the annual depreciation of the protective system must be lower than the amount spent on repairing the damages."[1]

To put it in engineer's terms, we could say that the cost of the lightning protection and its maintenance must be significantly less than the average damage of a lightning stroke multiplied by the probable number of direct hits in the life expectancy of the building. This simple equation becomes more complex when one considers that:

1. The protection cost is up-front money, while the cost of lightning damage is only a possibility.
2. When the risk comprises human lives, the cost aspects are of secondary importance and protection must be provided.

Once a satisfactory economic criterion has been devised, the probability of lightning strokes on the unprotected building can be calculated from the local keraunic levels, i.e., the average number of thunderstorms days per year in this locality. The explanation of lightning stroke mechanism is far beyond the ambition of this book, and is well explained in Refs. 1 through 4, just to name a few. Let us say that in every country, the meteorological bureau keeps the lightning statistics in form of isokeraunic curves; that is, the lines which connect the places having "the same number of thunderstorm days per year." A few examples are shown in Figs. 9.1 through 9.3. Figures 9.4 and 9.5 show actual lightning events.

The number of probable earth flashes per year per km^2 can be approximated by:

$$N_f = 0.1 \text{ to } 0.16 \, N_k \qquad (9.1)$$

where, $\quad N_f$ = flashes/km^2/year or flash/density
$\qquad\quad N_k$ = keraunic level

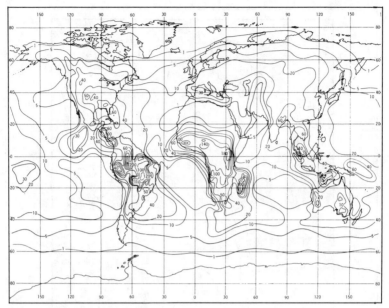

Figure 9.1—Average Annual Worldwide Thunderstorm Days

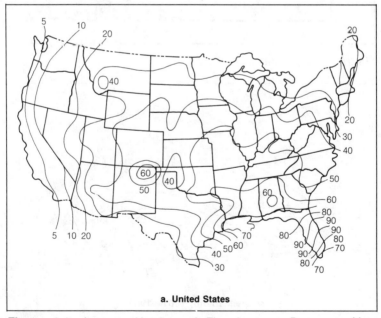

Figure 9.2—Average Number of Thunderstorm Days per Year (Isokeraunic Levels). The observation range for each point is about 100 Km^2. (continued next page)

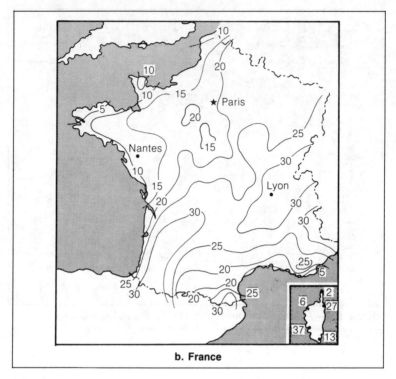

b. France

Figure 9.2—(continued)

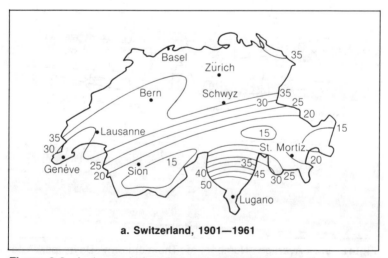

a. Switzerland, 1901—1961

Figure 9.3—Isokeraunic Levels (continued next page)

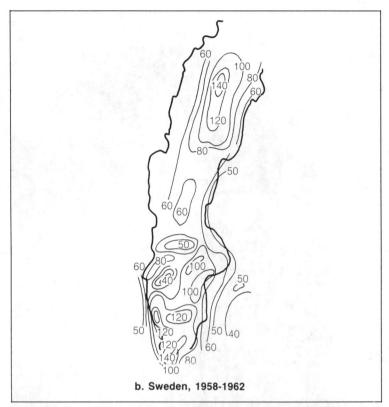

b. Sweden, 1958-1962

Figure 9.3—(continued)

Figure 9.4—Cloud-to-Ground Flash

Figure 9.5—Lightning-Induced Fire in Wichita, Kansas (courtesy of the "Witchita Eagle Beacon" Newspaper)

The N_k coefficient has been found empirically by comparing thousands of actual flashes. Although it contains widely varying parameters like the number of flashes in a stormy day, or the area surveyed per monitoring stations, this coefficient is fairly constant for a number of thunderstorm days per year not exceeding 30. For larger numbers, the flash density N_f follows approximately a $0.05\ N_k^{1.5}$ dependency which reaches, for instance, $N_f = 35$ for $N_k = 80$.

The striking distance of a lightning bolt approaching ground level varies according to the severity of the stroke (which can depend on the elevation of the building, so the two factors are interactive), its polarity and its orientation (i.e., vertical or slanted). The distance can range from 30 m (for a stroke in the lower decile of probability, i.e., 8 kA) to 120 m (for a severe stroke in the 60 kA range). The relationship derived from strike measurements is shown in Figs. 9.6 for the current amplitude and 9.7 for the striking distance.

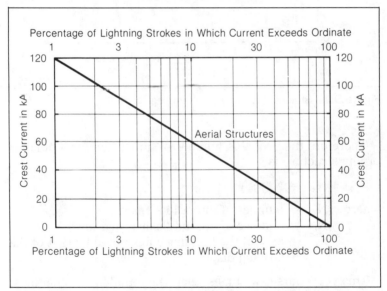

Figure 9.6—Amplitude Distribution of Currents in Lightning Strokes to Structures

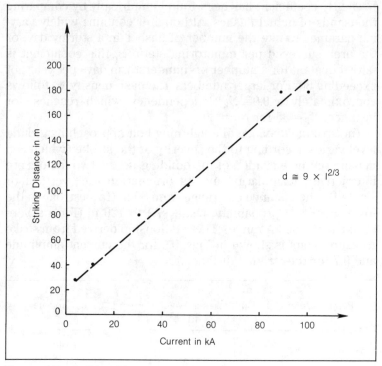

Figure 9.7—Striking Distance vs. Lightning Current

Therefore the probable number of direct hits for a building or any structure is:

$$N_x = N_f \times S_T \tag{9.2}$$

where, N_x = number of direct hits/year
N_f = number of ground flashes/year/km^2
S_T = area of the building, augmented by that of the striking distance

This, of course, assumes that the building is the most prominent structure in the vicinity. If another one exists whose area of attraction overlaps the one being considered, the buildings will share the probability of being struck in overlap area.

9.12

Illustrative Example 9.1

Assume a building with a projected area of 30 × 30 m, installed in a region with a keraunic level of 30 thunderstorm days per year. From Fig. 9.8, the attraction area will be taken as 90 × 90 m, or 0.01 km² (small strike) to 270 × 270 m, or 0.07 km² (worst case). Therefore:

$$N_x = 30 \times 0.1 \times 0.01 = 0.03 \text{ strikes/year, best case}$$
$$= 30 \times 0.16 \times 0.07 = 0.3 \text{ strikes/year, worst case}$$

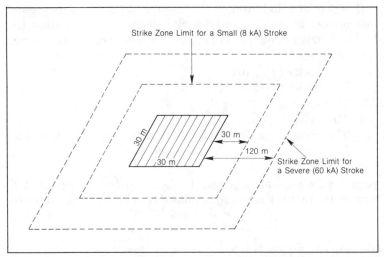

Figure 9.8—Example of Striking Zones for a Building with 30 × 30 m Projected Area

Therefore, the unprotected building has a high probability of being hit once every 30 years, with a worst-case possibility of once every 3 years (the average being about once in 10 years). A finer calculation can be made by weighing each current range by its probability of occurrence and summing up all the probabilities as shown in Table 9.2.

The use of this building and factors relating to human occupancy would modulate the risk assessment, but this building is a likely candidate for a roof aerial system.

The previous attraction assessment being based on the footprint of the building augmented by the striking distance, one might conclude that the height of the building has no effect on the number of strokes per year once it is established that it is the most prominent structure within the sample area. However, Fig. 9.9 shows that, given the worst-case striking distance d_{max} and the building height h, this building can attract any lightning whose striking distance is greater than h. Therefore if $h > d$, any lightning within the d radius will hit the building.

If $h < d$, the lightning will "choose" to strike the ground instead because the ground-strike distance is less than the building-strike distance. Therefore, there is a complex interaction between:

1. The area of capture
2. The building height
3. The striking distance d
4. The lightning current I_x
5. The percentage probability of lightning strokes exceeding I_x

Table 9.2—A More Precise Calculation of Illustrative Example 9.1, Accounting for the Percentage Probability of Lightning Current and for the Building Height

Stroke Amplitude Range	% Prob.	Striking Distance	Attraction Area in km²	Probable Strikes/Year $= \dfrac{N_k}{6} \times$ P% $\times$ Area
0 – 20 kA	50	55 m	0.02	$\dfrac{30}{6} \times 0.02 \times 50\% = 0.05$
20 – 40 kA	30	90 m	0.044	$= 0.066$
40 – 60 kA	10	120 m	0.07	$= 0.035$
60 – 100 kA	8	190 m	0.17	$= 0.028$

$$N_{TOT} = 0.18$$
or 1 event every 5.5 year

Note: If the building height "h" is less than the striking distance, the following derating applies =
If "h" exceeds 190 m = no derating
If "h" does not exceed 120 m, the Last Line is dropped and
$N_{TOT} = 0.152$/year
If "h" does not exceed 90 m, the two last lines are dropped and
$N_{TOT} = 0.117$/year, etc...

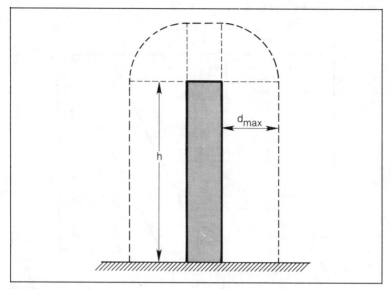

Figure 9.9—Area of Capture of a Structure, Counted from Stroke Distance d

Starting from the smallest building and increasing h, the number of cases where h exceeds d will accumulate until all the possible lightning strokes, from the least to the most severe, will be attracted by the building.

If this number is given in events/km^2, the dependency is like h^2, as evidenced by Fig. 9.10. The figure is taken from actual measurements. For any level $N_k \neq 10$, the numbers should be multiplied by $N_k/10$. Curve 1 is most applicable to regions with high values of N_k, while curve 2 is best for low values of N_k. Curves were obtained from regions with similar geographical and geological parameters. The h^2 dependency is obvious for both slopes.

As was illustrated in Figure 9.9, any tall structure can be seen as surrounded by a "capture" dome for a given striking distance d. A lightning stroke which would fall outside this dome "if the structure were not there" will still have its path unaffected. Inside the dome, the lightning will strike the structure.

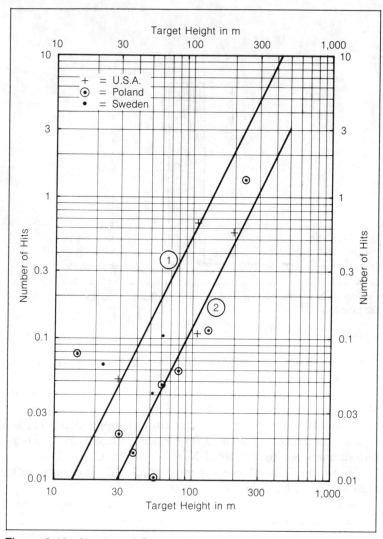

Figure 9.10—Number of Direct Hits per Year on Isolated Structures (Towers, Buildings, Etc.) Normalized to a Keraunic Level of 10. For Nk ≠ 10, multiply by Nk/10.

9.16

Several national codes such as set forth by the U.S. National Fire Protection Association or in British and Australian codes use rating tables to facilitate risk assessment and decide whether air terminals are needed. For instance, the *NFPA Risk Assessment Guide* contains six tables. Five of them are used to rate a building according to these indexes:

1. Type of structure
2. Type of construction
3. Relative location
4. Topography
5. Occupancy and contents

The sixth table rates the building by geographic location affecting the isokeraunic level (number of thunderstorm days per year) of the region.

The overall risk index is determined by adding the first five tables and dividing the sum by the index value obtained from the isokeraunic table. The following three illustrative examples show how the guide works.

Illustrative Example 9.2: A Three-Story, Wood Frame, Brick-Sided, Composition-Roofed Apartment Building Housing More than 50 Persons, Located in the Chicago Suburb of Palos Heights

Index	Value
A—Type of structure:	
Residential structure less than 15 m high	5
B—Type of construction:	
Wood frame, composition roof	3
C—Relative location:	
Large structure over 1,000 m^2	4
D—Topography:	
On a hillside	2
E—Occupancy and contents:	
Large assembly of people (50 or more)	6
F—Isokeraunic level:	
41 to 50 thunderstorm days per year	4

The formula:

$$R = \frac{A + B + C + D + E}{F}$$

9.17

yields:

$$R = \frac{5 + 3 + 4 + 2 + 6}{4} = 5$$

Referring to Table 1-2 of the *NFPA Risk Assessment Guide*, R values between 4 and 7 have an overall risk value of "moderate to severe."

Illustrative Example 9.3: A Steel-Framed, One-Story Factory with a Built-Up Roof and Employing 500 people, Located near Orlando, Florida

Index	Value
A—Factory building less than 15 m high	5
B—Steel frame, composition roof	3
C—Large structure over 1,000 m² but located in an area of lower structures	2
D—On flat land	1
E—Large assembly of people	6
F—Over 70 thunderstorm days per year	1

The result using the formula is:

$$R = \frac{5 + 3 + 2 + 1 + 6}{1} = 17$$

However, Florida is in the southwest section of the country where there happens to be a lower than average ratio of cloud-to-ground lightning flashes. Therefore, the R value 17 is multiplied by the factor 0.5, providing a risk figure of 8.5. This still is more than 7, so the risk for the factory is "severe."

Illustrative Example 9.4: A Steel-Framed Office High-Rise in Baltimore, Maryland

Index	Value
A—Office building 45 m or higher	8
B—Steel frame, composition roof	3
C—Structure extending more than 15 m above adjacent structures or terrain	10
D—On flat land	1
E—Large assembly of people	6
F—From 11 to 20 thunderstorm days per year	7

The result is:

$$R = \frac{8 + 3 + 10 + 1 + 6}{7} = 4$$

However, Baltimore is in the Northeast, where there is a heavy ratio of cloud-to-ground lightning discharges, so the R value is in this case multiplied by the factor 1.5. This results in a risk value of 6, "moderate to severe." A copy of U.S. Code NFPA 78 containing the Risk Assessment Guide can be purchased from the Publications Department, National Fire Protection Association, Batterymarch Park, Quincy, MA 02269.

9.1.1.2 Assessing the Protection Zone of the Aerial

Lightning aerials, sometimes termed **lightning rods** or **air terminals,** have the purpose of intercepting a lightning strike and deflecting it to the ground via the structure or earthing conductors. There is a common myth that lightning rods work by constantly "bleeding off" the cloud charges to ground, thus limiting the number and severity of flashes. This is impossible considering that the charge corresponding to an average lightning flash is about 30 coulombs: given that before the flash, the rod current due to slow discharge is on the order of 10 A, it would take about 800 hr to discharge harmlessly a thundercloud (see Golde, Ref. 1).

Indeed, the rod concentrates on itself all the chances of lightning striking within its area of influence. This is why it is so important, having "invited" the flash, to provide a dependable path to earth. Otherwise, the presence of a rod alone could make things worse. Two basic kinds of roof terminals are used, either alone or in combination: lightning rods and a set of more or less gridded conductors over the roof (ridge, edge, etc.). The roof metalized elements can be part of this latter net.

To decide which is appropriate, an evaluation of the protection zone offered by the aerial is needed. Figure 9.11 shows the principle of this protection zone. The protection is ensured for all objects within the dashed zone and for striking distances ≥ d; i.e., for strokes whose I ≥ $(d/9)^{3/2}$ (ref. Fig. 9.7), the left part of the building shown is at risk.

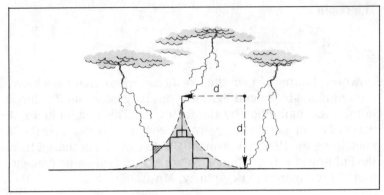

Figure 9.11—Protection Zone of a Rod

The lightning is viewed as a traveling leader carrying around it a "sphere of influence" whose radius is the previously described striking distance d. When the sphere is tangential to the soil surface and the lightning rod, these are the farthest and only objects the stroke can reach. Any object protruding inside the sphere (Fig. 9.11) can be hit.

However, a protection zone is valid only for a given striking distance d. Since this distance depends on the current, it seems conservative to consider the highest possible current with the percentage of risk being covered. Unfortunately, this means that lightning strikes with less current could arc over to lower parts of the building instead of being deflected by the rod. This situation is shown in Fig. 9.12. In summary, a protection zone devised for the most damaging current may leave the building vulnerable to less severe (but possibly more frequent) flashes, especially side flashes.

The implication of this is that if all flashes were to be intercepted, the roof would have to be covered with such a close array of conductors that it would make the installation costly and impractical. So each country's national code has more or less embraced a compromise whereby the lightning strokes which are likely to bypass the aerial have a sufficiently small intensity to do minimal damage.

Incidentally, we see in Fig. 9.11 that the height of the rod extending beyond the striking distance is of little interest, although a high rod increases the chance of capturing a flash with a small striking distance.

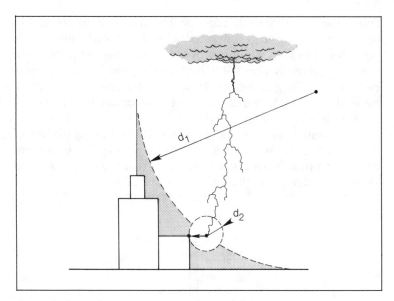

Figure 9.12—Object Within the Protection Zone for a Striking Gap d_1 Can Still Be Hit with Smaller Flashes Having a Striking Distance d_2.

For small houses, the simplest lightning aerial system is to use all-metallic gutters and rain pipes and to bond them together down to an earth rod. This method is only appropriate for a small building with moderate risk. For a building with larger dimensions and a more significant loss potential, a system of real lightning aerials should be installed.

For buildings with relatively small roof areas, e.g., no more than 10×10 m, one lightning rod is generally sufficient. For step roofs, the protection is made by one rod at each end, connected by a ridge wire. Structures with larger roofs would require many lightning rods, so a compromise is generally made by using several rods which are separated by no more than 20 m and interconnected by a belt wire. A standard rooftop protection system is shown in Fig. 9.13.

The U.S. Code stipulates air terminals at 6 m intervals or less on roof high points, chimneys, dormers and other protrusions, interconnected with braided conductors. For high-rise buildings where a steel frame or reinforced concrete is used, the advantage of an existing metal net exists. A combined arrangement is generally used where all the metal members of the roofing are interconnected and equipped with short aerials (15 to 45 cm) which are evenly distributed. A roofing element is considered to be a valid part of the protection net if its metal surface is directly accessible by the flash and if it is interconnected with the general net. How large the mesh cells can be depends on each national code, but a maximum distance of 10 to 20 m is generally specified.

The aerials must be made noncorrodible either by the use of stainless steel or by a nickel or chrome plating. If the rods are on top of a plant with chimneys and corrosive smoke, each rod should be adequately plated.

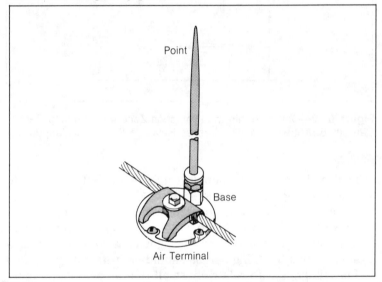

Figure 9.13—A Standard Rooftop Protection System

9.1.1.3 Protection of Rooftop Equipment

All metal bodies present on the roof (air conditioners, water tanks, vents, elevator machinery, antennas, etc.) should be tied to the general aerial system to prevent side flashing. The risk of side flashing to roof-mounted objects is depicted in Fig. 9.14.

For antennas, since relying just on the coaxial braid of antenna feeder to sink the lightning current would be highly hazardous, each antenna is required to have a lightning arrestor which will temporary ground the aerial to the general roof mesh or to the lightning rod main conductor. To prevent side flashing as well, the exact position of all metal services (water pipes, electricity, etc.) **under** the roof must be known. If their distance to the closest aerial conductor is sufficiently small that an arc can exist, they should be connected to this aerial. A quick assessment of the risk of arcing is made by considering the expected lightning current, its rise time and the total impedance to earth of the aerial system and its down conductors.

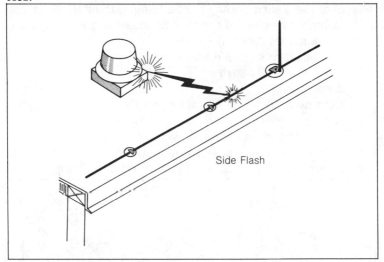

Figure 9.14—Risk of Side-Flashing with Roof-Mounted Object at Arcing Distance

Assuming, for instance, a 15 m high building with an inductance to earth of 15 μH for a down conductor and a lightning current slope of 30 kA/μs, the transient voltage on the roof versus earth will be:

$$V = L \, dI/dt = 15 \times 10^{-6} \times 3 \times 10^{4}/10^{-6} = 450 \text{ kV}$$

Given an average breakdown voltage of 10 kV/cm in the air, any object within 45 cm of the aerial network should be grounded to it. More severe current slope or a higher structure will result in more stringent requirements.

9.1.2 Down Conductors

Once a lightning flash has been intercepted by the aerial, the corresponding current must be directed to the earth electrode(s) by a path which is both the shortest (i.e. the least impedant) and the least damaging as possible. This is the role of the down conductors. Much lightning damage occurs in buildings which are equipped with aerials but where the down conductors fail to drain the current to ground. This makes the whole protection system worse than having no aerial at all.

An additional benefit of down conductors, if there are several of them surrounding the building, is their effect against side flashing, especially if they are arranged in a Faraday cage. Down conductors can consist of:

1. One or more stranded wires
2. One or more flat strips
3. Rods or tubes
4. Existing gutters and metal liners
5. Faraday cages
6. Any combination of the above

Figure 9.15 shows aerials and down conductor arrangements with an average-size, traditional-construction building.

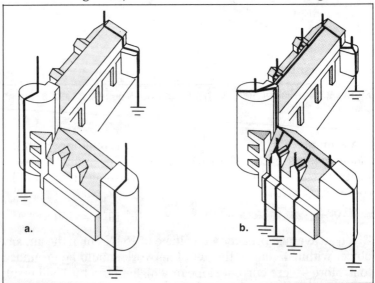

Figure 9.15—Aerials and down-conductors arrangement with average size, traditional construction building—the choice of high rods with individual down-conductors (a) or distributed short rods with gridded down-conductors (b) is generally made on feasibility and aesthetic criterias.

9.1.2.1 Down Conductor for Small Constructions

For small domestic or industrial buildings, down conductors are generally of the wire or strip type, whose impedance is mostly inductive. By paralleling two or more conductors, provided that they are separated by a sufficient distance (roughly equal to their length), their combined inductance is equal to a single inductance divided by n, the number of conductors in parallel.

As their separation decreases, their combined inductance is more than 1/n times that of a single conductor. Consequently, several codes recommend a minimum of two down conductors, even for the smallest buildings. The first reason invoked is that, by selectively opening the test joints which must be provided with all down conductors, the continuity can be tested readily during regular inspection.

The second reason is the risk of a single down conductor being severed, leaving the aerial system unearthed for long periods. This is of course speculative, and what can happen to one conductor can also happen to two or more. Therefore, the presence of two or n conductors does not preclude the need for periodic system inspection.

But the third reason is the most prominent one: by doubling the down conductor, the voltage gradient between the highest point and ground is divided by two, reducing the risk of side flashing with roof-mounted or inner parts. Whether or not they recommend a minimum of two down conductors in every case, all codes agree that an additional conductor must be added for each 20 to 30 m of perimeter above the first 30 m (or 100 m^2 ground surface).

Another aspect which may govern the number of down conductors is the quality of the earth terminal they connect to. If the earth conductivity is poor and several earth terminals are necessary, this will dictate a need for a corresponding number of down conductors. Here again we see that the lightning protection must be viewed as a system whose components can be separately studied but whose interaction must be understood.

Conductors should be evenly distributed around the perimeter, with building angles the preferred locations. Each should follow the shortest path to its earthing terminal, which guarantees a low inductance. When figuring the shortest path, the designer has to consider the three-dimensional aspect of this path. Right-angle bends should be minimized and tortuous paths avoided as much as possible. This is sometimes easier said than done since parapets and ornamental features may force some pointed angles and re-entrant loop, as shown in Fig. 9.16.[1] Such a loop, when carrying a high dI/dt, can create a high voltage difference which can cause an arc, damaging the structure comprised within the loop.

For instance, in the same figure we see that the loop inductance L represents about 4 μH. For a 30 kA/μs current, the voltage across the loop ends will be:

$$\Delta V = 4.10^{-6} \times \frac{30.10^3}{10^{-6}} = 120 \text{ kV}$$

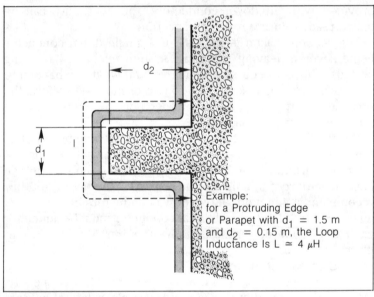

Example:
for a Protruding Edge
or Parapet with d_1 = 1.5 m
and d_2 = 0.15 m, the Loop
Inductance Is L ≈ 4 μH

Figure 9.16—Problems of Down Conductor Inductance Created by Re-entrant Loops (Parapets, Building Edges, Decorations, Etc.)

A voltage of 120 kV across 15 cm represents 8 kV/cm, which is in the range of breakdown voltage in air. Since the medium is not air but some construction material like concrete, bricks, etc., the breakdown voltage of the specific material should be known to carry out a valid calculation. However since these materials can be porous or compact, wet or dry, etc., their arcing voltages vary from slightly less to substantially more than that of air.

Therefore, conservatively, the same value as for air can be retained. Several codes handle this by stipulating the l/d ratio not to exceed a given value (20 in the German code, 8 in the British code). In our example for instance, the l/d ratio is $(2d_1 + d_2)/d_2 = 21$, so even the most permissive code is slightly exceeded. In such case, the conductor should be laid through instead of around the parapet.

Figure 9.17 shows another unacceptable routing of a down conductor, presenting a safety hazard for somebody walking underneath wearing wet clothing or carrying a long metal object.

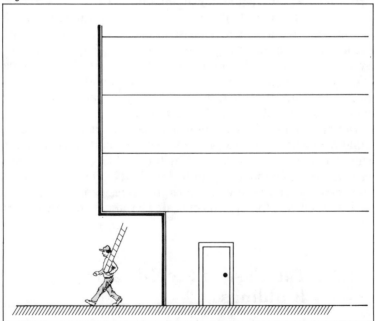

Figure 9.17—Inadmissible Positioning of Down Conductor on Building with Cantilevered Upper Floors (British Code)

9.1.2.2 Materials for Down Conductors

Depending on the system used (special conductors or existing building parts), down conductors are made of copper, copper-based alloys, aluminum or steel. If the supporting structure is made of aluminum, the down conductors and their fasteners must be made of aluminum as well. Minimum cross section varies between countries but is in the 20 to 50 mm^2 range for copper and 25 to 75 mm^2 for aluminum.

Although, legitimately, steel conductors should be sized according to their lesser conductivity, i.e., have about six times more cross section than copper, this is generally not done since the inductive part of the impedance by far dominates its resistive part, not to mention the skin effect. So mechanical strength and longevity dictate the minimum size as much as the cross section offered to current. Most codes accept the same cross section for steel as for aluminum.

The use of "natural" down conductors like rainfall pipes is permitted provided their cross-sectional area meets the above values and that their bonding to the rest of the protection system is secure and cannot be tampered with. For instance, the building owner must be warned that, should gutters and rain pipes be replaced by plastic ones, "artificial" down conductors would have to be installed.

Down conductors may spoil the aesthetic aspects of some buildings when they expand excessively and loosen in hot sunlight. If the artistic aspect of the building facade is that critical, down conductors can be installed inside service ducts provided that (a) they are not accessible to residents, but can still be inspected, and (b) they do not share elevator shafts or electrical cable trays.

9.1.2.3 The Case of Steel-Frame Buildings

Steel-frame or reinforced concrete construction offers the natural advantage of multiple parallel paths with greatly reduced inductance (see Chapter 2). With regard to protection to side flashing, i.e., lightning strikes "escaping" the influence of the aerials such a building behaves as a sort of Faraday cage.

Thus, they require no down conductors. It may even be possible to save the aerials, provided that the metal structure of the building sufficiently covers the roof. Even though there are no artificial down conductors, the steel frame structure still needs to be earthed via low-resistance terminals as will be explained in Section 9.1.3.

9.1.2.4 The Case of High-Rise Buildings and Structures

The consideration for down conductors of high-rise buildings, towers, etc. are identical to those discussed before. However, tall structures generally present the following particularities:

1. Their height is so great (50 m, 100 m or more) that the down conductor inductance becomes extremely high. This causes more and more risk of secondary side flashing with internal structures in the upper stories because of the large voltage gradient between the upper part of the conductors and the ground.

2. Above 100 m, the structure reaches a transmission line condition for the fastest rise times, therefore not only a forward current pulse but a reflected current pulse as well needs to be taken into account. This current reflection is due to the mismatch between the structure characteristic impedance (typically a few hundred ohms) and its "terminating" impedance, i.e., the earth electrode which is much lower (typically a few ohms to a few tens of ohms). During the first microseconds of the strike, the current at each point of the down conductor is the sum of the forward and backward currents, while the voltage is the difference between the forward and backward voltages.

3. In contrast to short buildings, tall buildings typically have the roof full of protrusions such as air conditioning exchanges, water tanks, flag poles, observation decks, strobe lights, elevator machinery, etc.

4. Fortunately, modern high-rise buildings are almost always of the metal-frame or reinforced concrete type. Thus the considerations given before to steel frame construction acting as a Faraday cage are perfectly applicable here

(see Figs. 9.18 and 9.19). In Fig. 9.19, the only addition to the existing material (besides earthing) is the roof conductive belt, which also encompasses the ventilation tower.

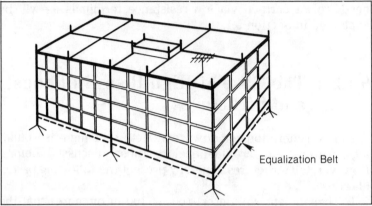

Figure 9.18—"Faraday-Cage" Style Lightning Conductor System for a Modern but Nonmetallic Building (from Golde, Ref. 1)

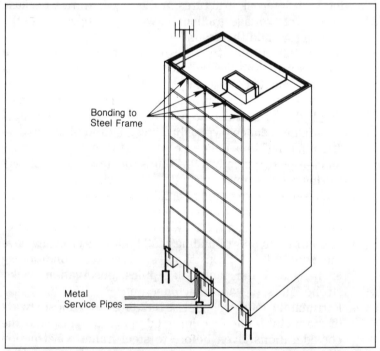

Figure 9.19—Protection of High-Rise Building, Using Metallic Structure as Down-Conductor/Faraday Cage Combination (from Golde, Ref. 1)

Given the above considerations, it is recommended that the reinforcing bars or building girders be electrically connected at intersections to provide a reliable path. Since we are dealing with grounding network impedances in the range of several ohms, it is superfluous to seek bonding quality of a few milliohms like the ones described in Chapter 3. Several tests have proven that ordinary binding wire or rivets provide a sufficient pressure between the crisscrossing bars. When they are finally embedded in concrete, their connection more or less stabilizes. Intensive tests have shown that as long as the two intersecting bars are touching, the electrical contact is good enough and no rupture of the concrete block occurs. Moreover, the first large lightning currents may cause a fusion welding. In contrast, if no bonding is made, gaps as small as a few millimeters can cause the concrete to erode around the intersection. **Note that these principles apply to lightning considerations only. If the building must also provide some RF shielding to ambient VHF or UHF noise, or withstand an EMP field, the framework intersections must be treated much more carefully.**

At each story level, all internal metal parts like lift rails, HVAC pipes, water pipes and floor grids must be connected horizontally to the vertical sides of the "Faraday cage." To do this, it is important for the architect and the builder to plan in advance to allow excess lengths of rebars to extend outside from the concrete blocks.

The Faraday cage behavior of the reinforced concrete is supported by both analytical and practical studies. For instance, Fig. 9.20 shows a comparison of two reinforced concrete buildings having a height of 42 m and separated by 40 m.[6] A surge generator was used to deliver an 8 A pulse (20 to 80 percent rise time of 5 μs) in the two buildings in series. The bases of the buildings were interconnected by a low-impedance grid.

In a first experiment, all the parameters being known or measured, it appears that the equivalent inductance of one building is 18 μH, giving for such a typical building a linear inductance of 0.43 μH/m. If we assume that no subsequent flashover would exist in the building, these results can be linearly extrapolated up to several kiloamperes, i.e., the 8 A being replaced by 8 kA and the voltage scale of Fig. 9.20 being replaced by kilovolts.

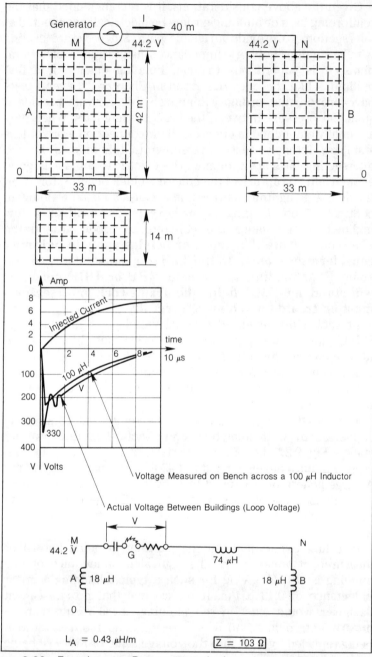

Figure 9.20—Experiment to Demonstrate the Impedance of Reinforced Concrete Buildings

In the second experiment, the left building is overlaid with a set of six vertical down conductors, tied together at the top but not touching the building except at ground level. Analyzing the second wave form, it has been concluded that the new inductance of the left-hand branch was 16.9 μH, not very different from the natural grid provided by the building (Fig. 9.21).

Finally, tying-up the six down conductors with the top of the building structure results in a total inductance of 17.9 μH, showing that they are closely coupled and that additional ground conductors over a metal-framed building are practically useless in reducing the overall inductance. However, they still divert about half of the current from the interior of the building structure, decrease the dc resistance of the down conductor net and allow easy inspection.

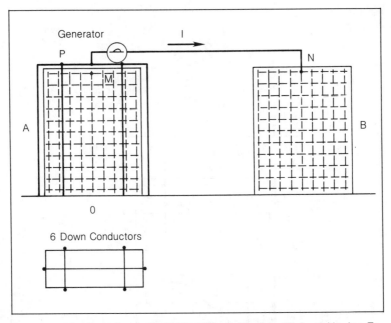

Figure 9.21—Experiment Showing Little or No Benefit from Having External Down Conductors when the Building Has a Steel-Reinforced Structure (continued next page)

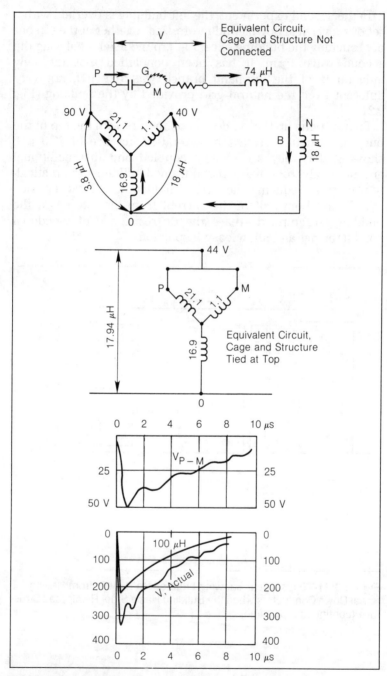

Figure 9.21—(continued)

9.34

9.1.2.5 Clearances to Avoid Internal Side Flashing

There are many cases where buildings with good aerial and earthing conductor systems still fail to protect people and property inside, causing death, injury and material damage. The reason is almost always ignorance or negligence regarding internal side flashes. Figure 9.22a shows such an example. The down conductor has a height of 15 m, and the lightning current has a peak value of 60 kA, with a slope of 30 kA/μs. The resistance of the earthing rod is 20 Ω. The rise of potential at the top of the down conductor is:

$$\Delta V = Ri + L \, dI/dt \tag{9.3}$$

Actually, the ohmic and inductive voltage drops are not exactly in phase and should not be added arithmetically, but for simplification and conservatism we will keep this expression. Considering that $L = 15$ m $\times$ 1 μH/m $= 15$ μH, we have:

$$\Delta V = 20 \times 60 \times 10^3 + 15 \times 10^{-6} \times 30 \times 10^3/10^{-6} = 1{,}600 \text{ kV}$$

Notice that because of the mediocre earth conductivity, the resistive contribution to this voltage rise is larger than the inductive contribution.

The arcing distance for 1,600 kV is about 2 m. If the water tank of Fig. 9.22a is closer than 2 m from the down conductor, a flashover will take place with all the ensuing risk of injuries and damage. Practically all national codes give minimum clearances between down conductors and metal objects like tanks, radiators, ducts, plumbing and faucets, etc.

The concept of "clearance" is a result of the dilemma of whether every metallic part in the building should be connected to earth. If so, it may flash over with a nearby lightning conductor. Or, should every metallic part in the building be connected to the nearest lightning conductor? In this case they may become dangerous for people inside the building.

The clearances, calculated from the worst-case peak current and dI/dt in the country of concern, must be understood as follows:

1. Any metal object within the clearance must be bonded to the down conductor system.
2. Any metal object outside this clearance can be kept isolated.

9.35

Although there are differences between national codes which reflect the particulars of keraunic levels and typical earthing resistances of each country, a typical formula to calculate the minimum clearance is:

$$D = 0.25\,R + \frac{h}{15n} \tag{9.4}$$

where, D = clearance in meters

R = earthing resistance of the entire earthing system

h = average height of down conductors

n = number of down conductors in parallel

Figure 9.23 shows a plot of this formula for few typical values of R and n. An absolute minimum of 0.5 m is also shown. Unfortunately, any code is of a somewhat academic nature, and many of these national codes fail to recognize the following reality: Once an inner metal object has been connected to a down conductor, it becomes itself an extension of the lightning conduit and is submitted to about the same voltage rise since it is too close to lower the path inductance significantly. And this extension "arm" may now be within flashing distance of other objects which were previously outside the clearance zone. Figure 9.22b shows an example of this possible cascade of secondary side flashings reaching an electrical wall outlet where the building electrical wiring (whose neutral is earthed somewhere at ground level) can be subjected to side flashing. Furthermore, people (themselves being more or less conductive) can be victims of these extension arms of the down conductors, especially in kitchens, bathrooms, urinals, etc. with all sorts of unpleasant results (Fig. 9.22c).

We can see that some inner parts of buildings, especially those with regular or casual human occupancy, have to be connected to down conductors. Therefore, it is a better practice to tie together all the metal girders, rebars and pipes to form a horizontal equipotential layer with the down conductor at that particular floor level. The French construction rules, for instance, extend these bonding practices even to the window and door frames, stair rails, etc.

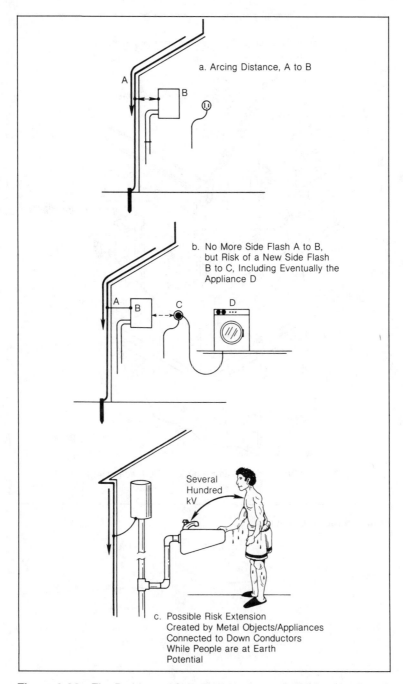

a. Arcing Distance, A to B

b. No More Side Flash A to B, but Risk of a New Side Flash B to C, Including Eventually the Appliance D

Several Hundred kV

c. Possible Risk Extension Created by Metal Objects/Appliances Connected to Down Conductors While People are at Earth Potential

Figure 9.22—The Problem of Side Flashing Inside Buildings (continued next page)

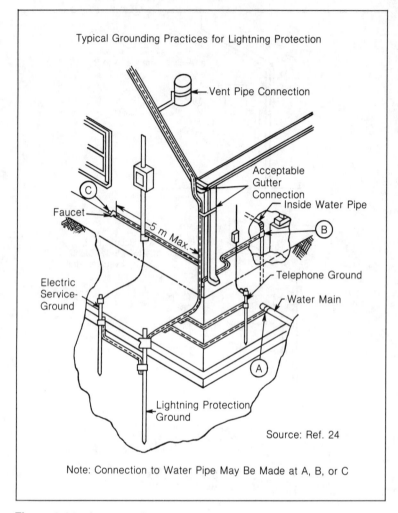

Figure 9.22—(continued)

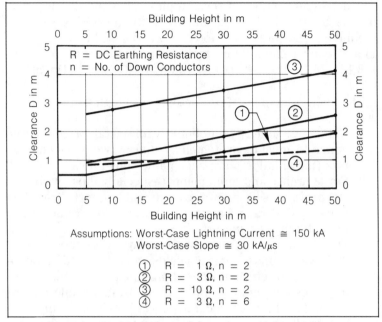

Figure 9.23—Minimum Clearance between a Lightning Conductor and a Metal Component Inside the Building.

9.1.2.6 Constructions with Especially High Risks

Construction types are termed **high-risk** either because their height or shape invariably makes them prime lightning targets or because building contents demand outstanding precautions. In the first category are chimneys, cooling towers, antenna masts, observation towers, lighthouses, rocket launching towers, etc. The second category includes buildings in which the artistic, financial or human value of the building is of prime importance. This is also the case for plants or storage areas for ammunition, explosives, fuels, etc.

A detailed coverage of these topics is beyond the objective of this book, which deals mostly with the EMI aspects of grounding. The subject is thoroughly addressed by Golde (Ref. 1) and, concerning military facilities and aircraft by MIL-STD-188-124, MIL-STD-1542 (USAF) and AFSC Design Handbook DH 1-4.

The main principles of protecting these high-risk structures are:

1. Chimneys, unless built entirely of metal or reinforced concrete, must be protected by at least two down conductors (metal ladders are acceptable substitutes).

2. For churches and monuments (especially those with high steeples), observation terraces and so forth, the bell house, guard rails, balconies, etc. must be connected to the lightning conductors.

3. Television towers, microwave relays, etc. should have their waveguides, coaxial shields and other feeders bonded to the structure at several intermediate heights.

4. In places containing explosives, fuels, flammable materials, and such, mechanical fasteners between metal members (bolt, rivets, etc.) must be treated as, or doubled by, secure electrical bonds (see Chapter 3). The Joule effect and mechanical strains caused by lightning currents, which in an ordinary building is simply dealt with by some cross-section requirement, are to be thoroughly considered in these buildings. Sometimes, to completely isolate the building from the lightning current, a system of shield wires and masts is installed around and above the facility.

9.1.3 Earthing Terminals of Lightning Conductors

The earth termination of a lightning conductor (rod, grid or plate) has the function of distributing the current into the surrounding mass of earth. The earthing resistance of rods and buried grids, their material and construction has been covered at length in Section 2.7. In a sense, the earth electrode is the extension of the down conductor into the earth. An excessive voltage rise between the down conductor end and the surrounding soil would create a safety hazard by side flashing, either above or just below ground level (with nearby utility conduits, for instance). Therefore it is recommended that the metal service pipes be bonded to the earth terminal near this building entry point.

In the past, underground water pipes have been excellent media due to their large amount of contact area and sufficient depth to prevent freezing. However, there is an increasing number of cases where water and gas pipes are either prohibited for use as grounds or are not accessible for electrical grounding purposes, i.e., where ground rods and meshes are to be used in lieu of National Electrical Code requirements. The 1972 U.S.A. National Electrical Code reads as follows:

> Where available on the premises, a metal underground water pipe shall always be used as the grounding electrode, regardless of its length and whether supplied by a community or a local underground water piping system or by a well on the premises. Where the buried portion of the metal water pipe (including any metal well casings effectively bonded to the pipe) is less than 10 feet long or where the water pipe is or is likely to be isolated by insulated sections or joints so that the effectively grounded portion is less than 10 feet long, it shall be supplemented by the use of an additional electrode specified by Sections 250-82 and 250-83.

National Electrical Code requirements are generally adhered to for industrial and commercial use. However, various private concerns and branches of the armed services prescribe techniques to be used to provide earth grounding of structures and equipments using ground rods and meshes.

Increasingly, bonding to water pipes is becoming ineffective because of the introduction of plastic pipes. In addition, natural gas transmission engineers object that bonding gas pipes to lightning conductors creates a risk of explosion. (On the other hand, not bonding them creates a risk of side flashing which could even be worse!) It therefore is wiser to use independent earth electrodes while still connecting them to all earthed metal services entering the building.

9.1.3.1 Connection of Down Conductors to Earth

Figures 9.24 through 9.26 show the various terminations of down conductors into earth. For small, nonmetallic houses where one or two down conductors are used, they simply connect to their respective earth electrode. A means of disconnection is always provided to check both the earthing resistance and eventually the down conductor integrity.

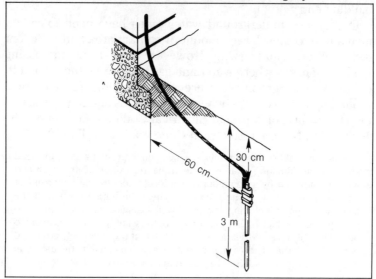

Figure 9.24—Grounding in Moist, Clay-Type Soil

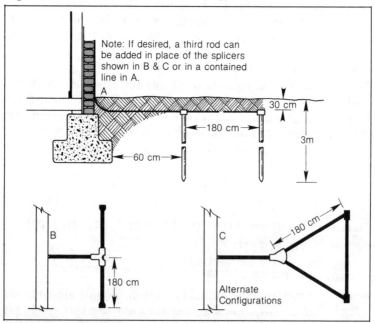

Figure 9.25—Grounding in Sandy or Gravelly Soils

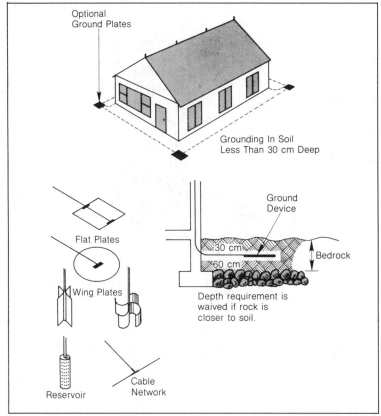

Figure 9.26—Alternate Forms of Grounding in Shallow or Rocky Soil

For buildings with metal frame or reinforced concrete (see Figs. 9.27 and 9.28), many investigations have concluded that concrete foundations with reinforcing bars are fully acceptable as lightning earth terminals (but this does not imply that they are acceptable as power earthing terminals). Measurements have shown that steel bars buried in concrete footing offer about the same earthing resistance as a copper electrode of same contact area. In other words, the volume resistivity of the concrete is sufficiently less than that of earth, so it does not increase significantly the total resistance. However, single bolts anchored in concrete footing are totally insufficient as earth electrodes because of their too small contact area. In this case, the mounting of Fig. 9.28 should be used.

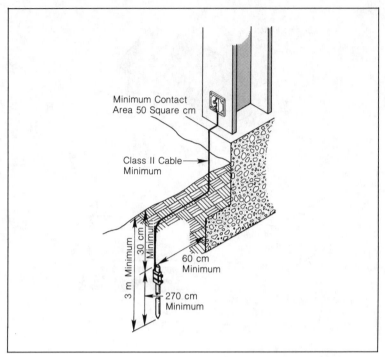

Figure 9.27—Connection of Down-Conductors to Earth Electrode by Building Structure

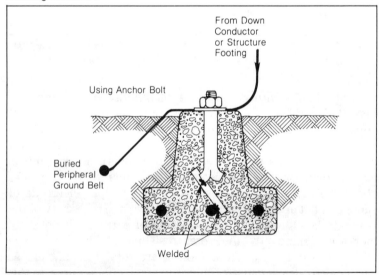

Figure 9.28—Connection of Down Conductors to Earth Electrodes Using Anchor Bolts

The final decision as to whether the concrete foundations are good enough electrodes should be based on an actual resistance measurement or prediction. If it meets the initial objective or specific codes requirements which themselves vary from 2.5 Ω (Holland) up to 30 Ω (South Africa), the concrete foundations are an acceptable substitute. Otherwise, they must be supplemented by a real electrode system.

Figure 9.29 summarizes lightning aerials, conductors and earthing techniques as employed in a modern building.

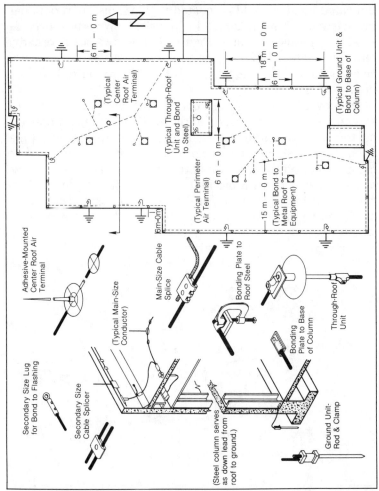

Figure 9.29—Summary of a Modern Building Lightning Aerial, Conductor and Earthing System. Steel-framed buildings can use columns as down conductors, but these must be bonded to a roof aerial network.

9.1.3.2. Method of Connecting Ground Rod to Structure and Grid Mesh

Figure 9.30 illustrates preferred techniques for connecting ground rods to structures and grid meshes. The portion of the ground wire making contact between the Joslyn washer and the base shoe should be tinned to reduce the effects of galvanic corrosion. All bolts and nuts should be securely tightened to prevent bond-impedance deterioration with age and wear. Indicated bonds should be coated with a moisture-proof coating capable of maintaining its physical properties over an extended period of time. Figure 9.31 shows an alternative technique where an intermediate collector plate, easier to access and maintain, is used to relay the ground rod connection.

The cover, which is placed over a portion of the ground rod extending above the surface of the earth, may be of a nonconductive medium as long as it remains waterproof over time. Such covers should be removable or provide entrance to facilitate periodic inspection of the ground-rod connection and measurement of earth resistance. The bonding cable can be a 4/0 or solid 6 mm (1/4″) copper wire, or larger sizes. Techniques displayed in Fig. 9.30 can be applied to all types of building structures with steel frames and base shoes.

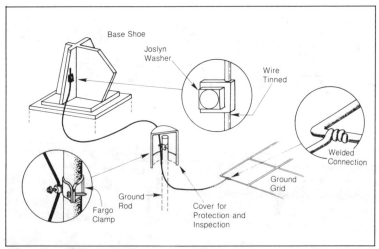

Figure 9.30—Method for Connecting Ground Rods to Structure and Grid Mesh

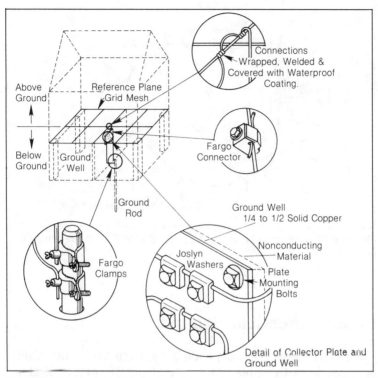

Figure 9.31—Alternate Method for Connecting Rods to Structure and Grid Using Collector Plate

9.1.3.3 Method for Connecting Earth Ground Grid to a Structure

Figure 9.32 illustrates a preferred technique for connecting an earth ground-grid to a structure. The end of the bond cable should be tinned where connection is made with the structure's base shoe in order to reduce effects of galvanic corrosion. A double connection is made between the bond cable and the grid mesh to reduce the possibility of bond deterioration with age and wear. All connections should be wrapped, welded and covered with a protective coating as indicated. All structure base shoes should be connected in a like manner to the grid mesh. Techniques illustrated in Fig. 9.30 should be followed when grid meshes are used in conjunction with ground rods.

9.47

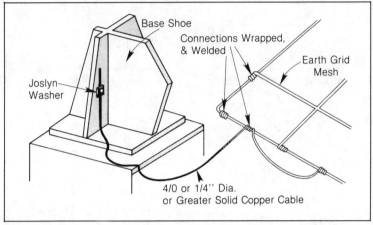

Figure 9.32—Method of Connecting Earth Grid to Structure (When Grid Is Used Instead of a Rod)

9.1.3.4 Chemical Grounds

We have seen that, depending on local code, maximum permissible earthing resistances vary from 2.5 Ω up to 30 Ω. In the U.S.A., most power companies look for a ground resistance of 10 Ω or less. It was shown in Section 2.7.3 that artificial salting of the soil or immersion in a saltwater solution was a way to decrease either the soil resistivity immediately around the rod or the electrode contact resistance.

There are numerous drawbacks and constraints to this method, including:

1. The need for more frequent inspections
2. A risk of polluting the water tables
3. Augmented corrosion of nearby buried services

As a result, the chemical ground is to be employed only as a last resort. One simple method is to dig a circular trench of about 0.30×0.30 m depth at a radius of 0.60 m around each electrode. The trench is filled with an electrically conductive chemical such as magnesium sulfate, copper sulfate or sodium chloride which is kept wet. The treatment must be renewed every few years. More elaborate methods use a real well surrounding the rod.

9.2 Lightning Protection of Utilities

This section explains lightning protection measures for the various services running along and entering the building, and their grounding rules. Essentially, they are:
1. Radio and television cables
2. Power lines
3. Telephone and data lines

9.2.1 Radio Service Aerials and Their Descent Cables

Radio antennas invariably constitute lightning targets, not only when mounted on the roof but even when installed in attics beneath nonmetallic roofs. In all cases (even if close to a lightning aerial), the antenna mast and clamps must be bonded to the lightning conductor. If the antenna is within the protection zone of the lightning aerial, no further precaution is needed. Unfortunately, such positioning of the antenna may cause unacceptable performance alteration (echo, dead angle, change in the gain pattern, degradation of front-to-back ratio, etc.). In many cases, the antenna has to be kept deliberately away from the lightning aerials and placed on some high point of the roof. Thus, the antenna will be hit and the bonding described above, although necessary, is insufficient. Part of the lightning current will flow on the cable and may even reach the radio receiver or transmitter, causing damage or injury.

If the radio equipment uses a coaxial or waveguide feeder, its envelope must be connected to the roof conductor system, i.e., the top of the lightning down conductors. In addition, a surge arrestor must be installed between the center conductor and the shield since the product of the lightning current times the shield impedance can still cause an excessive longitudinal voltage inside the coaxial line. Details on these arrestors and their mounting will follow. If the radio equipment uses a bifilar line for its antenna connection, both wires need to be equipped with surge arrestors.

The surge arrestors are bonded to the nearest down conductor or to the building steel frame if this latter is used as a down conductor. The surge arrestors mounted on a bifilar line are usually the three-terminal type; that is, they clamp each wire to ground in case of overvoltage but also provide differential (wire-to-wire) surge protection.

9.2.2 Electrical Supply and Telephone or Data Lines

These services are provided either by underground cables or overhead lines. If they are underground cables (buried in accessible trenches), the cables almost invariably have an outer armor. This armor must be bonded to the building earthing network as any other service pipe.

Obviously, as a result of this bonding, the cable sheath will rise to some voltage with respect to earth during the flow of lightning current. This in turn will couple transient voltages into the power or telecommunication wires contained in this cable, so they may have to be protected by surge arrestors. These are generally prescribed by the power or telephone companies.

If the service enters the building via an overhead line, or if the building is supplied by a buried line which becomes an overhead line within the striking area of this building, the line will be subject to both direct hits and induced voltage from nearby flashes. In any case, an overhead line presents a higher risk than a buried one. Depending on the type of service, the line is balanced (symmetrical versus ground) or unbalanced, and the two cases need to be considered separately.*

9.2.2.1 Open Balanced Wires

This is typically the case of telephone lines, remote control or remote sensing lines and, generally, any two or more open-wire lines, even though the source and load may not be ideally

---

*Typically in exposed areas, power and telephone companies install a "messenger wire" which is a protection wire placed atop their normal line. Its capture zone encompasses all the wire to be protected. This messenger is earthed regularly, like at every pole. This concept can be extended to buried lines if their burial depth is insufficient.

balanced. The overhead wires are subjected to both direct hits and induction fields. In addition, telephone wires often share some paths and poles with power lines, and a remotely induced surge on the power line can couple with the telephone line over their common runs. All these surges generally appear as common-mode interference, but in addition, they invariably carry a more or less severe differential-mode component for two reasons:

1. The common-mode voltage pulses may exhibit a slight phase shift between the several wires of the line.
2. One of the lines may become temporarily grounded either by a flashover or by the very operation of an upstream arrestor.

Therefore, at the building entry, the lines must be equipped with a surge protector of the high-energy type, capable of carrying the most severe lightning-induced pulse typical of the area. Many codes or local practices stipulate these waveforms, whose shape and amplitude may depend on the line exposure. One often recommended value for outdoor lines is the 6 kV, 1 µs/50 µs waveform (open-circuit voltage of a simulator having 50 Ω of internal impedance).

The surge protector is usually mounted in a three-terminal arrangement as shown in Figure 9.33 such that the arrival of a common- or differential-mode transient, or both, will fire the device and divert most of the surge to the building earthing. For those power line service entrances where a stepdown transformer is provided, transient protectors are necessary on both the high-voltage (primary) and low-voltage (secondary) sides of the transformer.

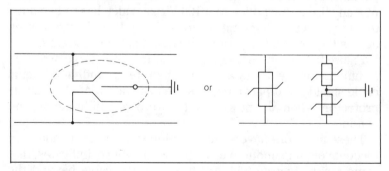

Figure 9.33—Differential- and Common-Mode Surge Protection with Three-Electrode Gas Tube (left) or Three Discrete Surge Suppressors (right)

Until the 1960s, surge protectors were merely carbon-block limiters or air-gap devices. These are being progressively phased-out and replaced by more elaborate gas-filled tubes or metal-oxide varistors whose setting voltages and VI curves are more predictable and dependable. A description of surge arrestors and their selection method is presented in Volume 5, *EMC in Components*, of this handbook series.

Regarding protection of the lines entering the building, the task of surge protection is generally split into two functions and two types of protective devices (primary and secondary). The first ones are installed either:

1. At power service entrance, for power lines
2. At the main distribution frame (MDF), for telephone lines
3. At the cable junction box, for other types of cables

The mission of these primary protective devices is to divert the bulk of the lightning pulse carried by the wire to building ground. Therefore they have to be earthed as close as possible to the point where the cable penetrates the building. The importance of this is both administrative and technical. In many cases the line belongs to the power or telephone company, and they need easy access to the protective equipment. Also, the lightning current diverted by the surge protector should have the least possible chance to couple with other circuits inside the building, creating another problem. Because the entry box, panel or plate of these services is metallic, it provides a good protection against arcing.

Finally, the connection of the surge arrestor leads to the line and earth must be short and wide to have the least possible parasitic inductance. With a slope of 10 kA/μs, each centimeter of lead wire corresponds to a 100 V rise which has to be added to the protector clamping or arc voltage. It is therefore seen across the line by the protected equipment downstream.

Figure 9.34 shows some typical mounting of surge arrestors at building entry. Parts a and b illustrate grounding of signal cable shields, and part c depicts the installation of a line surge protector when ac power is fed through an underground conduit.

These arrestors have some reaction time, and this added to the unavoidable inductive drop shown above indicates that some residual surge will still travel on the cable beyond the surge arrestor (Fig. 9.35). Furthermore, the rest of the wiring branches inside the building, although less exposed than the outside net, can still pick up some indirect lightning effects, especially if inner wires run along structure members, etc. For these reasons, secondary protections with lesser energy requirements are generally installed either at floor or room distribution panels, or inside the equipments themselves. The distance (or performance ratings) of the secondary surge protectors versus the primary ones must be such that there is no risk that the secondary device will operate before the primary one.

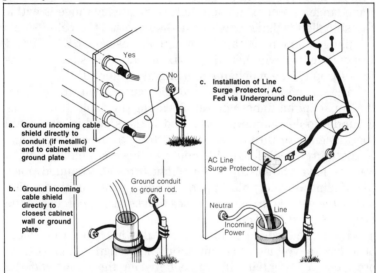

Figure 9.34—Grounding of Primary Surge Suppressors and Cable Shields at Building Entry

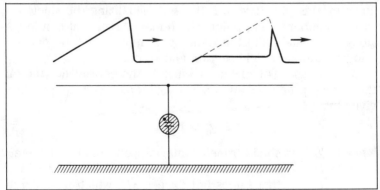

Figure 9.35—Residual Surge Due to Response Time of High-Energy Surge Suppressors

9.2.2.2 Unbalanced Lines (Coaxial)

Many services like cable TV, local area networks, etc. use coaxial cables. Although providing some protection against noise coupling (see Chapter 7 of this book), the braided shield may be totally insufficient against lightning. The transfer impedance concept (see Section 7.2) can be used to predict the behavior of a coaxial cable carrying a lightning current.

Given a lightning current rise time of 1 μs or more, the quasi-totality of its spectrum exists below 300 kHz. Since the transfer impedance of a coaxial cable in this frequency range is within the so-called "Ohm's Law" or dc-like region, the cable shield coupling can be predicated from the dc resistance of its braid. Depending on whether the coaxial cable is suspended or underground, the mechanism is slightly different.

With suspended cables, the shield current will travel from the impact point in both directions along the cable. If there are grounded poles along its path, and if the shield is connected (permanently or through surge diverters) to these poles, some of the current will leave the shield at these grounding points. Studies have shown that after about 3 to 30 grounded poles (depending on the pole impedance and pole earthing resistance), the shield current decreases to less than 3 percent of the original stroke current.

With buried shields, the current flowing over the shield produces a voltage gradient along its length. This voltage produces a potential difference between the cable and the surrounding ground until the shield-to-earth voltage exceeds the jacket breakdown voltage. Some of the lightning current flows by this puncture into the soil, equalizing the shield-to-earth potential at that point. The remaining current continues along the shield until eventually a new puncture occurs, bridging another shield section and so on.

In both cases (overhead or buried), the current flowing on the shield produces an inner longitudinal voltage gradient given by:

$$\Delta V = Z_t \times l \times I \tag{9.5}$$

where, Z_t = shield transfer impedance in ohms per meter
l = length of the cable segment in m (provided that l does not exceed $\lambda/4$, which for a surge

rise time of 1 μs corresponds to about 60 to 70 m of cable)

I = lightning current in amps

Considering the progressive decrease of the shield current over the cable length when moving away from the impact point, and given the fact that the $Z_t \times l \times I$ product is only meaningful as long as the segment being considered carries a uniform current, the biggest contributor to that inner voltage gradient is the first segment that extends a few hundred meters beyond the strike point. (The velocity of current in the shield is about 20 m/μs.) The ohmic-region value of Z_t varies from 3 mΩ/m for excellent, tight copper braid to 50 mΩ/m for cheap, lightweight shields. Taking an average length of 100 m, this corresponds to voltages ranging from 300 V/kA to 5 kV/kA of lightning current. Therefore, even though the shield provides some degree of decoupling, it is notoriously insufficient to protect the circuits at each end. Surge protectors are also required.

Normally, coaxial cable shields should be connected to the building earthing at their entry point. However, we encounter the dilemma explained in Chapter 7 regarding ground loops since a coaxial shield also carries the signal return current:

1. If the shield is grounded to buildings at both ends, all steady noise existing between these two earthings will be continuously imposed on the signal, degrading the S/N ratio or even exceeding the signal level.

2. If the shield is grounded at one end only or floated up to the 0 V planes of the transmitting and receiving equipments, the link will function but will be exposed to destructive and hazardous overvoltages during a lightning event.

So the solution is either to use a double braid with an insulation between the braids or to connect the shield at both ends at building entry through a surge arrestor which will set the path only if a shield-to-ground voltage of few hundred volts is reached. In this case no primary protectors are necessary between the center conductor and the shield at building entry point, but secondary protectors are still needed at room or equipment levels.

9.3 Various Electrical Returns and References, Internal to Building

The green safety wire, grounding rods and grounding grids of buildings are intended to control lightning and shock hazards to personnel and prevent damage to equipment. However, since nearly all equipments in a given building (see Table 9.1) will share the same green safety wire and building ground system, they become polluted with both transient and steady-state electrical current flow and noise voltage drops.

For example, at 60 Hz, a 30 m run of No. 12 AWG green safety wire exhibits an impedance of 0.16 Ω and may have 50 equipments connected thereto. Even if all are not in operation at any one time, each may contain two 0.1 μF capacitors for electrical noise suppression between phase or neutral and green lines, each one draining 5 mA from the 120 V ac. Thus, 50 equipments $\times$ 0.005 A $\times$ 0.16 Ω yields 40 mV of 60 Hz contamination on the frames of all equipment. Consequently, if frames or shields of sensitive equipment cables and circuitry are returned to these grounds, the common-mode impedance coupling may completely degenerate their EMC performance.

The foregoing situation is shown in Fig. 9.36. The 50/60 Hz, ac power source in reality is also a source of RF noise pollution since it contains pickup from the electromagnetic ambient due to the antenna effect of the source-feed system complex. These source voltages produce drops across the green wire as shown in the equivalent circuit of Fig. 9.37. When the frame of any circuit k is also the return side of a sensitive network, a portion of both the 60 Hz and RF common-mode voltages appear at its input terminals. If the associated frequency-amplitude levels are above the circuit sensitivity, EMI may result. Furthermore, some energy from transients developed in equipment e_1 can cross-couple to equipment e_k due to the finite impedances of the black, white and green wires. Therefore, as discussed in Chapters 6 and 8, the options available are to segregate the currents or reduce the common-ground impedance.

In the latter perspective, it has been shown (Chapter 2) that no wire can achieve a reasonably low impedance beyond about 100 kHz and that a ground plane or grid is the only possible low-impedance reference when dealing with dimensions as large as a room or an entire building floor area. This is also consistent with the criteria set forth in Section 8.2 for multi-point grounding where it was shown that, for equipment separation exceeding 10 m, a multipoint bonding to a low-impedance plane was the best tradeoff above a few megahertz.

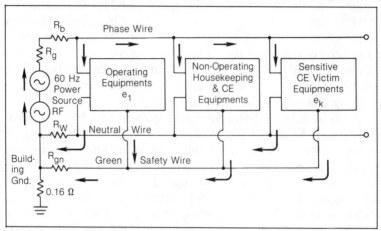

Figure 9.36—60 Hz Power and RF Noise Coupling to Green Safety Wire and to Chassis/Frame of Victim Equipments

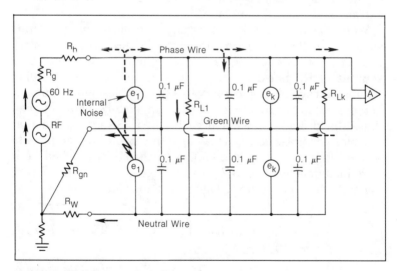

Figure 9.37—Equivalent Circuit of Figure 9.36 Showing Green-Wire Common-Impedance Coupling of Both 60 Hz and RF Noise

All buildings and structural complexes housing electronic equipment which is susceptible to or capable of generating RF energy should be supplied with a low-impedance reference plane, ground-grid mesh or green wire bus-bar system as applicable. Conductive shielding media used for the purpose of attenuating RF energy are dependent upon a low-impedance reference plane for effectiveness. Shields that are connected to a relatively high-impedance reference plane are ineffective in attenuating RF electric fields and may radiate energy which results from potentials induced on the reference plane by extraneous users of the plane.

All buildings and structural complexes housing electronic equipment which is susceptible to or capable of generating RF energy should be supplied with a low-impedance reference plane, ground-grid mesh or green wire bus-bar system as applicable. Conductive shielding media used for the purpose of attenuating RF energy are dependent upon a low-impedance reference plane for effectiveness. Shields that are connected to a relatively high-impedance reference plane are ineffective in attenuating RF electric fields and may radiate energy which results from potentials induced on the reference plane by extraneous users of the plane.

While earth ground is not essential to performance at this stage, a single connection to earth is desirable for safety protective purposes. When sensitive equipment and significant sources of RF noise are to be located in the same building (almost always), it is necessary to shield cables and equipment housings and to provide a very low-impedance path between these shields and the EMI source. Figure 9.38 shows a situation in which the noise sources may be either cables or equipments which exhibit capacitive coupling to their victims, and both have impedances (Z_1 and Z_2) to some ground reference. From Fig. 9.39, the coupled noise signal e_s to the victim voltage e_v is:

$$\frac{e_v}{e_s} = \frac{R_v}{R_v + R_s + R_1 + R_2 + R_g + jX_c/2} \tag{9.6}$$

$$— \approx \frac{R_v}{R_v + R_s + R_g + X_c/2}$$

for R_1 and R_2 << both other R_s and X_c values.

In an effort to reduce EMI, the Faraday shield (i.e., cable or equipment shield) is placed around the noise source, the victim or somewhere in between. For illustrative purposes, the latter is shown in Fig. 9.40. From the equivalent circuit of Fig. 9.41, the new emitter-receptor, coupled-signal ratio is:

$$\frac{e'_v}{e'_s} = \frac{R_b}{R_b + R_s + R_1 + R_g/2 + jX_c} \times \frac{R_v}{R_v + R_2 + R_g/2 + jX_c}$$

$$= \frac{R_b R_v}{R_s R_v + X_c(R_s + R_v) + X_c^2} \tag{9.7}$$

for R_1, R_2 and $R_g \ll$ both other R_s and X_c values,

where, R_b = bond impedance to reference of the Faraday shield.

To determine the decoupling shielding effectiveness (SE) of the shield, the ratio of Eq. (9.7) (after shielding) to Eq. (9.6) (before shielding) is:

$$SE = \frac{R_b (R_v + R_s + R_g + X_c/2)}{R_s R_v + X_c (R_s + R_v) + X_c^2} \tag{9.8}$$

$$= \frac{R_b(R_v + R_s + R_g)}{R_s R_v} \text{ for } X_c \ll R_s' \text{ at highest value} \tag{9.9}$$

For the shield to perform well in Eq. (9.9):

$$R_b \ll R_s \text{ and } R_v \tag{9.10}$$
$$R_g \ll R_s \text{ and } R_v \tag{9.11}$$
$$R_b \text{ and } R_g \ll X_c \text{ at highest frequencies} \tag{9.12}$$

The bond impedance, R_b and the reference plane impedance R_g both increase with frequency while X_c decreases with frequency. Thus a crossover frequency will be reached at which the shield is no longer effective. In fact, it can become resonant and radiate.

Since R_s, R_v and X_c can take on any value between any two equipments in a building, there is no unique solution to the problem. Notwithstanding the above, in an attempt to quantify R_b and R_g, somewhat arbitrary criteria will be selected. R_s and R_v may likely be of the order of 100 Ω. To obtain a 40 dB minimum SE, R_b and R_g must be ≤ 0.5 Ω in Eq. (9.9) at the highest frequency for which the building noise source and victim are separated by a distance of $\lambda/20$. Table 9.3 summarizes this.

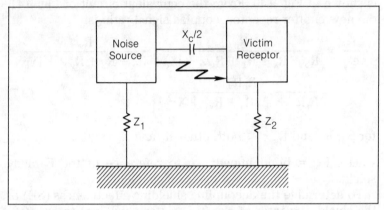

Figure 9.38—Capacitive Coupling between Noise Source and Victim

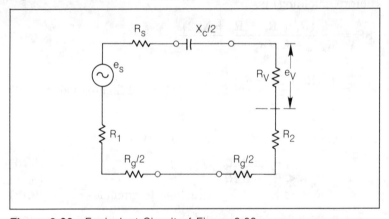

Figure 9.39—Equivalent Circuit of Figure 9.38

From Table 9.3, a second criterion can be generated to give the required impedance of both the shield bond and ground reference plane as a function of building floor length and frequency to yield a 40 dB SE. This is shown in Fig. 9.42 in which it is presumed that a dc resistance of 3 mΩ is the lowest that can be practically attained without substantial cost. Thus, the RF impedance becomes asymptotic to this value below the notch frequency.

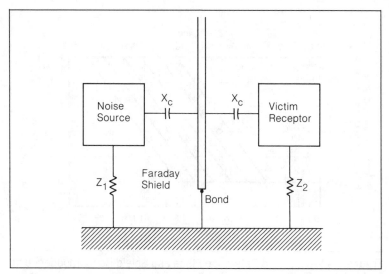

Figure 9.40—Inserting a Faraday Shield in Figure 9.39

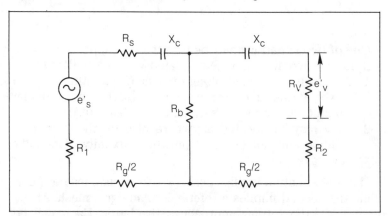

Figure 9.41—Equivalent Circuit of Figure 9.40

Table 9.3—Shield Bond and Reference-Plane Impedance at Maximum Useful Frequency

Source-Victim Distance in m (ft)		Maximum SE Frequency	R_b and R_g at Max. SE Freq.
1	(3)	15 MHz	0.5 Ω
3	(10)	5 MHz	0.5 Ω
10	(30)	1.5 MHz	0.5 Ω
30	(100)	500 kHz	0.5 Ω
100	(300)	150 kHz	0.5 Ω
300	(1,000)	50 kHz	0.5 Ω

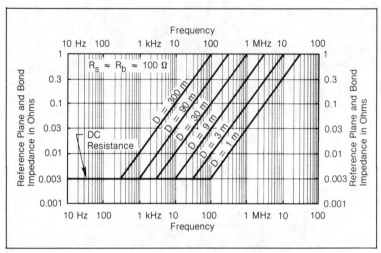

Figure 9.42—Required Reference Plane and Shield Bond Impedance of Buildings vs. Frequency and Building Floor Length

One of two situations may be presumed to apply to communication electronics equipment located within a building:

1. They will be located along or near (say, within 2 m) of power wiring raceways or cable trays. (Ordinary tubular conduit cannot be considered as a substitute.)
2. They may be located anywhere else on the floor of a building and not benefit from the proximity of metallic raceways.

The first situation implies perhaps a few bus lines per floor, while the second implies a reference plane grid mesh. At the outer limit, the former approaches the latter. Each will be discussed separately.

In a sense, a **reference grid** can be to an equipment deck what the metal chassis is to an electronic apparatus. (Sometimes it is called a **signal reference grid,** but this is an improper term because the grid is seldom a part of the normal signal circuits.) Unfortunately, the principle of this grid or plane, so clear in theory, becomes unclear when blueprints are laid over a table and the architect asks what has to be done.

For instance:

1. Should this floor mesh be connected to building structure? Where and how?
2. Can the reinforced concrete rebars be used as a substitute? If so, how?
3. If both items 1 and 2 are required, should they be connected or isolated?
4. Can either 1 or 2 be used as an **instrument ground**? If not, how does this instrument ground relate to 1 and 2?

The answers normally should be found in the myriad of installation standards and practices dealing with grounding. However, depending on the industry or institute that has issued them, these documents generally optimize the specifics of their particular discipline or application, assuming others are of secondary importance or fall in the category of common sense. For instance, a building may:

1. Contain low-frequency, sensitive analog equipment requiring a single-point ground and dedicated ground buses
2. Contain telecommunication equipment working in the HF, VHF or UHF bands
3. Contain computing centers and other large interconnected digital equipments
4. Have to be immune to severe lightning strikes or NEMP

Depending on which of the above features is advanced, the building grounding rules may be different. Since a large building may represent any combination or even all of the above, the installation designer is typically faced with several different practices, some of which are irreconcilable. Even the fact that safety always takes precedence may not be enough to sort out the "best" option. The next paragraphs offer some guidelines for making this choice.

9.3.1 Various Types of Room-Level Ground References

The **room-level plane,** or **pseudo-plane** can be in several forms:

1. A continuous sheet of copper, aluminum or zinc-plated steel

2. A mesh of round conductors
3. A mesh of flat copper straps or braid
4. The natural grid offered by the raised metal floor structure

The impedance of these structures has been described in Section 2.6. Figure 9.43 shows the realization of RF reference grids by discrete conductors. For places where a false floor is used, an effective and less expensive alternative to a ground grid is the raised floor supporting frame (Fig. 9.44). For this solution to work, the requirements are:

1. Individual metal members (stringers) must be bolted to each pedestal. They must be free of oxide and dirt. Standard bolts are required rather than speed nuts or sheet metal screws.
2. Members, pedestals and their top plates must be suitably plated so that a low-resistance bond exists from member to member.

Experience has shown that it is not necessary that the floor tiles themselves make a low-resistance contact with the supporting grid provided their surface resistance is still low enough (10^9 Ω or less) to avoid static charge buildup.

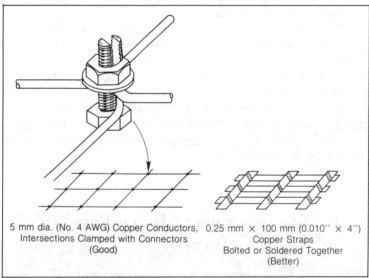

5 mm dia. (No. 4 AWG) Copper Conductors,   0.25 mm × 100 mm (0.010'' × 4'')
Intersections Clamped with Connectors   Copper Straps
(Good)   Bolted or Soldered Together
(Better)

Figure 9.43—Realization of Room-Level Reference Grid

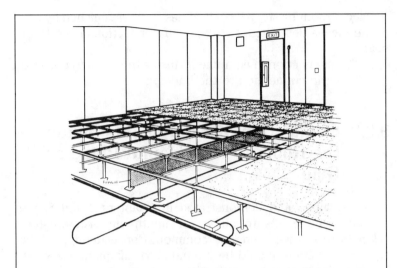

1. Bolted down stringers (struts between supporting posts) assure low electrical resistance joints.
2. Isolation from building steel except via computer system grounding conductors, conductor to computer systems central grounding point and to power source ground.
3. Ideal floor height for crawling access is 75 cm. Less than 45 cm restricts air flow. For large computer rooms, install firewall separation barriers to confine fire and Halon extinguishing gas.

Figure 9.44—Raised Floor Supporting Structure as a Signal Reference Grid (from Ref. 8)

It should be remarked that, although the floor underneath the equipments seems to be a normal medium to support this grid, it is nowhere stated that the grid has to be at this level. Electrons do not flow by gravity and, in such installations where a floor grid is impractical, the grid can be laid under the ceiling or on top of the equipments. This, however, requires that all other attachment rules for cable trays, cabinet bonding straps, etc. are also turned from downside to upside. Also, one must remember that by no means should this EMI grid or plane be considered a substitute for the safety grounds, i.e., the green or green-yellow earthing conductors.

Once a room or story-level grid has been established by one of the means described, two types of connections need to be made:

1. The connection of equipments inside the room to this grid
2. The grid connection to the building

9.3.2 Connection of Equipments inside the Room to the Ground Plane or Grid

As explained and demonstrated in Chapters 2 and 8, the ground plane exists to allow for multipoint grounding of cabinets to a low-impedance common. Consequently, all the equipment frames should be grounded to this plane via wide, low-impedance straps (see the discussion on straps in Section 2.3). These straps will not substitute for the green safety wire which must still be connected to each equipment containing hazardous voltages. In this respect, aircraft, vehicles and ships are in a totally different situation from buildings because they use, by nature, a continuous metal plane for both power, safety and RF ground.

In the case where the reinforced concrete grid is used as ground plane, the above provisions must have been done at construction time. Otherwise, getting access to the buried bars will require some heavy construction rework.

9.3.3 Connection of the Ground Plane or Grid to the Building Structure

If noise were the only problem, it would be generally better to leave this ground plane floated since its purpose is to act as an RF reference for all the equipment in the room. However, right from the beginning, this option is made impossible by the fact that equipment chassis are grounded to the power earthing terminal via their safety wires. In addition, keeping this plane floated would create safety issues because of possible voltage gradients between this grid and the rest of the building in case of power fault or lightning (side flashes). Therefore, the generally recommended scheme is shown in Fig. 9.45, option A where the floor grid is connected at one point (generally the room power distribution panel) to the safety bus. This terminal can also collect the Faraday shield of the isolation transformer.

All pipes (HVAC, plumbing, conduits, etc.) also should be bonded to the grid at this point, if practicable, or at least at the point where they penetrate the grid perimeter. These metal ducts and tubes usually travel over long paths in the building, sometimes come from the roof (air conditioning towers, etc.) and are therefore very likely to carry direct or induced lightning currents.

The connection of the grid to the building structure at more than one point is not recommended because this would re-create low-frequency ground loops which would allow all the building coupled noise, machine leakages and fault currents to flow on the reference grid. One might object that due to the high capacitance between the grid and the building risers and beams, this coupling will exist sooner or later. But the advantage of a single-point connection of the ground plane to the building structure still remains indisputably superior against low-frequency EMI. Another objection to this single-point connection is the possible side flashing or hazardous voltage gradients between the building structure or lighting down conductors and the far ends of the ground plane or grid. This risk can be serious and should be checked using the criteria developed in Section 9.1.2.5 for proper clearances.

In buildings where EMC grounding checks are regular maintenance practices, the single-point connection of the ground plane can be reliable. Unfortunately, in many buildings, these checks may be nonexistent. Little by little, all sorts of pipes, ducts, etc. will touch or be attached to the ground plane (especially in the case of raised metal floor) making the single-point ground a utopian concept. Even in this case, the fact remains that the EMI "fire fighter" sometimes will have to chase down and eliminate these loops to reduce interference.

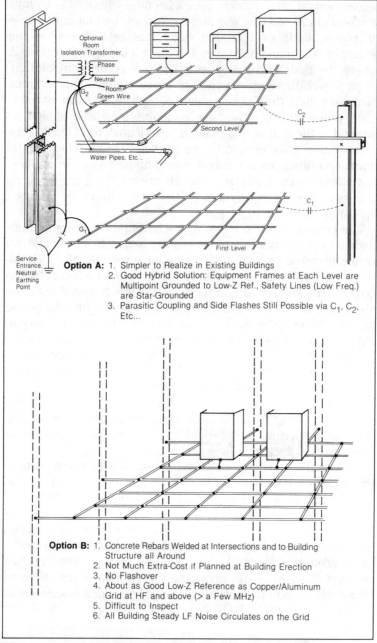

Option A: 1. Simpler to Realize in Existing Buildings
2. Good Hybrid Solution: Equipment Frames at Each Level are Multipoint Grounded to Low-Z Ref., Safety Lines (Low Freq.) are Star-Grounded
3. Parasitic Coupling and Side Flashes Still Possible via C_1, C_2, Etc...

Option B: 1. Concrete Rebars Welded at Intersections and to Building Structure all Around
2. Not Much Extra-Cost if Planned at Building Erection
3. No Flashover
4. About as Good Low-Z Reference as Copper/Aluminum Grid at HF and above (> a Few MHz)
5. Difficult to Inspect
6. All Building Steady LF Noise Circulates on the Grid

Figure 9.45—Connection of Room Grid to Building Structure

9.3.4 Use of Concrete Rebar as a Ground Plane

It has been suggested that a possible substitute to a dedicated RF ground plane would be the reinforced concrete grid. This solution is viable under certain conditions:

1. Electrical bonding of equipment cabinets, chassis, etc. to this grid must be possible and practical as described in Section 9.3.1.

2. At the time of construction, each intersection must make a good electrical contact. Arc welding would be electrically suitable, but some architects prohibit it as weakening the strength of the steel bars. In this case, brazing or cadwelding is recommended instead. This takes into account the fact that the ordinary loose binding wires used to tie the bars may be sufficient for lightning purposes, where contact resistances in the ohm(s) range are acceptable but cannot match the lower resistance requirements for an EMI and noise-control reference plane.

The above constraints imply that the use of the reinforced concrete grid as an electrical ground plane has been planned before the building is erected (see Fig. 9.45, option B). Provided that these conditions are met, such a ground grid will be an excellent means of decreasing transient common-mode voltages in case of EMP or lightning, and an acceptable RF ground to avoid voltage differences between equipments processing digital signals.

However, this kind of grid cannot be used when the system requiring a ground reference processes low-level analog signals such as voice communications, instrumentation signals, analog transducer signals, etc. This is because, primarily, these systems require a low-impedance common ground at low frequencies (i.e., where the conductors' resistivities and contact resistances are the dominant parameters). They suffer fewer common-impedance problems at frequencies above few hundred kilohertz, where any grid becomes an acceptable ground plane substitute. This will be discussed in a later section.

9.3.5 Transient Plates

In cases where a ground plane cannot be installed and where the reinforced concrete grid cannot even be accessed, a backup solution exists. Called the **transient plate,** this solution has been widely used by IBM installation planning engineers, among others. The principle is to install a square plate of copper or galvanized steel. The plate should measure at least 1.20×1.20 m, or any other dimension providing that the above minimum area is achieved and that the length-to-width ratio does not exceed 3. The principle of this plate is shown Fig. 9.46. Understanding that the "real" ground is too far away to be accessible, this transient plate, due to its large capacitance to the building structure (typically 300 to 1,000 pF), provides an efficient sink for EMI filters, varistors and transformer Faraday shields. The power line common-mode transients are more efficiently decoupled to the building structure or earthing this way than via the green wire, which is totally incapable of offering a low-impedance reference.

This transient plate must collect the dedicated grounding straps from all the equipment frames in the room. So, ideally, the plate should be installed at the approximate geometric center of all these frames. Another acceptable location is near the room distribution panel, since the transient plate will connect to the safety ground post of this panel. The closer this plate to the concrete grid the better, so the plate is generally laid over the floor concrete rather than over the false floor. The plate must connect to the building safety bus to avoid hazard, should the plate become energized. Even when properly installed, a transient plate cannot match the performance of a true ground plane or grid, but it can be an acceptable fix in many cases.

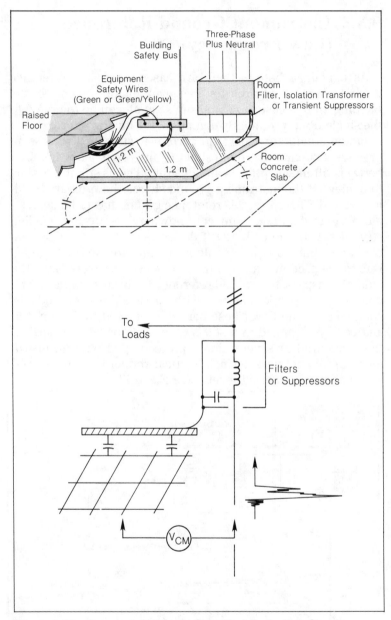

Figure 9.46—Transient Plate and Simplified Equivalent Circuit

9.3.6 Instrument Ground Reference (Low-Frequency)

As explained before, there are cases where the reference ground plane is required for low-level analog systems in the building. In this case, no compromise at all can be tolerated to the single-point ground. By definition, the analog reference is a common conductor where **no** current is supposed to flow. In practice a maximum ground shift of 1 mV (dc to a few hundred hertz) is often accepted as an objective. This is still impossible to achieve if the instrument ground shares the ordinary building ground. Therefore, this reference ground has to be dedicated to the system and connected nowhere else to the building structure. It would be better if the users of this ground system could be confined to a same floor or same area in the building. Due to the predominance of the low-resistance aspect over the inductive aspect, the ground reference of these systems can be made of large copper bus bars with threaded holes or studs for equipment grounding. These bars do not need to form a grid and can be arranged in a star system at floor level or against the room wall. If several floors are equipped with an instrument ground network, a single vertical copper bar will be used to connect the different levels (see Fig. 9.47).

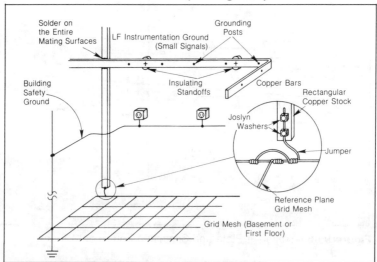

Figure 9.47—Instrument Ground Bus for DC or Low-Frequency Signal Reference (see also Fig. 9.30, 9.31 and 9.32)

It is extremely important to mount the copper bars of the instrument ground on insulating standoffs to avoid possible contact with conductive parts of the building walls or floor. In some cases, the instrument ground conductors are covered with insulating sleeves or painted with a certain color code to identify them and prevent undesirable connections. Connections should be made only with copper hardware or a galvanically compatible metal.

The instrument ground should be connected to earth ground for protection of personnel and equipment from hazardous potentials. Various precautions must be taken to ensure that such measures are implemented in a manner which will not affect the primary purpose of the reference net.

The instrument ground must be earthed at only one point. The building ground can be expected to carry large amounts of power system fault currents and possibly large currents due to lightning discharges. Such loop currents must be prevented from circulating in the instrument ground. Figure 9.47 illustrates a method for connecting the instrument reference grid or bus to earth ground. Such procedures can be applied to any building using a reference plane and ground rods. In situations when earth-ground meshes are used in lieu of or to complement ground rods, techniques indicated in previous should be used for making earth-ground connections, using, for instance, a ground well.

Ground-well installations should be made readily accessible for inspection and repair if necessary. Such installations should be installed in basements or in spaces between structural flooring and ground. More than one contact between the reference plane and ground well and between the ground well and earth ground is desirable to prevent loss of earth ground by a fault on one contact (see Fig. 9.31).

9.3.7 Cable Trays and Raceways

Metallic cable trays can help in reducing installation noise. Properly used and integrated in the general grounding system, metallic cable trays can:

1. Reduce crosstalk by increasing the cable-to-ground capacitances

2. Reduce common-mode field pickup or radiation by bringing a metal plane close to the cables

3. Augment or actually become the reference grid

For instance, a cable tray of 20 cm width, 5 cm sides and made of 0.8 mm thick sheet metal will have the following resistance per meter of length:

$$aluminum = 0.065 \text{ m}\Omega/\text{meter}$$
$$steel = 0.24 \text{ m/meter}$$

Up to about 10 m length, such trays can compare favorably with more expensive ground planes. If one wants to integrate these trays in the grounding network, the various sections of the cable trays must be reliably bonded together.

The dc resistance of each bond connection should stay below 5 mΩ. Since each floor level will typically have more than one cable tray running, all the trays can be bonded at their various intersections. This begins to form a grid, even though the size of the mesh is large. While the low inductance of metal raceways makes a fairly good RF grid, their dc or 60 Hz resistance can be improved by copper cables, as shown in Fig. 9.48.

Figure 9.48—Bonding of Cable Raceways

To summarize Sections 9.1 to 9.3, the essentials of the grounding and earthing guidelines discussed in this section are illustrated in Fig. 9.49.

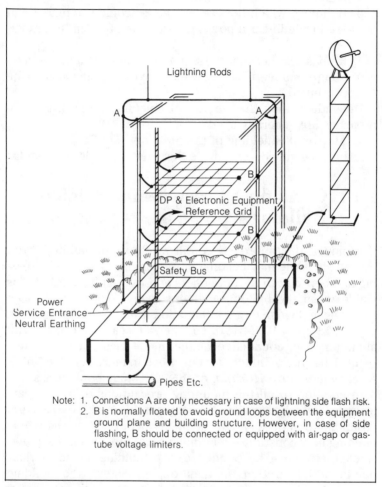

Note: 1. Connections A are only necessary in case of lightning side flash risk.
2. B is normally floated to avoid ground loops between the equipment ground plane and building structure. However, in case of side flashing, B should be connected or equipped with air-gap or gas-tube voltage limiters.

Figure 9.49—General View of a Complete Building Grounding/Earthing.

9.4 Grounding Aspects with Shielded Buildings and Shielded Rooms

There are a growing number of cases where some amount of electromagnetic shielding has to be offered at the building level, because of either the severity of the outside threat or the vulnerability of the inner system. Examples include:

1. Buildings where EMI/RFI testing is performed
2. Hospitals using nuclear magnetic resonance (NMR) scanners
3. Buildings which host sensitive electronic equipment and are located near a powerful broadcast transmitter, radar, etc.
4. Embassies, headquarters and government facilities handling confidential data where eavesdropping has to be prevented

Depending upon the amount of shielding desired, two approaches are generally used:

1. An overall shielding of the building
2. Internal shielded rooms, either custom-made or modular

9.4.1 Grounding Practices for Shielded Buildings

Although this approach is still rarely used, buildings with overall shielding may become more common with the increasing number of both EMI offenders and victims. This solution is viable when the building contains many rooms which need shielding and when target attenuation levels are rather modest, say, 40 dB up to 100 MHz or so. The walls can be covered with aluminum foil, conductive textile, metal mesh or conductive paint. This type of building is described in more detail in Vol. 3, *Electromagnetic Shielding*, of this EMC handbook series.

In addition to all the mounting precautions to avoid seam leakages (which are out of the scope of this book), two general grounding practices should be mentioned. Because the whole building now constitutes a Faraday cage, cable conduits, pipes, shields, etc. must be bonded to the building shield at their points of penetration. In addition, for safety, the building overall shield must connect to the earthing conductor.

9.4.2 Grounding Practices for Shielded Rooms

When superior attenuations are needed, e.g., 80, 100 or 120 dB, a real shielded room is installed. To avoid alteration of the Faraday cage performance by its installation, the following principles should be observed:

1. The shielded room must be connected to the building safety ground conductor. This connection is to be made at the exterior of the room, preferably at the power input box or filter. Metal ducts, pipes, etc. must be electrically interrupted with a dielectric spacer at the point where they penetrate the shielded cage. The entry hole then needs to be equipped with a waveguide or honeycomb barrier to preserve the high attenuation of the room to HF fields.

2. The grounding of the room down to the earthing terminal can be made by a dedicated conductor, but in this case precautions to avoid ground loops are required, i.e., no other ground connection must be made to the shielded room. This may demand a serious checking of all ancillary equipment which may interconnect through the room shield via coaxial connectors.

3. A dedicated earth rod is not recommended since it would pose both a noise problem and a safety issue (two earthing resistances in series) in case of a power fault to ground. If a dedicated rod has to be driven close to the shielded room, because of the excessive distance to the normal service ground rod, both rods should be connected by a copper wire to obviate the safety hazard. Then, a Faraday shielded isolation transformer is mandatory to break the EMI ground loop. Figure 9.50 shows some common mistakes in the grounding of a shielded room, and their cures.

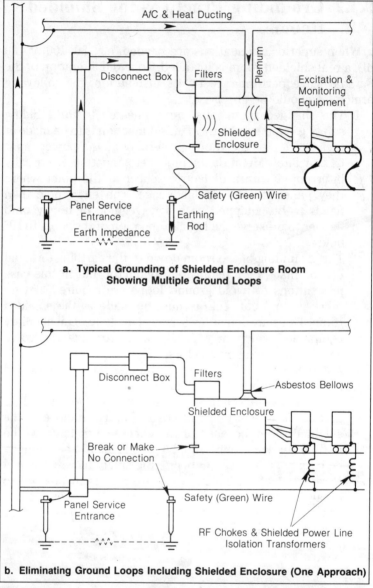

a. **Typical Grounding of Shielded Enclosure Room Showing Multiple Ground Loops**

b. **Eliminating Ground Loops Including Shielded Enclosure (One Approach)**

Figure 9.50—Bad (a) and Preferred (b and c) Grounding Practices for Shielded Enclosures in a Building (continued next page)

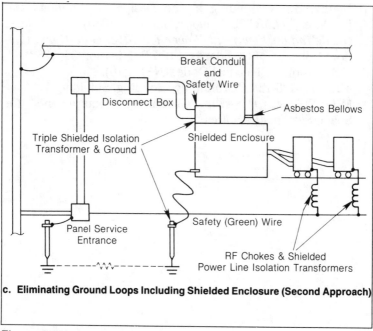

c. **Eliminating Ground Loops Including Shielded Enclosure (Second Approach)**

Figure 9.50—(continued)

9.5 References

1. Golde, R.H., *Lightning Protection*, (New York: Chemical Publishing Company).
2. Uman, M., *Lightning*, (New York: McGraw Hill, 1969).
3. Uman, M.; Krider, E.P.; and Master, M.J., "A Comparison of Lightning Fields with the NEMP in the 10 kHz to 10 GHz," (*IEEE EMC Transactions*, November, 1982).
4. St. Privat D'Allier Group, "Eight Years of Lightning Experiments," (Revue Generale de l'Electricite, No. 9, 1982).
5. Frydenlund, M., "Grounding for the Control of Lightning," (*EMC Technology*, January, 1983).
6. Bodier, G., "EDF and ORTF Installation Practices for Lightning Protection of Telecommunication Centers," (Electricite de France, Internal Reports).

7. Denny, H., "Grounding in the Design of Buildings and Facilities," (*EMC Technology*, January, 1983).

8. *Guideline on Electrical Power for DP Installations*, (National Bureau of Standards, FIPS Publication 94, 1983).

9. U.S. National Electrical Code, (NFPA 70).

10. MIL-STD-188-124, "Grounding, Bonding, Shielding."

11. MIL-STD-1542 (USAF), "Grounding Requirements for Space Systems Facilities."

Chapter 10

Ground System Tests and Maintenance

A basic ingredient of engineering is the performance and interpretation of measurements. Unfortunately, because of the wide frequency range over which a grounding network can influence system behavior, and because of the physical extent of a network (often many wavelengths long), we are somewhat limited in our ability to make effective measurements that provide results directly related to network performance. One of the reasons that ground system design and analysis tends to be viewed as an art rather than a science may be the unavailability of a comprehensive measurement process. For example, throughout this book it has been repeatedly emphasized that dc and low-frequency properties do not define the high-frequency properties of a grounding network. Yet, low-frequency measurements are the only easy and unambiguous ones to make.

High-frequency measurement results include the effects of resonances, standing waves and radiated pickup, all of which render interpretation difficult. However, indirect inferences can be made of high-frequency performance from low-frequency measurements with considerations of geometry and the other interference elements of coupling and shielding. The preceding chapters have established relationships between these factors and overall grounding network performance.

Therefore, certain applicable measurements are set for use in this chapter. In addition, some suggestions for interpreting the results are listed.

10.1 Test Procedures

Procedures for testing the performance of a grounding network at all its operational frequencies do not exist. Low-frequency measurements can be made, however, and the results evaluated for comparative performance. The principal measurements now available are bond resistance, ground system noise current and differential noise voltage.

10.1.1. Bond Resistance

This test is intended to give a general indication of bond adequacy based on the dc resistance of the bond.

Equipment Requirements:
1. A dc resistance bridge capable of measuring to about 0.001 Ω or better is the first requirement. The bridge should be portable and position-insensitive. Connection of the test sample to the bridge terminals should be easily performed without cumbersome adaptors of special tools. An instrument with separate potential (voltage) and current terminals is preferred to a two-terminal device.
2. A pair of heavy-duty spring clip leads is needed for connection between the bridge and the bonded junction. Clip leads may be connected to braided straps and lugs to make connection to the bridge. The total resistance of external connectors and leads should not be greater than 0.001 Ω.

Equipment Setup:
1. Using the heavy-duty spring clips and braids or low-resistance wire, connect the leads to the bridge.
2. Place the bridge in operation according to the manufacturer's operating manual.

3. Zero the bridge, including leads, and connect the clip leads across the bonded junction as shown in Fig. 10.1. By placing the current leads away from the junction while placing the potential leads near the junction, the effects of the probe contact resistance are minimized. If the bond to be measured is internal to a metallic grid such that other current paths exist between the current probes in parallel to the path through the bond under test, the potential and current probes should be connected near the same point (one potential probe and one current probe on each side of the bond). Otherwise, a gross error may result. When multiple parallel paths exist, this procedure may not adequately indicate the true condition of the specific junction of interest. But it will indicate the total resistance between both sides of the junction.

Test Procedures:
1. Adjust the bridge balance until a null is obtained.
2. Record the indicated resistance.

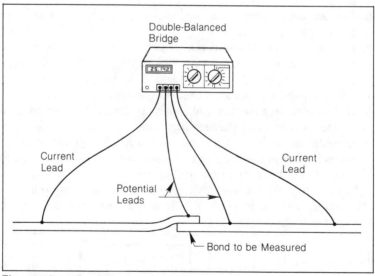

Figure 10.1—Bond Resistance Measurement

10.1.2 Ground System Noise Current

This procedure measures the stray currents on safety grounds, signal grounds and cable shields. These frequently are causes of common-mode noise interference within a facility.

Equipment required:
1. Oscilloscope
2. Oscilloscope current probe (Hall-effect) or EMI current probe (passive)
3. Oscilloscope camera

Equipment Setup and Test Procedure:
1. Connect the current probe, current probe amplifier and oscilloscope as shown in Fig. 10.2.
2. Observe the oscilloscope-displayed ambient level at each test point.
3. Photograph the ambient level at each test point.
4. Set the oscilloscope to trigger at a level slightly above the ambient.
5. Set the oscilloscope for single-sweep operation and open the camera shutter.
6. Let the camera shutter remain open for five minutes or until the oscilloscope is triggered, whichever occurs first. (Longer sampling periods may be used if desired.)
7. Record pertinent information on the test photograph.
8. If a spectrum analyzer plug-in is available for the oscilloscope, perform the current measurements in the frequency domain as well as the time domain. (Frequency-domain measurements can be of great assistance in identifying the source of interference currents.)

Notice that one of the advantages of this technique is that the pickup device is perfectly floated relative to the circuit being checked.

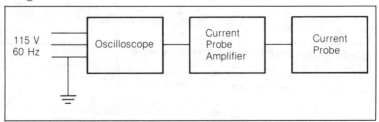

Figure 10.2—Test Setup for Stray Current Measurements

10.1.3 Ground Differential Noise Voltage

Equipment Required:
1. Oscilloscope with differential plug-in (or spectrum analyzer)
2. Power line isolation transformer, to avoid creation of a third ground by the safety wire. By default, one can disconnect the safety wire, but this creates a safety issue. A battery-powered oscilloscope would be an excellent alternative.
3. Oscilloscope camera
4. Isolation transformer
5. Required lengths of shielded cable

Equipment Setup and Test Procedure:
1. Set up the equipment as shown in Fig. 10.3. Note that the signal probe and the ground reference probe are connected to each of the two points between which the voltage differential is desired.
2. After an adequate warmup time, photograph the ambient noise level in both time and frequency domains. Figure 10.4 shows two examples of time-domain results provided by this technique.
3. If transient data are required, proceed as indicated in Steps 4 through 7 of Section 10.1.2.

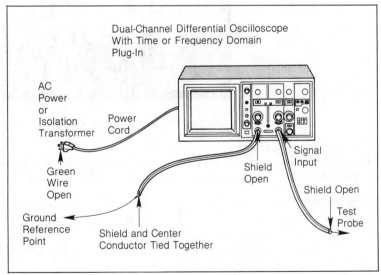

Figure 10.3—Oscilloscope Connections for Measuring Voltage Levels on Ground Systems

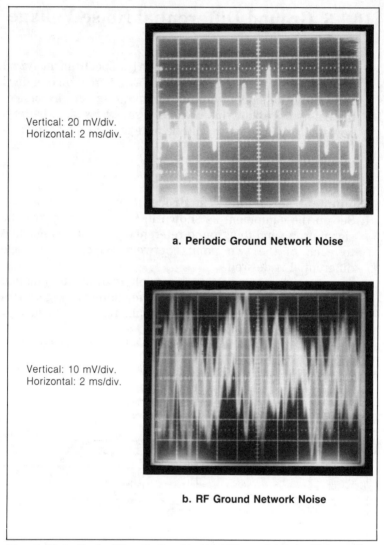

Vertical: 20 mV/div.
Horizontal: 2 ms/div.

a. Periodic Ground Network Noise

Vertical: 10 mV/div.
Horizontal: 2 ms/div.

b. RF Ground Network Noise

Figure 10.4—Typical Results Provided by Differential Noise Voltage Test

Notice that, in contrast with ground current measurement, this setup is not floated at the pickup point. Even though common-impedance problems cannot create measurement errors, the loop area formed by the two probe wires can intercept an ambient field. This field will induce a series voltage in the loop which will add to the real ground voltage being measured. The shields are no help in this case, as can be seen in Fig. 10.5. The voltage V_i induced by radiation may be from an external source or from a noise source within the installation itself. In the later case, the error can be doubly misleading because it would be correlated with the operation of the system being tested, yet that ground voltage would not correspond to reality since it has been introduced by the measurement setup itself.

To reduce this possible pickup, leads should be arranged with the minimum loop height and length. For instance, the two coax cables can be run side-by-side from the oscilloscope down to the ground plane, split and laid over it as close as possible until reaching the points being probed.

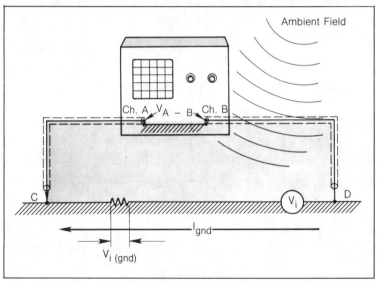

Figure 10.5—Possible Misleading Measurement Caused by a Too-Large Loop of the Probe Wires, in the Presence of EM Ambients

10.1.4 Ground Plane and Chassis Currents

In many cases of EMI investigations implying ground currents, the current does not flow on a wire but on a metal chassis, deck, wall, etc. It is useful to know the amplitude distribution of this current across the plane.

A surface-current probe can be used. This accessory measures the HF current under its effective footprint without making any direct contact. By moving the probe in discrete increments across the surface, the total RF current can be determined.

Figure 10.6 shows the principle of this probe, similar to the standard clamp-on probe. Typical values for the transfer impedance (volts per ampere) of such probes are in the 0.3 to 3 Ω range. With typical EMI receivers or spectrum analyzers, this allows measurement sensitivities of 1 μA or less. These probes can handle several hundred amperes before saturation.

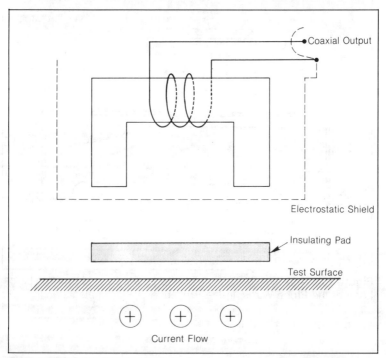

Figure 10.6—Surface Current Probe (continued next page)

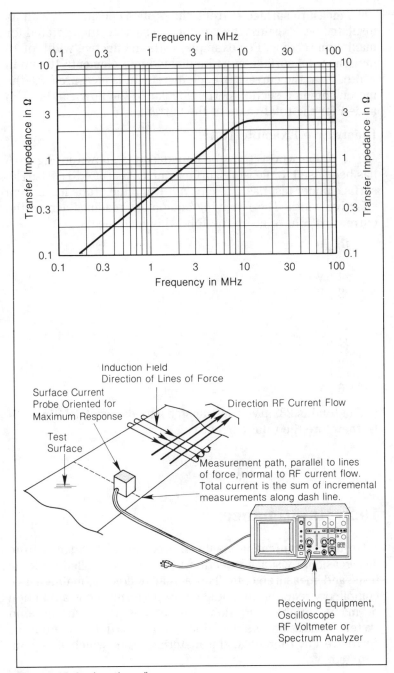

Figure 10.6—(continued)

To measure surface current, the probe is positioned with its insulated base against the conducting surface, then rotated for maximum reading. For example, with an effective width of 10 mm, the total surface must be divided into elements 10 mm in width. Then the current in each increment is measured. All the increments in a section perpendicular to the flow can be then added for the total value of the current.

Illustrative Example 10.1:

The probe whose transfer impedance is shown in Fig. 10.6 has been used to measure surface currents around 1 MHz. The surface under test has a 10 cm width, and the probe has a 1 cm effective width. The receiving equipment readings across the current path have given the following increments:

$$10 \ \mu V$$
$$16 \ \mu V$$
$$24 \ \mu V$$
$$32 \ \mu V$$
$$32 \ \mu V$$
$$40 \ \mu V$$
$$34 \ \mu V$$
$$26 \ \mu V$$
$$12 \ \mu V$$
$$6 \ \mu V$$

The total is 232 μV. The transfer impedance at 1 MHz is 0.4 Ω, therefore the total current is:

$$\frac{232}{0.4} = 580 \ \mu A$$

10.2 Maintenance

Ground system maintenance efforts can run the gamut from an occasional visual inspection to rigidly controlled periodic tests and measurements. The actual degree of maintenance complexity required for satisfactory performance is a function of many variables. Predominant among these are ground system utilization, its location with regard to weather or corrosive environments, the materials from which it is constructed, etc.

10.2.1 Inspection

As a minimum, ground system maintenance should include a periodic visual inspection of all possible interconnections and bonded joints. During these inspections, indications of corrosion at the interface between mated metal surfaces and broken or disconnected ground conductors should be noted and corrected. Joints bonded together by bolts or clamps should be specifically inspected for corrosion. Emphasis should be directed to inspections for broken or disconnected ground conductors in areas of new construction and where flexible metal straps are used to bond movable devices to the ground system.

10.2.2 Measurements of System Ground Bus

In addition to visual inspections, it is desirable to conduct minimal tests to provide a quantitative indication of ground system adequacy.

10.2.2.1 Bonds

1. Concurrent with or following visual inspection of the bonds, perform bond resistance measurements. Select 5 to 10 bonds that visually appear tight, well-made, and free of corrosion. Measure their resistances. The sampling should include structural bonds, equipment-to-structure bonds, connections between safety ground wires, conduit-to-conduit or conduit-to-cabinet joints, bonds in lightning down conductors (to include structural columns if used for lightning discharge paths) and others as appropriate. Also measure all bonds exhibiting visible defects.
2. For every bond exhibiting a resistance greater than 1 mΩ, check for looseness. If the connections are loose, tighten the fastener and measure the resistance again after tightening. If the resistance is still greater than 1 mΩ and the joint can be readily disconnected, disassemble the joint and check for

corrosion, debris, paint and other nonconductive materials. Remove the material, reassemble the bond and remeasure the resistance.

3. The green safety wire should be connected to the power common (neutral) only at the power service disconnecting means. Facilities which can be temporarily removed from service should be de-energized and the main power switch locked or otherwise secured open. With electrical power removed, disconnect the neutral from ground at the service disconnecting means and check for isolation between the neutral and the grounding conductor (see Fig. 10.7). A low resistance reading ($<10\ \Omega$) indicates that the neutral is connected to ground somewhere other than at the service disconnect. This ground connection must be located and removed.

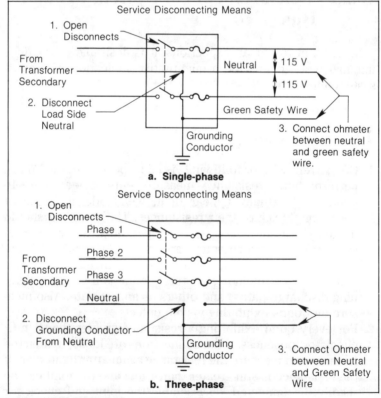

Figure 10.7—Method for Determining the Existence of Improper Neutral Ground Connections

10.2.2.2 Ground Network Resistance

Where low-frequency ground networks exist in a facility, measure the resistance between those points on the network where equipment interconnections are made. In Fig. 10.8, typical examples of this measurement are between equipment boxes D and E, between E and B, and between G and K. This resistance should not exceed 20 mΩ. Furthermore, measure the resistance between the ground terminals of equipments that are also interconnected with signal cables and control lines.

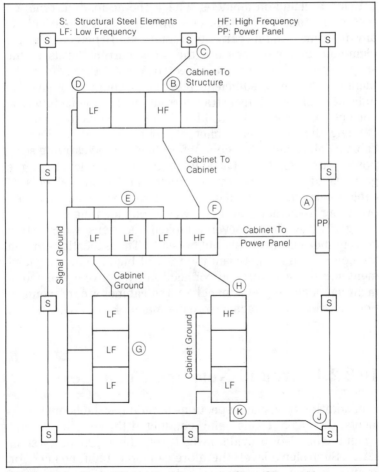

Figure 10.8—Typical Bond Resistance and Stray Current Measurement Locations in an Electronic Facility

On systems employing the equipment chassis or cabinet as a signal ground (e.g., most HF and RF systems), measure the cabinet-to-cabinet (or chassis-to-chassis) resistance, particularly on those interconnected with signal cables (see connections BF and FH). Also measure the cabinet-to-structure resistance (see connections BC and KJ). These two resistances should be less than 5 mΩ.

10.2.2.3 Stray Current Levels

Using a clamp-on ammeter, check the ac load currents on the conductors of three-phase supply lines. Note particularly any differences in line currents greater than 10 percent. Using a clamp-on ammeter, measure the stray current levels in the safety ground network at selected points throughout the facility. Choose a sufficient number of points to give an indication of the relative stray current level in the facility. The current levels should be < 0.1 A at power mains frequency.

Using the clamp-on ammeter, probe signal ground wires, cable shields, and other conductors likely to be carrying stray power currents. Note particularly the current levels in the grounds of low-frequency equipment and in the shields of cables carrying video, data or other types of signals with operating frequencies in the power-frequency range.

Figure 10.8 shows several typical locations where stray current measurements should be made. These locations are on the connection BC between the rack of high-frequency equipment and the structure, on connection AF between the equipment bay and the power panel, on the cabinet ground connection between low-frequency equipments E and G, and on connection JK.

10.2.2.4 Ground Network Noise Level

In addition to visual inspections and dc resistance measurements, the signal levels being conducted through the ground system can also provide insight regarding ground system status. Such signal levels therefore can indicate of the need for ground system maintenance. Using the test procedure of

Section 10.1.2, measure the stray current levels on a selected number of shields surrounding sensitive signal cables, on conduit and on equipment ground cables. Document the test details (i.e., vertical sensitivity and sweep rate) on the photographs made of the oscilloscope displays.

Using the test procedure described in Section 10.2.3, perform differential-noise measurements between interfaced equipment between the low-frequency (or other) signal ground network and structural ground, between equipment signal grounds and the point of connection to the earth electrode system, between widely separated points on ground networks and between any other two points where common-mode voltages are causing system or equipment noise problems.

Oscilloscope displays should be retained to provide a relative indication of the ground system status as a function of time or system activity level. Signal levels in both time and frequency domains at ground points of interest during periods of minimum activity should be recorded. Then, during periods of heavy activity, photographs of these same ground points should be made again. The two photographs for each ground point should be retaken at regular intervals and immediately following major structural or equipment modifications or additions. This historical record will then permit detection of short-term compromises and long-term deteriorations in the grounding system.

10.2.2.5 Star Ground Compromises

The simplest method to reveal that uncontrolled ground loops exist in a star (single-point) ground is to temporarily disconnect the signal ground from chassis at the identified single point. An ohmmeter across that gap should measure a quasi-infinite resistance (or at least several hundred kilohms). However, this technique does not say much about the location of any detected leakages.

A measurement technique useful for identifying undesired short circuits between various elements of the single-point ground system is illustrated in Fig. 10.9. The technique, designated the **current induction** method, utilizes a convenient length of wire, a clamp-on ammeter and a toroid coil through which 60 Hz current is passed. To determine if isolation is maintained between the signal ground and the facility ground, the auxiliary wire is threaded through the coil and is connected between the signal ground point and the facility ground. The normal connection between the signal ground and facility ground is then broken as shown in Fig. 10.9a. A voltage is induced in the auxiliary wire. Currents I_1, I_2 and I_3 are measured, and if either of them is not equal to zero, the single-point ground system is compromised.

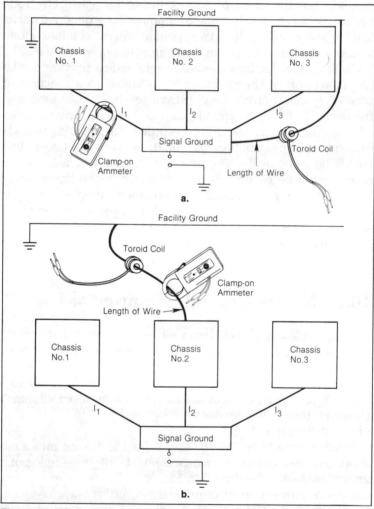

Figure 10.9—Determination of Single-Point Ground System Compromises with the Use of Induced Currents

The auxiliary wire is then connected between each chassis and the facility ground to determine where the compromise is, as indicated in Fig. 10.9b. Using the toroid coil, the current induced into each chassis is measured separately. The relative magnitude of these currents indicates the particular chassis in which the short circuit exists. For example, if the short circuit current induced in chassis no. 3 is significantly larger than the currents induced in the other chassis, the compromise is at chassis no. 3. (Removal of the undesired short circuit in chassis no. 3 should be followed by a complete recheck of the entire system.) Notice that the method is not restricted to 50/60 Hz and that, using a signal generator, higher frequencies can be injected to reveal where stray capacitances are degrading the star ground operation.

10.2.3 Corrective Action

The following guidelines may be used to help evaluate results of measurements and to help define the corrective actions which should be taken. This set of guidelines is not to be considered all-inclusive. Specific situations can be expected that will not be adequately covered by the guidelines. These need to be dealt with on an individual basis.

1. Review electrical wiring diagrams and the electrical equipment distribution within the facility to determine possible direct or indirect coupling paths between noisy equipment and susceptible electronic apparatus. Apply corrective measures such as:
   a. Relocate the equipment.
   b. Redistribute the electrical load so that potentially interfering equipment units are served by separate feeders.
   c. Install electrical feeders in steel conduit or raceways to reduce magnetic fields.
   d. Relocate signal lines to sensitive equipment at the maximum possible distance from power conductors feeding noisy equipment.
2. Correlate, if possible, any evidence of equipment malfunctions due to electrical noise on signal or control cables with the measured values of stray currents or voltages on grounding conductors and on cable shields. If such a

correlation exists, determine the probable cause of such noise voltages using the principles set forth earlier.

Then apply the techniques described to reduce the noise to a level which is acceptable to the equipment in the facility:

1. If operational experience (as indicated by maintenance logs or outage reports and operator comments) reveals problems with system noise and interference attributable to grounding deficiencies, choose the most appropriate noise attenuation procedures and implement them.
2. If a significant number (e.g., 10 percent) of the bonds measured exhibit a resistance greater than 1 mΩ, all bonds should be inspected carefully and the resistance measured. Each one found to be deficient should be redone.
3. Record all changes made during the maintenance process.

10.3 Earthing Resistance Measurements

It is necessary to know, at least approximately, the value of the resistance at the ultimate terminal of building grounding network, i.e., the earthing resistance. However, as simple as it looks, earthing resistance is a complex parameter as explained in Section 2.7. In fact, the resistance to earth, beyond the point where the safety or ground wires attach to the earth electrode, consists of the following components:

1. The resistance of the earth rod itself. Being in the milliohm range, this one can be neglected in favor of the next two.
2. The contact resistance of the electrode to the surrounding earth
3. The earth volume resistance, or resistivity

Components 2 and 3, of course, are the dominating parameters and need to be measured. The contact resistance of the ground rod to the earth is an installation variable and needs to be checked periodically. The earth resistance is a result of the earth resistivity at this location and is out of our control. However, at least at the outset, it is necessary to determine it to establish the type and number of electrodes required in the earthing system (see Section 2.7). To optimize the combination of components 2 and 3, it would be stupid to fight for a contact resistance less than 1 Ω in a ground whose earth resistance exceeds, for instance, 100 Ω.

Reciprocally, it would be regrettable to accept a contact resistance of several ohms in a soil which has only 2 or 3 Ω resistance. Component 3 can be measured. Component 2 cannot be measured independently of 3, so the measure of 2 plus 3 is done instead.

10.3.1 Measurements of Earth Resistivity

To validate (or eventually correct) the hypotheses made on the basis of soil resistivity, hypotheses which allowed computation of the expected earthing resistance, a measurement of earth resistivity is recommended when large installations are planned. A simple method uses four electrodes as seen in Fig. 10.10. A current is forced between A and D, and the voltage drop is measured between B and C. The distance d ranges from 10 to 100 m, depending the area under examination.

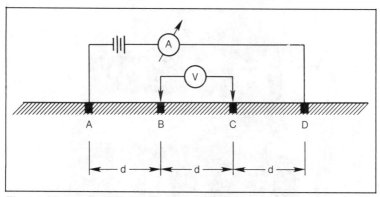

Figure 10.10—Four-Electrode Method of Measuring Ground Resistivity

The resistance between B and C is:

$$R_{BC} = \frac{V}{I} \ \Omega$$

Then the resistivity will be:

$$\rho = R_{BC} \times 2\pi \times d \text{ in ohm-meters}$$

Provided the voltmeter has a high impedance, and since no current is flowing into electrodes B and C, their own contact resistances do not spoil the measurement significantly.

10.3.2 Measurement of Earthing Resistance

Three techniques are widely used to measure the earthing resistance:

1. The Megger® method (Megger is a trade name for the instrument made by James G. Biddle Co. as shown in Fig. 10.11)
2. The simple voltage-drop method
3. The three-point method (the most widely used)

The "Megger" is an instrument combining an ohmmeter and a calibrated voltage source. It can use only two points; that is, only one rod is driven in addition to the one being measured. As with an ohmmeter, the dial reads the resistance directly.

Figure 10.11—Economical, Battery-Powered Earth Tester (Courtesy of Biddle Instruments Co.)

The simple voltage-drop method uses two auxiliary rods, one for the voltage and one for the current (see Fig. 10.12). Preferably, this auxiliary ground should be located at a distance that is large compared to the dimensions of the ground under test since interaction of the ground current distributions at the two electrodes is undesirable. For instance, the German VDE 141 recommends that both distances be 20 m. A voltage is then measured between the ground point under test and a reference ground point which is located somewhere between the two current-carrying electrodes. This reference ground should also be so located that it is not in the electric field of either of the current-carrying electrodes. Assuming that the current density is negligible at the reference electrode, the resistance of the ground under test is:

$$R = \frac{V}{I}$$

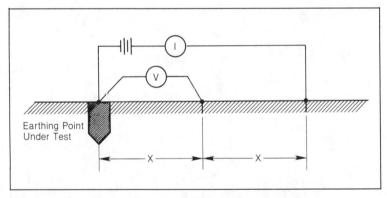

Figure 10.12—Voltage-Drop Method

The three-point method also uses two auxiliary rods and an ohmmeter (Fig. 10.13). Three sets of measurements are taken, and in each set two readings are taken (the second with reversed ohmmeter leads). For accuracy, the length of the auxiliary rods should be close to the one being checked. They also should be located at least six meters apart to prevent overlapping of their respective grounding zones. The unknown resistance R_X can be computed with the following equation:

$$R_X = \frac{1}{2} (R_{XB} + R_{XC} - R_{BC})$$

where,

$$R_{XB} = \frac{R_{XB} + R_{BX}}{2}$$

$$R_{XC} = \frac{R_{XC} + R_{CX}}{2}$$

$$R_{BC} = \frac{R_{BC} + R_{CB}}{2}$$

That is, each term is the average of the two measurements made with direct and reverse polarities (this dual measurement allows cancellation of parasitic effects due to other circulating ground currents plus possible nonlinearities in the electrode-to-ground junction).

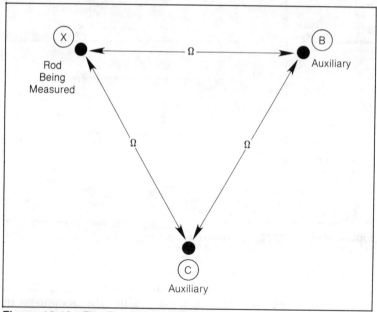

Figure 10.13—The Three-Point Method

Illustrative Example 10.2:

In an actual measurement, the following readings were obtained:

$$R_{XB} = 83\ \Omega,\ R_{BX} = 77\ \Omega$$
$$R_{XC} = 93\ \Omega,\ R_{CX} = 79\ \Omega$$
$$R_{BC} = 76\ \Omega,\ R_{CB} = 102\ \Omega$$

$$\text{Average } R_{XB} = \frac{83 + 77}{2} = 80$$

$$\text{Average } R_{XC} = \frac{93 + 79}{2} = 86$$

$$\text{Average } R_{BC} = \frac{76 + 102}{2} = 89$$

$$R_X = \frac{80 + 86 - 89}{2} = 38.5\ \Omega$$

This resistance is quite high, and after these measurements some corrective action needs to be taken such as driving the rod deeper, using several rods in parallel or wetting the soil. When measuring the ground resistance of an extensive structure, it may be difficult to place the auxiliary current ground and the reference ground far enough from the ground under test to prevent interaction of electric fields from the electrodes. It has been shown that substantially correct measurements can be made if the reference ground is located at 0.6 times the distance between the auxiliary ground and the ground under test.

If the system is large, errors may be encountered which result from stray currents in the ground from outside power sources. These tend not to affect the measurements when using a self-contained ground tester since the current frequency of the test set is generally different from the frequency of the interfering currents. Such interfering currents can also be balanced out in the measuring instrument.

The resistance between a ground rod and earth can be obtained by the **fall-of-potential** test method. Test rods have to be driven into the earth whether the fall of potential or other methods are used to determine the resistance between a ground rod and earth. Ten test rods are necessary. In Fig. 10.14, the rods are spaced at 15 m intervals in a straight line up to a distance of 150 m from the periphery of the earth ground system.

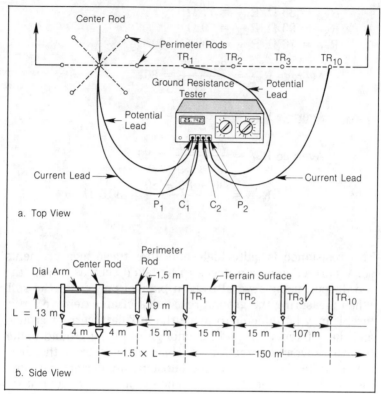

Figure 10.14—Physical Layout of Radial Ground System

The earth-ground system consists of a number of rods driven 10 m into the earth in a circular arrangement with one center rod down 13 m. Initially, the rods are not connected. Enough of the rod should be exposed above the terrain surface to attach a test lead. The test rods should not be interconnected. A ground-resistance tester or equivalent passes a 90 Hz current so that any 60 Hz currents in the ground do not alter the resistance reading from the ground system ground rod to the test rod. The potential drop is measured on a meter calibrated in "ohms" resistance. The ground-resistance testers are four-wire types in that there are two voltage leads and two current leads; therefore the lead resistances do not become part of the resistance reading.

The measurements are made successively at 16 m intervals from the ground system rods. When the resistance to each test rod is plotted against the distance of the test rod from the ground system ground rod, the resultant curve approaches zero resistance in the vicinity of the grounding system, then slopes abruptly upward. From a 30 m distance to about a 120 m, the curve remains horizontal with little change in resistance. Beyond 120 m, the resistance again increases.

The flat portion of the curve establishes the resistance to earth of the ground system ground rods. The resistance to earth is then the average reading of the horizontal position of the curve. Figure 10.15 illustrates a typical ground rod resistance curve obtained by the fall-of-potential test method. After the tests are made with the individual ground rods, the earth-ground system is radially interconnected, as described in the previous section, and the complete earth-ground system is tested.

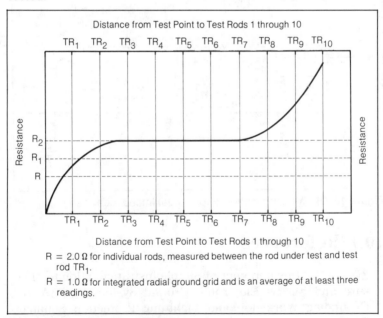

Figure 10.15—Ground-Rod Resistance to Earth

10.3.3 Measurement of Earthing HF Impedance

More and more often, it is desirable to evaluate the high-frequency behavior of an earthing electrode, recognizing that its dc or 100 Hz measurements can be insufficient as an indicator (see Section 2.7.8 of this book). Although no standard method is universally acknowledged, a useful setup has been devised by Kouteynikoff (Ref. 6, 7) adapted from the Conventional three-point method. The test method is shown in Fig. 10.16. The earthing impedance is found from the ratio V/I of the probe-to-earth voltage to the injected current. The impedance values shown in Fig. 2.41 (Chapter 2) have been obtained by such setup.

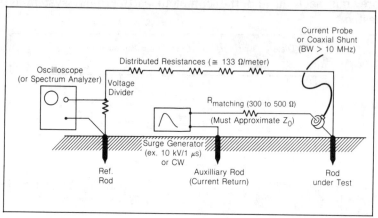

Figure 10.16—Measuring the HF (or Surge) Impedance of an Earth Rod

10.4 References

1. Zych, J.F., "Development of Simple Instrumentation to Measure and Assess Electronic Ground Systems," (FAA/GIT Grounding Workshop and Lightning Protection Seminar, FAA-RD-106, Atlanta, GA, May 1975, AD A013 618, pp. 45-62).
2. Denny, H.W., et. al., *Grounding, Bonding and Shielding Practices and Procedures for Electronic Equipments and Facilities*, Volumes 1-3, (Report No. FAA-RD-75-215, Contract DT-FA72WA-2850, Engineering Experiment Station,

Georgia Institute of Technology, Atlanta, GA, Dec., 1975, AD A022 332, AD A022 608, and AD A022-871).
3. "Final Report on the Development of Bonding and Grounding Criteria for John F. Kennedy Space Center," WDL-TR-4202, Volumes 1-3, (Philco-Ford Corp., Contract NAS10-6879, Palo Alto, CA, June, 1970).
4. Corey, L.E., "Engineering for Electromagnetic Interference/ Electromagnetic Pulse Protection in NORAD Cheyenne Mountain Complex," (*ADC Communications and Electronics Digest*, ADCRP-100-1, Volume 22, No. 4, April, 1972, pp. 24-30).
5. Instruction Manual for Surface Current Probe Model 95210-1 (Eaton, ex. Singer).
6. Kouteynikoff, P., "Impulse Response of Grounding Electrodes," CIGRE Symposium, 1981 (Stockholm).
7. Kouteynikoff, P., "HF Impedance in a Semi-Conducting Space," 1983 EMC Symposium, Tregastel, France (in French).

Other Books Published by ICT

1. Carstensen, Russell V., *EMI Control in Boats and Ships*, 1979.
2. Denny, Hugh W., *Grounding for Control of EMI*, 1983.
3. Duff, Dr. William G., *A Handbook on Mobile Communications*, 1980.
4. Duff, Dr. William G. and White, Donald R.J., Volume 5, *Electromagnetic Interference Prediction & Analysis Techniques*, 1972.
5. Feher, Dr. Kamilo, *Digital Modulation Techniques in an Interference Environment*, 1977.
6. Gabrielson, Bruce C., *The Aerospace Engineer's Handbook of Lightning Protection*, 1987.
7. Gard, Michael F., *Electromagnetic Interference Control in Medical Electronics*, 1979.
8. Georgopoulos, Dr. Chris J., *Fiber Optics and Optical Isolators*, 1982.
9. Georgopoulos, Dr. Chris J., *Interference Control in Cable and Device Interfaces*, 1987.
10. Ghose, Rabindra N., *EMP Environment and System Hardness Design*, 1983.
11. Hart, William C. and Malone, Edgar W., *Lightning and Lightning Protection*, 1979.
12. Herman, John R., *Electromagnetic Ambients and Man-Made Noise*, 1979.
13. Hill, James S. and White, Donald R.J., Volume 6, *Electromagnetic Interference Specifications, Standards & Regulations*, 1975.
14. Jansky, Donald M., *Spectrum Management Techniques*, 1977.
15. Mardiguian, Michel, *Interference Control in Computers and Microprocessor-Based Equipment*, 1984.
16. Mardiguian, Michel, *Electrostatic Discharge—Understand, Simulate and Fix ESD Problems*, 1985.
17. Mardiguian, Michel, *How to Control Electrical Noise*, 1983.
18. Smith, Albert A., *Coupling of External Electromagnetic Fields to Transmission Lines*, 1986.
19. White, Donald R.J., *A Handbook on Electromagnetic Shielding Materials and Performance*, 1980.
20. White, Donald R.J., *Electrical Filters—Synthesis, Design & Applications*, 1980.
21. White, Donald R.J., *EMI Control in the Design of Printed Circuit Boards and Backplanes*, 1982. (Also available in French.)
22. White, Donald R.J. and Mardiguian, Michel, *EMI Control Methodology & Procedures*, 1982.
23. White, Donald R.J., Volume 1, *Electrical Noise and EMI Specifications*, 1971.
24. White, Donald R.J., Volume 2, *Electromagnetic Interference Test Methods and Procedures*, 1980.
25. White, Donald, R.J., Volume 3, *Electromagnetic Interference Control Methods & Techniques*, 1973.
26. White, Donald R.J., Volume 4, *Electromagnetic Interference Test Instrumentation Systems*, 1980.
27. Duff, William G., and White, Donald R.J., Volume 5, *Prediction and Analysis Techniques*, 1970.
28. White, Donald R.J., Volume 6, *EMI Specifications, Standards and Regulations*, 1973.
29. White, Donald R.J., *Shielding Design Methodology and Procedures*, 1986.
30. *EMC Technology 1982 Anthology*
31. *EMC EXPO Records 1986, 1987, 1988*

Index

I.1